BUILDING CONTRACTS COMPARED AND TABULATED

(Second edition)

BUILDING CONTRACTS COMPARED AND TABULATED

(Second edition)

by

Vincent Powell-Smith
and
David Chappell

Legal Studies and Services (Publishing) Ltd

Building Contracts Compared and Tabulated
Second edition (1990) published by:
  Legal Studies & Services (Publishing) Ltd
  57/61 Mortimer Street
  London W1N 7TD

First published in 1986 by: The Architectural Press Ltd

ISBN 1.85271.118.3

Typeset by: Prima Graphics, Camberley, Surrey.
Printed by: The Bath Press, Lower Bristol Road, Bath BA2 3BL.

Dr Vincent Powell-Smith, LLM, D Litt, FCIArb, MBAE, was for many years Lecturer in Law at the University of Aston Management Centre. He now acts as a consultant specialising in construction contracts and as a practising arbitrator. Well-known as a conference speaker in both the United Kingdom and the Far East, he has been Legal Correspondent of "Contract Journal" since 1974 and is joint editor of "Construction Law Reports". He has written a number of highly successful books on construction law including "Construction Arbitrations – A Practical Guide" with John Sims, "Engineering Contract Dictionary" and "A Contractor's Guide to the JCT Standard Form of Building Contract (JCT 80) (second edition) for Legal Studies and Services Ltd.

Dr David Chappell, MA, PhD, ARIBA, has previously worked as an architect in public and private sector practice, as contracts administrator for a building contractor and as a lecturer in construction, building law and contractual procedures. He is now a senior consultant with James R Knowles and Associates. He is a regular contributor to "Architect's Journal" and "Building Today" and has written "Contractual Correspondence for Architects", "Contractors' Claims: An Architect's Guide", "Understanding JCT Contracts" amongst others. He is also joint author with Dr Vincent Powell-Smith of "Building Contract Dictionary", "JCT Intermediate Form of Contract: An Architect's Guide" and "JCT Minor Works Form of Contract: An Architect's Guide" all published by Legal Studies and Services Ltd.

Preface

Legal principles have been tabulated since the time of the code of Hammurabi, the Babylonian king, who about 1750 BC issued a code in 282 sections. Our objective is different from that of Hammurabi: it is to set out the essentials of all the commonly-used standard form building contracts in tabular form, accompanied by a brief commentary.

The method of approach adopted is based on a series of articles in *The Architect's Journal*, which between 1983 and 1985 published a series of Practice Guides in its pages, devoted to some standard form contracts. *AJ* readers evidently found the tabular approach helpful and we hope that it will also appeal to a wider readership. We have in fact carried the idea a stage further, not only analysing the major contracts in terms of the powers and duties of the parties and of the architect but also providing other tabular summaries where this would be helpful. Flowcharts have also been included where they make the position clearer and we have added diagrams in appropriate cases.

This book will be helpful as a summary of the main standard forms of building contract to several groups of people: architects, quantity surveyors, builders and other members of the building team. It should also assist students by providing an introduction to the changing world of building contracts. The second edition takes account of the substantial changes made to many of the standard forms since the first edition in 1986, and also recent case law developments. It also considers the 1987 JCT Standard Form of Management Contract.

We concentrate on the practicalities rather than the legalities, though inevitably we have made reference to case law, which illuminates dark corners. The book is a guide and not a definitive treatise and the bibliography gives further reading on the various forms of contract. In practice, of course, it is not only the terms of the contract which are important but how they are administered and here the architect carries a heavy burden. It is for him to administer the contract fairly and justly between the parties and in so doing he must steer between Scylla and Charybdis.

We are grateful to Geoffrey Trickey FRICS ACIArb and John Sims FRICS FCIArb for permission to use their ideas and material in Chapter 1. We also acknowledge the help and support of the new publishers, Legal Studies & Services Ltd.

Funchais, Portugal **Vincent Powell-Smith**
Wakefield **David Chappell**

Contents

Chapter 4   The JCT Agreement for Minor Building Works (MW 80)

Chapter 5   The JCT Standard Form of Management Contract (JCT 87)

Chapter 6   The JCT Fixed Fee Form of Prime Cost Contract

Chapter 7   JCT Form with Contractor's Design

Chapter 8   The ACA Form of Building Agreement (ACA 2)

Chapter 9   The Government Conditions of Contract (GC/Works/1)

Bibliography

1: Contract Choice and Comparison

1.01   Introduction

All contracts are about allocation of risk and responsibility and there is a whole range of different types of standard form building contracts available. These cover a variety of clients' needs, and each standard form modifies the common law position to a greater or lesser extent.

The common law position is straightforward:

- In the traditional form of building contract, the employer and his professional advisers assume responsibility for design. The contractor merely agrees to erect the structure as designed.
- In so doing, the contractor is obliged to:
  - Do his work in a "good and workmanlike manner"
  - Supply good and proper materials
  - Complete the work by the date for completion stated in the contract.
- Corresponding duties are imposed on the employer.

These implied obligations are often modified by the standard form contracts in common use, and the choice of which form of contract to use is a difficult one.

The broad elements of any building project are:

- Preparation of the brief
- Development of the design
- Specifying standards of materials, workmanship and construction, and ensuring that these standards are achieved

- Determining the price to be paid
- Setting the period for construction
- Commissioning the completed project.

There are several ways in which these basic responsibilities can be apportioned as between the employer and his design team and the contractor, including management contracting, which is a relatively new method of procurement. **Table 1.01 illustrates the basic position.**
The choice of contract form is a vital matter; which set of conditions is used will (or should have) an effect upon price. The most important criteria involved in this choice are:

- The type of project: complexity, probable cost, etc
- The time factor. This can be critical for a variety of reasons and the need for completion on time can dictate the contract conditions.

Table 1.02 shows a comparison of extension of time clauses in standard forms.

1.02   Who is to Design?

The basic choice is between employer-designed works and works which are designed wholly or partially by the contractor, and this choice is reflected in the standard forms of contract which are currently available.
The Joint Contracts Tribunal – parent of the majority of forms discussed in the text (**see Table 1.03**) – appreciates this fundamental truth in its Practice Note 20 which contains sound guidance on choosing the appropriate JCT main contract form. As regards employer-designed works, the Practice Note points out that the employer must decide whether he requires a lump sum price, ie the amount he will pay (subject to variations, etc) or whether he merely requires a budget price or indication only of the price at tender stage. If he opts for the latter, a further choice must be made between a re-measurement contract, where all work executed is measured and valued, and a cost-plus contract.
Where the employer has decided to go for contractor-designed works, the Joint Contracts Tribunal offers a limited choice of contract form: between a full design and build contract – when the JCT Standard Form of Building Contract with Contractor's Design, may be used – or partial design and build contract, in which case the ordinary JCT Standard Form of Contract 1980 edition in its with quantities version must be used, as modified by the JCT Contractor's Designed Portion Supplement.
The Joint Contracts Tribunal's present intention is to provide a range of standard forms for every construction activity, and the list of JCT standard forms currently available is illustrated in **Table 1.04**. In fact, the JCT Practice Note over-simplifies the position and is, in any event, limited to guidance on the Tribunal's own forms.

In effect, therefore, the first thing to be decided is whether the project in hand is one for which the traditional methods of design and construction are best. From the employer's point of view this will mean:

- Engaging professional advisers: architect, quantity surveyor, consulting engineer and so on
- The design team preparing a full design and all construction details
- Selecting a contractor by competitive tender.

This is not always the best route to choose. If time is critical, the contract may need to be let urgently and there may be insufficient time for a full design to be prepared and for competitive tenders to be obtained. This is where the design and construct contract comes into its own. There are, however, several drawbacks which are discussed later.

There is no set boundary which delimits design and construct contracts from construct only contracts. The contractor's design input will vary according to the nature of the project, although traditionally a design and construct contract is regarded as one where the contractor undertakes the primary responsibility for the design of the structure and for the preparation of the necessary construction drawings.

Until recently, there has been no adequate standard form of contract for design and construct projects, but many projects have been completed successfully on this basis under specially-drafted conditions of contract. The basic minimum requirements for a design and construct contract are:

- Design responsibility imposed on the contractor, to ensure that the building is constructed to adequate standards, fulfils its intended purpose, and the requirements of the employer
- Preparation of drawings and specification and other construction information and obtaining of necessary consents
- Selection of materials and standards of workmanship
- Provision for variations
- Provision for regular inspection on behalf of the employer
- Payment and price
- Contract period.

These objectives are achieved by the two design and construct contract forms available: that sponsored by the JCT, and the ACA Agreement in its design and construct mode.

The advantages claimed for design and construct contracts are:

- Maximum overlap between design and construction is permitted
- Construction expertise reflected in design development
- Early commitment to the maximum price.

Disadvantages are:

- Since the design is not fully developed at tender stage, competition may be less than is desirable
- Tendering is an expensive overhead in this type of contract
- The best designer is not necessarily the best constructor. Design and construction are different processes and require different skills
- The contractor's design liability is limited either by the terms of the contract itself or, more practically, by the fact that most design and construct contractors are limited liability companies.

1.03 Management Contracting

This method of construction procurement involves the management contractor co-operating with the employer's professional team. The contractor manages the project, the actual construction work being carried out by works contractors. There is a low commercial and contractual risk on the management contractor. The project is designed from concept to scheme design and is in two stages:

pre-construction stage and the construction stage. A cost plan is agreed and if the employer decides to proceed with construction, the works contracts are let sequentially. An early start is possible on early works contracts packages, eg groundworks. The remaining detailed design proceeds in parallel with construction.

Cost control is vital since the project is based on a cost plan; methods controlling and monitoring cost are essential.

Management contracting is suitable where:

- Independent designers are used. Design and construct projects are not suitable
- Early completion is needed
- The project is a substantial one
- Flexibility is needed, eg where there is need to keep options open until a late stage.

Until 1987 there was no standard form of management contract and most management contractors operated under their own in-house forms. This situation has altered with the publication of the JCT Standard Form of Management Contract 1987, and its associated documentation.

1.04   Choosing the Appropriate Contract

Once the basic choice has been made, consideration must be given to which set of contract conditions is best suited for the project in hand. All too often, a particular set of contract conditions is adopted because of familiarity with the procedures under it. Familiarity is not a good criterion for contract selection and in each and every case consideration must be given to the best set of conditions for the job in hand: **see Table 1.05**.

The preliminary choice is between those sets of conditions sponsored by the Joint Contracts Tribunal, and the Association of Consultant Architects' Form of Building Agreement. For central government projects, there is a special set of conditions (form GC/Works/1) and it must be said that, with appropriate amendments, form GC/Works/1 is equally suitable for commercial projects. It should be noted that forms ACA 2 and GC/Works/1 are not negotiated like the Joint Contracts Tribunal's sets of conditions, and therefore they may be taken to be the employer's "written standard terms of business" for the purposes of the Unfair Contract Terms Act 1977. Amended JCT forms may be similarly caught by the Act. Whether this will have any practical effect will depend on all the circumstances but must be taken into account when the choice is being made.

The JCT forms of contract currently available are:

- The Standard Form of Building Contract 1980 – With Quantities and Without Quantities versions. These are both lump sum contracts, providing for interim payments monthly unless otherwise stated
- The Standard Form of Building Contract With Approximate Quantities. This is suitable where, at tender stage, it is made clear to tenderers that the quantities are approximate and are subject to re-measurement. The tender sum is converted to an ascertained Final Sum on measurement and valuation, but interim payments are made monthly or at other appropriate intervals
- The Fixed Fee Form of Prime Cost Contract. In the view of the JCT this form is suitable "where the nature of the work is such that it cannot be fully

16

described in advance of work being carried out" and also "where an early start is required, eg after fire damage". The Fixed Fee form differs entirely from the other JCT forms, except from the new management contract. *Practice Note 20*, para 7 says: "[The] contractor is paid the actual cost he incurs in carrying out the work on site plus a previously agreed lump sum for his overheads and profit. Thus the employer will be particularly dependent on the efficiency and reliability of the contractor".

- The Intermediate Form of Building Contract 1984. Again, this is a lump sum contract, and its use is subject to various limitations as to the nature of the work
- The Agreement for Minor Building Works 1980. Another lump sum contract with broad outline conditions, suitable only for projects of limited monetary value and with a short contract period
- The JCT Standard Form of Management Contract 1987. This is not a lump sum contract. A Contract Cost Plan is prepared by the quantity surveyor based on the project drawings and specification, the total of which is subject to the management contractor's consent. The actual cost of building the project (the prime cost) is what the employer actually pays, together with a fee to the management contractor for his services.

The use of all these forms of contract presupposes employer-designed works. Where there is to be design input by the contractor – design by him in whole or in part – one of the following can be used:
- The Standard Form With Contractor's Design
- The Standard Form of Building Contract 1980 in its With Quantities version, modified by the JCT Contractor's Designed Portion Supplement.

All these forms are the product of consensus among the constituent bodies of the Joint Contracts Tribunal, which represents all interests, ie employers, contractors, sub-contractors, and consultants. They are negotiated forms of contract and thus represent what is essentially a compromise between the various interests involved. The principal advantage claimed for the JCT contract forms is that they are well-known and widely accepted.

The Joint Contracts Tribunal currently consists of the following organisations:
- Royal Institute of British Architects
- Building Employers' Confederation
- Royal Institution of Chartered Surveyors
- Association of County Councils
- Association of Metropolitan Authorities
- Association of District Councils
- Confederation of Associations of Specialist Engineering Contractors
- Federation of Associations of Specialists and Sub-Contractors
- Association of Consulting Engineers
- British Property Federation
- Scottish Building Contract Committee.

The JCT also publish appropriate supporting sub-contract documentation and there is a Scottish Supplement to the JCT Standard Form of Building Contract 1980, published by the Scottish Building Contract Committee, which is also responsible for a series of documents relating to nominated sub-contractors under that form.

In contrast to the JCT forms, a set of standard conditions has been made available through the initiative of the Association of Consultant Architects.

17

The document is called The ACA Form of Building Agreement 1982, 2nd edition 1984 (and referred to as ACA 2) and the Association also publishes a supporting form of sub-contract, various pro forma certificates and a *Guide* to the contract. This is not a negotiated document but there was informal consultation with all interests during the original drafting, and in the preparation of the second edition there was a considerable input from the British Property Federation. The allocation of risk and responsibility differs from that of the JCT forms but the contract is by no means an employer's document, as some critics have suggested.

Amongst other things, the ACA Agreement provides a number of alternatives within one document:

- It can be used with or without bills of quantities
- It can be used conventionally, where the architect undertakes the design and provides all construction information. Alternatively, the architect may produce a finite set of drawings and require the contractor to provide construction information
- There is a wide choice of alternative clauses. For example, there are alternative provisions for extensions of time, under one of which the contractor assumes the risk of delays to completion by any cause other than acts, defaults, etc of the employer or the architect, the other provision being in the JCT mould
- It is assumed that the contractor will price for the risks involved, depending on the alternatives chosen
- Adjudication followed by arbitration is offered as an alternative to conventional arbitration as a method of dispute settlement. Indeed, neither of these options need be chosen, as an optional clause also provides for litigation in the courts
- There is a choice between liquidated damages and general damages as the sanction for late completion
- Many of the ambiguities in the JCT forms have been done away with.

Another standard form of unilateral provenance is GC/Works/1: the General Conditions of Government Contracts for Building and Civil Engineering Works, 2nd edition 1977. These conditions can be used as a full bill form of contract, as a schedule form of contract or as a lump sum form. It is an exceptionally well-drafted set of contract conditions and strikes a fair balance between the competing needs of the parties. With some modifications, it can be used for private work, though it is generally disliked by contractors.

Table 1.06 summarises the broad advantages and disadvantages of the various forms mentioned in this section. **Table 1.07** compares the clauses in more detail.

1.05   The JCT Standard Form of Building Contract 1963 edition

Although the Joint Contracts Tribunal has withdrawn its sanction from this form, and printed copies of it are no longer available, it is known that JCT 63 is still used. Even at the time of writing, several years after its withdrawal, contracts are being let on JCT 63 terms.

There are a good number of legal and practical reasons why JCT 63 should not be used in any circumstances at all. It is defective in several important respects as regards protecting the employer's interests. For example:

- Fluctuations are not frozen at the due date for completion, in contrast to the position under JCT 80. Under JCT 63 (except where formula adjustment applies) the employer has to bear all the additional cost of items covered by the fluctuations provisions. The fluctuations clauses are not restricted to the completion date but extend throughout the whole period until the construction work is completed
- The JCT 63 extensions of time clause is gravely defective. It makes no provision for such defaults of the employer as failure to give agreed access to the site
- Since the JCT has withdrawn its sanction to the document, as a matter of law any ambiguities in the document – and there are many ambiguities in it – will be interpreted against the person putting the form forward, ie the employer.

Indeed, many authoritative commentators consider that an architect recommending the use of this form to a client may well be holding himself open to an action for professional negligence if the employer suffers loss as a result.

Admittedly, JCT 80 is somewhat more complex administratively – notably as regards nomination of sub-contractors – but that is not a reason for using JCT 63. The latter contract is not discussed in this book, but **Table 1.08** compares the provisions of JCT 63 with those of JCT 80.

1.06   The Standard Forms Outlined

The JCT Standard Form of Building Contract 1980
JCT 80 is very widely used for a range of building projects. It is available in a number of versions:

- For private or local authority users
- With or without bills of quantities as a contract document defining what is to be done for the price
- With either firm or approximate quantities.

In all its versions the form is long and complex. Its characteristics include:

- An architect and a quantity surveyor must be appointed. The architect has wide but strictly-defined power to issue instructions, etc on behalf of the employer and also acts as independent certifier of payments, quality of work, the contractor's performance, and so on. The quantity surveyor is responsible for the valuation of work, variations etc
- Provision for the nomination of specialist sub-contractors designed to safeguard the interests of the main and sub-contractor against each other and with consequential involvement of the architect in the process of nomination and in the administration of the resulting sub-contracts
- Elaborate provisions for dealing with delays to and disruption of the work
- Lengthy and complex insurance provisions
- Detailed provisions for bringing the contractor's employment to an end in the event of default or insolvency by either party.

JCT Practice Note 20 (revised July 1984) contains valuable guidance on its use, and the choice between bills and specification. In the Tribunal's view, the use of bills is generally desirable where the estimated value of the works is £100,000 or more at 1984 prices, and their use may well be desirable below that figure if the works are very complex.

The JCT Intermediate Form of Contract 1984

IFC 84 is widely used. It bridges the gap between JCT 80 and the Minor Works Form discussed below. Even though it is somewhat shorter than JCT 80 it is still very complex. Its characteristics include:

- Flexibility. It may be used for both local authority and private employers and with or without bills of quantities as the control document
- Provision for specialist sub-contractors to be "named" either in the contract documents or subsequently. Although these provisions (which are complicated) attempt to protect the interests of both main and sub-contractors, they do not involve the architect in the administration of the sub-contract, although the procedure for naming sub-contractors is administratively complex and involves the use of specially-prepared documents
- Shorter but still complex provisions for dealing with delays to and disruption of the work
- Lengthy and elaborate insurance provisions
- Improved provisions for determination of the contractor's employment (see **Table 1.09** for a comparison of determination clauses in standard forms)
- Power for the employer to defer giving of possession of the site.

Because it is shorter and less detailed than JCT 80, there is a real danger that the Intermediate Form will be used in situations it was not designed for, as has happened in practice with the Minor Works Form.

The JCT Form of Agreement for Minor Works 1980

MW 80 is a simple form of contract for use on very small projects but the conditions provide a bare outline. It is acceptable for such projects as domestic extensions and in general should not be used where the contract value exceeds £70,000 at 1987 prices. Its simplicity, while an advantage on the sort of project for which it is designed, makes it a dangerous document to use on larger projects where its lack of provisions dealing with many matters that may go wrong may leave the employer in an exposed position.

The JCT Standard Form of Management Contract 1987

This complex document followed JCT 80 in its philosophy and drafting. The employer appoints a professional team which prepares project drawings and a specification describing the general scope of the project. Detailed drawings, specifications and bills of quantities are then prepared at appropriate times for use in the various works contracts which are entered into by the management contractor as and when required. It is not a lump sum contract. The employer pays the actual cost incurred by the management contractor in building the project, together with a management fee.

At the end of the pre-construction period, the employer may instruct the management contractor that he is not to proceed, in which case he receives the pre-construction period fee specified in the contract Appendix. A notable provision of the contract is that the architect is empowered to instruct acceleration of progress of the project or to alter its timing or sequence provided the employer has stated in the Appendix that he wishes these provisions to apply.

The JCT Fixed Fee Form of Prime Cost Contract 1967 (last revised 1976)

This Fixed Fee form, which is now of considerable age, is quite close in its drafting to JCT 63. While it is intended for use where, for whatever reason, it is not possible to obtain a firm price for the work in advance, it assumes that the design of the work has been developed to a point at which it is possible to estimate its probable cost with considerable accuracy, since such an estimate is required to be inserted and forms the basis for the fixed fee.

In its characteristics, it is akin to JCT 80, but without the improvements to that form as compared with the 1963 edition. It makes no provision for variations to the work as such and may well be considered too inflexible for the majority of projects. It also deals hardly at all with the monitoring of the prime cost or for the exclusion of costs arising from the contractor's inefficiency. Its main disadvantages are twofold.

- It is difficult to obtain satisfactory competitive tenders because of the limited nature of the contract documentation
- There is really no certainty about the ultimate price.

The JCT Form with Contractor's Design 1981

As its name suggests, this form is for use where a contractor is engaged at the outset to design as well as construct the whole of the project. There is also a supplement (Contractor's Designed Portion Supplement) for use where only part of the project is to be designed by the contractor and the remainder by the employer's design team. There is no provision for the appointment of an architect or quantity surveyor as such, but there must be an "Employer's Agent" who acts on behalf of the employer throughout. There is no provision for nomination or naming of specialist sub-contractors although it is possible for this to be done effectively through the Employer's Requirements which, together with the Contractor's Proposals constitute the control documents for the work provided the optional supplementary provisions issued in February 1988 are stated to apply. The Employer's Requirements will often take the form of a performance specification set out in considerable detail. In other respects the form is similar in style and content to JCT 80.

The ACA Form of Building Agreement 1982 (second edition 1984)

The principal characteristic of this form (ACA 2) is adaptability. It provides for the situation where the design has been fully developed by the employer's design team before the contractor is engaged, as well as for the situation where the design is developed to a certain point from which the contractor takes over the final design development. It can be used for variations between these themes. It has a number of alternative clauses for such other matters as contract documentation, extension of time and settlement of disputes and this makes it flexible in its application. It provides for the naming of sub-contractors – though these differ from "named persons" under the JCT Intermediate Form – and it points up the contractor's responsibilities.

There is also a version (the BPF edition) for use with the method of building procurement devised by the British Property Federation and this provides for a Schedule of Activities to be used as a control document as an alternative to bills of quantities.

Table 1.10 sets out some possible uses of the alternative clauses according to the type of project involved. Detailed instructions about the alternatives are found in the marginal notes printed in italics in each right-hand margin of the

Agreement itself and in particular the various time-periods may be changed if they are not appropriate. Full guidance on completion of the form is to be found in the *Guide to the ACA Form of Building Agreement* published by the ACA.

The Government Conditions of Contract (GC/Works/1)

This contract is widely and successfully used for central government work and has stood the test of time. A significant characteristic is that there are many contract conditions which give binding force to the decisions of the employer (called "the Authority" in the form). An essential document is the Abstract of Particulars, which can be used to modify the conditions themselves. This document will identify the employer, the superintending officer and the quantity surveyor and will also contain the details which are usually set out in an appendix to other forms of contract. GC/Works/1 is fair but firm and the superintending officer – on behalf of the employer – is firmly in control throughout. The provisions for prolongation and disturbance are in traditional form, with quite complex procedures, and provision is made for the nomination of specialists.

GC/Works/1 is now in its second edition and a radically revised third edition will be in use in 1990, for the time being alongside the second edition. Edition 3 of GC/Works/1 includes many unique features including a requirement for provision of a resource programme which is essential to the management of the contract.

Table 1.01 Various Ways of Apportioning Basic Responsibilities

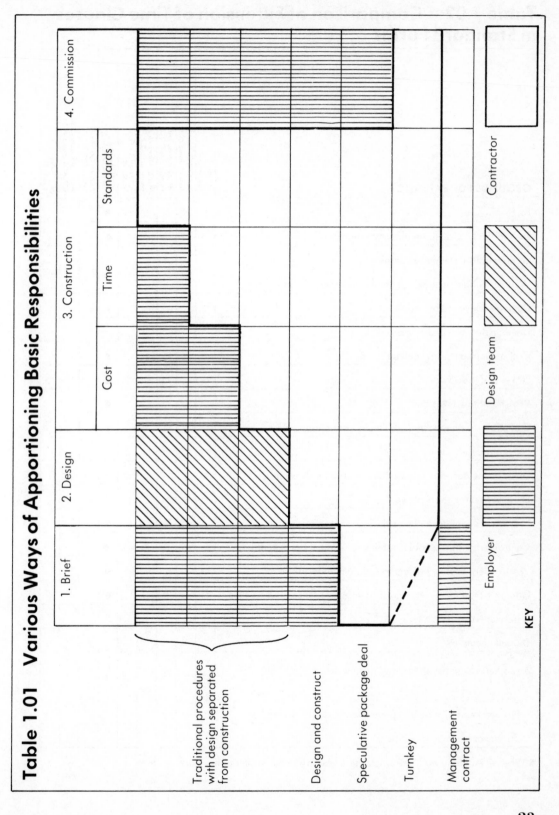

Table 1.02: Comparison of Extension of Time Clauses in Standard Forms

GROUNDS FOR EXTENSION	JCT 80 (clause 25.4)	JCT 81 With Contractor's Design (clause 25.4)	IFC 84 Intermediate Form (clause 2.3)	MW 80 Minor Works Form (clause 2.2)	JCT Fixed Fee Form (clause 19)	JCT Management Contract (clause 2.12)	ACA 2 alternative 1 (clause 11.5)	ACA 2 alternative 2 & BPF/ACA (clause 11.5)	GC/Works/1 (clause 28(2))
Force majeure	○	○	○	○	○	●		○	○
Exceptionally adverse weather conditions	○	○	○	○		●			
Exceptionally inclement weather				○	○				
Weather conditions making continuance of work impracticable				○					○
Damage due to insured risks	○	○	○	○		●		○	
Damage due to accepted risks									○
Civil commotion, riot, rebellion	○	○	○	○	○	●		○	○
Strikes and lock-outs	○	○	○	○	○	●			○
War, hostilities, invasion	○	○	○	○	○	●		○	○
Compliance with specified architect's instructions	○	○	○		○	●			○
Late instructions, etc	○	○	○	○	○	○		○	○
Delay on the part of nominated sub-contractors or suppliers	○				○	●			
Employer's direct work or supply	○	○	○	○	○	●			
Exercise of governmental power	○	○		○		●			
Contractor's unforeseeable inability to obtain labour or materials	○	○	○		○	●			
Work under statutory powers by statutory undertakers	○	○	○	○	○	●		○	
Employer's failure to give ingress or egress	○	○	○	○		●			
Deferment of possession	○		○			○	○		
Default of employer						○	○	○	○
Any other reason beyond control of contractor — Foreseen					○				
Any other reason beyond control of contractor — Unforeseen					○				○
Delay in receipt of necessary permission of statutory body		○							
Unforeseeable ground conditions									○

● Where it entitles a works contractor to an extension of time under the works contract.

Table 1.03: JCT Series of Contracts Arranged in Genealogical Form

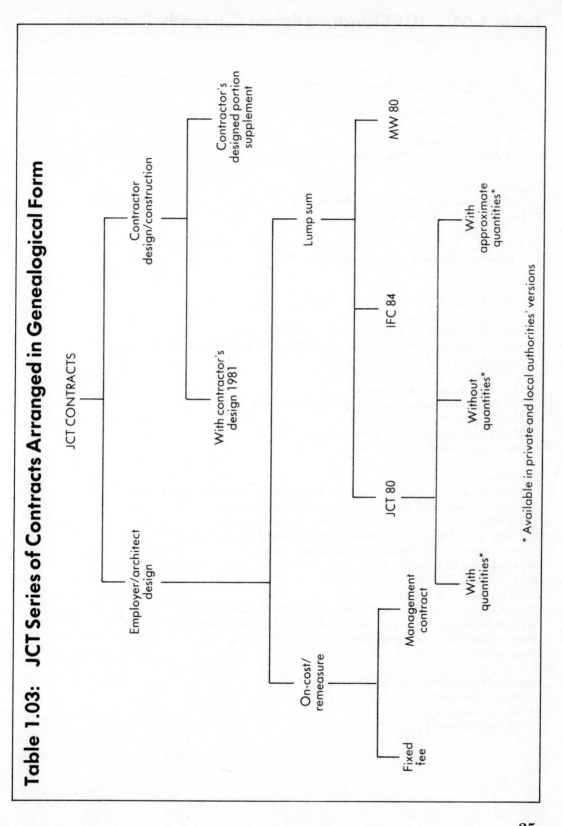

JCT CONTRACTS

Employer/architect design

Contractor design/construction

With contractor's design 1981

Contractor's designed portion supplement

On-cost/remeasure

Management contract

Fixed fee

With quantities*

JCT 80

Without quantities*

IFC 84

Lump sum

MW 80

With approximate quantities*

* Available in private and local authorities' versions

Table 1.04:   JCT Standard Forms Currently Available

Standard Form of Building Contract (JCT 80)
Local Authorities With Quantities
Local Authorities Without Quantities
Local Authorities With Approximate Quantities
Private With Quantities
Private Without Quantities
Private With Approximate Quantities

Supplements to JCT 80
    Fluctuations supplement (local authority)
    Fluctuations supplement (private)
    Formula rules
    Sectional completion supplement
    Contractor's designed portion supplement

Sub-contract forms
    NSC/1 Nominated sub-contract tender and agreement
    NSC/1a Nominated sub-contract tender
    NSC/2 Employer/nominated sub-contractor agreement
    NSC/2a Employer/nominated sub-contractor agreement (where NSC/1 not used)
    NSC/3 Nomination of a sub-contractor
    NSC/3a Nomination of a sub-contractor
    NSC/4 Nominated sub-contract
    NSC/4a Nominated sub-contract (where NSC/1 not used)
    TNS/1 Tender for nominated suppliers
    TNS/2 Warranty for nominated suppliers
Intermediate Form of Building Contract (IFC 84)

Related forms
    Fluctuations clauses and formula rules for sub-contracts and works contracts
    NAM/T Tender and agreement for named sub-contractors
    NAM/SC Sub-contract conditions for named sub-contractors
    NAM/SC/FR Sub-contract formula rules for named sub-contractors
    ESA/1 RIBA/CASEC Employer/specialist agreement
Agreement for Minor Works 1980
Minor Works Supplement
Fixed Fee form of prime cost contract
Agreement for renovation grant works (where architect employed)
Agreement for renovation grant works (where architect *not* employed)
Standard Form with contractor's design
Formula rules

Standard Form of Management Contract (JCT 87)
    Works Contract/1
    Works Contract/2
    Works Contract/3

Table 1.05:   Contract Selection

CRITERIA	JCT 80 With Quantities	JCT 80 Without Quantities	JCT 80 With Approximate Quantities	JCT 80 With Contractor's Design	IFC 84 Intermediate Form	MW 80 Minor Works Form	JCT 87 Management Form	JCT Fixed Fee Form	ACA 2	GC/Works/1
Negotiated	○	○	○	○	○	○	○	○		
Simple						○			●	
Comprehensive	○	○	○				○		○	○
Flexible				○	○		○		○	
Lump sum	○	○		○	○	○			○	○
Bills of quantities can be used	○		●		○				○	○
Schedule of rates can be used					○	○			○	○
Specification can be used		○			○	○	○	○	○	○
Alternative clauses									○	
Suitable for uncertain work								○		
Suitable for complex work	○		○	○			○		○	○
Suitable for early start work			○				○	○		
Suitable for contracts over one year	○	○	○	○			○	○	○	○
Suitable for project management contracts				○			○		○	
Suitable for contracts under £100,000	○	○	○	○	○	○		○	○	○
Suitable for contracts £100,000 to £800,000	○		○	○	●		○	○	○	○
Suitable for contracts over £1,000,000	○		○	○			○	○	○	○
Principal topics covered										
Architect/Contract Administrator	○	○	○		○	○	○	○	○	○
Quantity surveyor	○	○	○		○	○	○	○	○	○
Clerk of works	○	○	○		○		○	○		○
Contractor's obligations	○	○	○	○	○	○	○	○	○	○
Discrepancies	○	○	○	○	○	○	○		○	○
Statutory requirements	○	○	○	○	○	○	○	○	○	
Drawings	○	○	○	○	○	○	○	○	○	○
Ground conditions									○	○

Table 1.05: Contract Selection – (continued)

CRITERIA	JCT 80 With Quantities	JCT 80 Without Quantities	JCT 80 With Approximate Quantities	JCT 80 With Contractor's Design	IFC 84 Intermediate Form	MW 80 Minor Works Form	JCT 87 Management Form	JCT Fixed Fee Form	ACA 2	GC/Works/1
Access by architect	O	O	O	O		O	O	O	O	O
Contractor's supervision of the works	O	O	O	O	O	O	O	O	O	
Vesting of property	O	O	O	O	O		O	O	O	O
Insurance against injury to persons and property	O	O	O	O	O	O	O	O	O	
Insurance of the works	O	O	O	O	O	O	O	O	O	
Insurance against non-negligent damage to the works	O	O	O	O	O			O	O	O
Design indemnity insurance by contractor									O	
Disturbance to regular progress	O	O	O	O	O			O	O	O
Instructions	O	O	O	O	O	O	O	O	O	O
Valuation of variations	O	O	O	O	O	O	O		O	O
Assignment	O	O	O	O	O	O	O	O	O	O
Sub-letting	O	O	O	O	O	O		O	O	O
Named sub-contractors					O				O	
Nominated sub-contractors	O	O	O				O			O
Employer's licensees	O	O	O	O	O		O	O	O	O
Liquidated damages	O	O	O	O	O	O	O	O	O	O
Extension of time	O	O	O	O	O	O	O	O	O	O
Extension of time review	O	O	O	O	O				O	
Acceleration							O		O	
Postponement	O	O	O	O	O		O		O	O
Deferment of possession	O	O	O	O	O		O			
Practical completion	O	O	O	O	O	O	O	O	O	O
Defects liability period	O	O	O	O	O	O	O	O	O	O
Partial possession	O	O	O	O			O	O	O	O
Certification/payment	O	O	O	O	O	O	O	O	O	O
Fluctuations	O	O	O	O	O				O	O

Table 1.05:   Contract Selection – (continued)

CRITERIA	JCT 80 With Quantities	JCT 80 Without Quantities	JCT 80 With Approximate Quantities	JCT 80 With Contractor's Design	IFC 84 Intermediate Form	MW 80 Minor Works Form	JCT 87 Management Form	JCT Fixed Fee Form	ACA 2	GC/Works/1
Determination by employer	O	O	O	O	O	O	O	O	O	O
Determination by contractor	O	O	O	O	O	O	O	O	O	
Determination by either party					O		O		O	
Determination at will of employer							O			O
Antiquities	O	O	O	O			O	O	O	O
Hostilities	O	O	O	O			O	O		
Adjudication									O	
Arbitration	O	O	O	O	O	O	O	O	O	O
Litigation									O	

Table 1.06: Alternative Standard Forms of Contract

Name	Upper cost Limits	Contract documents	Advantages	Disadvantages
The ACA Form of Building Agreement 1984	No	Drawings Schedule of rates or bills of quantities or specification	Adjudication during contract period Simple scheme of payment Provision for design responsibility by contractor with professional indemnity cover Useful range of alternative clauses	Not yet widely accepted Time periods not always realistic
The JCT Standard Form of Building Contract 1980	No	Drawings Bills of quantities (variants with approx quantities or specification)	Comprehensive Widely accepted negotiated document Comprehensive selection of ancillary forms	Complex nominated sub-contract provisions Unrealistic fluctuations Printed conditions prevail over specially drafted ones Broad provisions for extensions of time Determination by contractor contains onerous provisions
The JCT Standard Form of Building Contract With Contractor's Design 1981	No	Employer's requirements Contractor's proposals including contract sum analysis	Flexible May be used with or without architect's assistance May save time	Good inspection procedures essential Contractor's obligations may be badly defined Likely to be increases in cost to achieve requirements Only limited responsibility for design on contractor
The JCT Intermediate Form of Building Contract for Works of Simple content 1984	Yes	Drawings Bills of quantities or Schedules of work or Specification	Provision for deferment of possession Flexible use Wide arbitration clause Wide testing provisions	Not suitable where specialist employed Not suitable for long or complex contracts
The JCT Agreement for Minor Building Works 1980	Yes	Drawings Specification or Schedules	Simple and easy to understand	No provision for financial claims No nominated sub-contractors Minimal fluctuations Liquidated damages cannot be deducted

Table 1.06:   Alternative Standard Forms of Contract – (continued)

Name	Upper cost Limits	Contract documents	Advantages	Disadvantages
				No insurance for non-negligent damage to other works
The JCT Standard Form of Management Contract 1987	No	Project Drawings Project Specification	Comprehensive Flexible Wide selection of supporting documentation	Complex in parts Low risk to contractor Residual risks on employer
The JCT Fixed Fee Form of Prime Cost Contract 1976	No	Specification with or without drawings	Useful where exact extent of work cannot be ascertained	Difficult to obtain competitive tenders Final cost uncertain No provision for variations Inflexible Closely related to JCT 63
GC/Works/1 Government Conditions of Contract Edition 2	No	Drawings Bills of quantities or Schedule of rates Specification	Clear Rarely the subject of dispute May be used for building or civil engineering works	Complex in parts Not a negotiated contract Unpopular with contractors

Table 1.07: Comparison of Clauses in Standard Forms of Contract

Description	JCT 80	JCT MW	JCT WCD	IFC 84	GC/Works/1	ACA 2	JCT Fixed Fee	JCT 87
Contractor's general obligations Co-operation with professional team	2	1	2	1	6 and/ or 13	1	2	1.4
Execution of works	2	1.1	2	1.1	6	1.1	2	—
Contractor's skill and care	—	—	2.5	—	—	1.2	—	—
Priority of documents	2.2	1.1	2.2	1.3	4	1.3	—	—
Bills of quantities	2.2	—	—	1.5	5	1.4	—	—
Ambiguities and discrepancies	2.3	4.1	2.3	1.4	4	1.5	—	—
Statutory requirements	6	5.1	6	5.1	14	1.6	5	—
Compliance with statutory requirements	6	5.1	6	5.1	14	1.7	5(1)	—
Drawings, details and information	5	1.2	5	1	4	2 Alternative 1	4(1)	—
Copies of contract documents	5.2	—	—	1.6	4(3)	2.1	—	1.9
Architect's drawings and details	5	1.2	—	1.7	4(3)	2.2	4(1)	1.10
Part of works	—	—	—	—	—	2.3	—	—
Drawings, details and information	—	—	5	—	—	2 Alternative 2	—	—
Copies of contract documents	—	—	5.2	—	—	2.1	—	—
Submission of contractor's drawings, etc	—	—	5.3	—	—	2.2	—	—
Return of contractor's drawings, etc	—	—	—	—	—	2.3	—	—
Architect's comments	—	—	—	—	—	2.4	—	—
Part of works	—	—	—	—	—	2.5	—	—
Ground conditions and artificial obstructions	—	—	—	—	—	2.6	—	—
Obligations in respect of drawings, details, documents and information	2 5	1.2	2 5	—	4	3	—	—
Errors in contractor's drawings	—	—	2.5	—	—	3.1	—	—
Effect on time schedule and contract sum	—	—	—	—	—	3.2	—	—
Confidentiality	5.7	—	5.6	1.8	—	3.3	4(2)	1.11
Effect of architect's comments	—	—	—	—	—	3.4	—	—
Samples	—	—	—	—	—	3.5	—	—
Visits to the works by the architect	11	—	11	—	—	4	9	3.17
Access for the architect	11	—	11	—	—	4.1	9	3.17
Visits by the architect	11	—	11	—	—	4.2	9	3.17
Supervision of the works by the contractor	—	—	—	—	—	5	—	—
Contractor's management of the works	—	—	—	—	—	5.1	—	1.8
Site manager	10	3.3	10	3.4	33	5.2	7(2)	3.13
Duties of site manager	—	—	—	—	—	5.3	—	—
Contractor's employees	—	—	—	—	13	5.4	—	—

Table 1.07: Comparison of Clauses in Standard Forms of Contract – (continued)

Description	JCT 80	JCT MW	JCT WCD	IFC 84	GC/Works/1	ACA 2	JCT Fixed Fee	JCT 87
Vesting of property, contractor's indemnity and insurance	16	6	15	1	3	6	8	—
Vesting of property	16	—	15	1.10 1.11	3(1)	6.1	8	—
Passing of risk	16	—	15	1.10 1.11	3	6.2	8	—
Contractor's indemnity and Insurance	20 21	6.1 6.2	20 21	6 —	47 —	6.3 —	14 15	6.7 6.9
Insurance of the works by the contractor (new buildings)	22A	6.3A	22A	6.3A	47	6.4 Alternative 1	—	—
Insurance of the works by the employer (existing buildings)	22B 22C	6.3B	22B 22C	6.3C	47	6.4 Alternative 2	16A	6.1 6.4
Insurance against collapse, subsidence, etc	21.2	—	21.2	6.4	—	6.5	15(2)	6.4
Professional indemnity insurance	—	—	—	—	—	6.6	—	—
Contractor's insurances	22A	6.4	22A	6.3A	47	6.7	—	—
Premiums	22A	—	22A	6.3A	47	6.8	—	6.4
Breach by contractor	22A	—	22A	6.3A	47	6.9	—	6.4
Claims by employer	22B 22C	6.3B —	22B 22C	6.3B 6.3C	47 —	6.10 —	16A 16B	— —
Insurance for loss of LAD	22D	—	22D	6.3D	—	—	—	6.6
Employer's liability	26	—	26	4.11	53	7	20	—
Disturbance to regular progress	26.1	—	26	4.11	53	7.1	20(1)	—
Notice of claim	26.1	—	26	4.11	53	7.2	20(1)	—
Submission of estimates	—	—	—	—	—	7.3	—	—
Agreement of estimates	—	—	—	—	—	7.4	—	—
Adjudication	—	—	—	—	—	7.5	—	—
Architect's instructions	4	3	4	3.5	7	8	3	1.8
Architect's instructions	4.1	3.5	4.1	3.5 3.6	7	8.1	3(1)	3.3
Valuation of architect's instructions	13	3.6	12.4 12.5	3.7	9	8.2	—	3.4
Oral instructions	4.3	3.5	4.3	—	7(2)	8.3	3(3)	—
Assignment and sub-letting	19	3	18	3.1	27	9	13	3.19
Assignment	19.1	3.1	18.1	3.1	27	9.1	13(1) 13(2)	3.19
Sub-letting	19.2	3.2	18.2	3.2	30	9.2	13(3)	—
Sub-contractors named in the contract documents	19.3 35 36	—	—	3.3	—	9.3	23 24	—
Architect's instructions as to named sub-contractors: provisional sums	19.3 35 36	—	—	3.3.2	38 39	9.4	23 24	—
Architect's instructions requiring sub-letting	35 36	—	—	—	38 39	9.5	23 24	—

Table 1.07: Comparison of Clauses in Standard Forms of Contract – (continued)

Description	JCT 80	JCT MW	JCT WCD	IFC 84	GC/Works/1	ACA 2	JCT Fixed Fee	JCT 87
Negotiation with sub-contracts	—	—	—	—	—	9.6	—	—
Termination of sub-contracts	35	—	—	3.3.3	44(6) 38(5)	9.7	—	—
Design by sub-contractors or suppliers	—	—	—	—	—	9.8	—	—
Contractor's responsibility for sub-contractors and suppliers	35.21 35.22	—	—	3.3.6	31 (2)	9.9	—	—
Employer's licensees	29	—	29	3.11	38 50	10	25	3.23-3.25
Employer's contractors	29	—	29	3.11	38 50	10.1	25	3.23-3.25
Instructions in relation to employer's contractors	29	—	29	3.11	38 50	10.2	—	3.23
Statutory undertakers	—	—	29	3		10.3	—	—
Adjustment to contract sum	14.2 3	—	26	4.11		10.4	26	—
Commencement and delays in the execution of the works	23	2.0	23	2.1	6 28	11	17	
Commencement and taking-over of the works	23	2.1	23	2.1	28	11.1	17	18
Certificate that works not fit and ready	24.1	2.4	24.1	2.5	—	11.2	18	2.9
Damages for delay	24.2	2.3	24.2	2.6	29	11.3	18	2.10
Adjustment of damages for delay	24.2	—	24.2	2.7	—	11.4	—	2.11
Grounds for extension of time	25.4	2.2	25.4	2.3	28(2)	11.5	19	2.13
Extensions of time	25.3	2.2	25.3	2.2	28(2)	11.6	19	2.12
Review of extension of time granted	25.3	—	25.3	2.2	—	11.7	—	—
Acceleration and postponement	—	—	—	—	—	11.8	—	3.6
Revision to the time schedule	—	—	—	—	—	11.9	—	—
Taking over and defective work	17	2.5	16	2.8 2.9	28 32	12	11	2.4
Taking over	17.1	—	16.1	2.8	—	12.1	11(1)	2.4
Defective outstanding work	17.2	2.5	16.2	2.9	32	12.2	11(2)	2.5
Costs of defective work	17.3	2.5	16.2	2.9	32	12.3	11(3)	2.5
Remedy for failure by contractor	17.4 4.1	2.5	16.4 4.1	2.9	32	12.4	3(2)	2.5
Taking over of part of the works	18	—	17	—	28A	13	12	2.8
Employer may take over part	18	—	17	—	28A	13.1	12	2.8
Date of taking over part	18	—	17	—	28A	13.2	12	2.8
Reduction of damages	18.1.5	—	17.1.5	—	28A(4)	13.3	12(d)	2.8
Antiquities	34	—	34	—	20	14	30	3.26
Property in antiquities	34.1	—	34.1	—	20(2)	14.1	30(1)	3.26
Instructions on discovery of antiquities	34.2	—	34.2	—	20(3)	14.2	30(2)	3.27

Table 1.07: Comparison of Clauses in Standard Forms of Contract – (continued)

Description	JCT 80	JCT MW	JCT WCD	IFC 84	GC/Works/1	ACA 2	JCT Fixed Fee	JCT 87
The contract sum	14	—	13	4.1	41	15	—	—
Adjustments to the contract sum	3	—	3	4.1	41	15.1	26	—
Quantity surveyor	Art 4	4th Recital	—	Art 4	1(2)	15.2	1(2)	Art 4
Duties of quantity surveyor	—	—	—	—	—	15.3	—	—
Payment	30	4	30	4	40	16	27	4
Interim applications	—	4.2	—	—	40(3)	16.1	—	—
Interim certificates	30.1	4.2	30.1	4.2	40	16.2	27(1)	4.2
Payment	30.1	4.2	30.1	4.2	40(2)	16.3	27(1)	4.2
Retention monies	30.5	4.2	30.4	4.2	40	16.4	27(4)	4.7
Deductions from retention	30.1	—	30.4	4.2	40	16.5	27(5)	4.8
Provisional sums	13.4	3.7	12.4	3.7	39	16.6	—	—
Value added tax	15	5.2	14	5.5	—	16.7	26A	5.6
Valuation of architect's instructions	13.4	3.6	12.4	3.7	9	17	—	—
Submission of estimates by contractor	—	—	—	—	—	17.1	—	—
Agreement of contractor's estimates	—	—	—	—	—	17.2	—	—
Failure to agree contractor's estimates	—	—	—	—	—	17.3	—	—
Withdrawal of instructions	—	—	—	—	—	17.4	—	—
Valuation if no agreement of estimates	—	—	—	—	—	17.5	—	—
Non-compliance by contractor	—	—	—	—	—	17.6	—	—
Fluctuations	38 39 40	A	36 37 38	4.8 8	11	18	—	—
Fluctuations on interim certificates	As above	A	As above	4.8	11	18.1	—	—
Fluctuations on final contract sum	As above	A	As above	4.8	11	18.2	—	—
Indices delay	—	—	—	—	—	18.3	—	—
Payment of the final contract sum	30	4.4	30	4.5	41	19	27	—
Final account	30.6	4.4	30.5	4.4	41	19.1	27(6)	4.12
Issue of final certificate	30.8	4.4	30.5	4.5	41	19.2	27(7)	4.12
Final payment	30.6	4.4	30.5	4.5	41	19.3	27(7)	4.11
Delivery of documents	—	—	—	—	—	19.4	—	—
Effect of certificates	30.10	—	30.9	4.6 4.7	—	19.5	27(9)	4.12
Termination	27 28	7	27 28	7	44 45	20	21 22	7
Termination by employer	27	7.1	27	7.1	44/45	20.1	21	7.1
Termination by contractor	28	7.1	28	7.5	—	20.2	22	7.5
Termination on insolvency	27.2 28.1	7.1 7.2	27.2	7.2 7.6	45	20.3	21(2) 22(1)(d)	7.2
Termination due to causes outside the control of both parties	(28) 22C 32.1	—	(28) 22C 32.1	7.8	—	21	(22) 16B 28(1)	7.7 — 7.9

Table 1.07: Comparison of Clauses in Standard Forms of Contract – (continued)

Description	JCT 80	JCT MW	JCT WCD	IFC 84	GC/Works/1	ACA 2	JCT Fixed Fee	JCT 87
Consequences of termination	27 28	7.0	27 28	7.4 7.7	46	22	21 22	7.4
Payment where employer terminates	27.4	7.1	27.4	7.4	46	22.1	21(3)	7.4
Payments where contractor terminates	28.2	7.2	28.2	7.7	—	22.2	22(2)	7.6
Payment where termination due to causes outside control of both parties	28.2	—	28.2	7.9	—	22.3	22(2)	7.9
Possession of site on termination	—	7.1	—	7.4(a)	46	22.4	—	—
Common law rights	27 28	7	27 28	7	46	22.5	21 22	7
Drawings	—	—	27.4	—	—	22.6	—	—
Contractors sub-contractors and suppliers	27.4	—	—	—	46	22.7	(21(3)(b)	—
Notices and interpreation	1	8	1	8	1	23	1	1
Notices to be given in writing	4.3	—	4.3	3.5	1(6)	23.1	3(3)	—
Interpretation	1	8	1	8	1	23.2	1	1
Finance (No 2) Act 1975	31	5.3	31	5.6 Supp Cond B	—	24	27B	5.9–5.17
Whether employer is "a contractor"	31	5.3	31	5.6 B	—	24.1	27B	5.10
The statutory deduction	31	5.3	31	B	—	24.2	27B	5.10
Form 715	31	5.3	31	B	—	24.3	27B	—
Calculation of the statutory deduction	31	5.3	31	B	—	24.4	27B	5.11
Breach by contractor of the Act	31	5.3	31	B	—	24.5	27B	5.11
Disputes adjudicator	—	—	—	—	—	25	—	—
The adjudicator	—	—	—	—	—	25.1	—	—
Matters referable to the adjudicator	—	—	—	—	—	25.2	—	—
Effect of adjudicator's decision	—	—	—	—	—	25.3	—	—
Appointment of another adjudicator	—	—	—	—	—	25.4	—	—
Arbitration on adjudicator's decision	—	—	—	—	—	25.5	—	—
Arbitration	—	—	—	—	—	25.6	—	—
Arbitrator's powers	—	—	—	—	—	25.7	—	—
Law of this agreement	—	—	—	—	—	25.8	—	—
Disputes arbitration	Art 5 and cl 41	Art 4 and cl 9	Art 5 and cl 39	Art 5 and s 9	61	25	31A 31B	Art 8 and s 9
Architect's rôle during execution of the works	—	—	—	—	—	25.1	—	—
Effect of architect's decision	—	—	—	—	—	25.2	—	—
Arbitration on architect's decision	—	—	—	—	—	25.3	—	—

Table 1.07: Comparison of Clauses in Standard Forms of Contract – (continued)

Description	JCT 80	JCT MW	JCT WCD	IFC 84	GC/Works/1	ACA 2	JCT Fixed Fee	JCT 87
Appointment of arbitrator	Art 5	Art 4	Art 5	Art 5	61(1)	25.4	31A 31B	
Reference to arbitrator	Art 5 and cl 41	Art 4 and cl 9	Art 5 and cl 39	Art 5 and s 9	61(1)	25.5	31A 31B	Art 8 and s 9
Law of this agreement	Art 5	—	Art 5	Art 5	61(3) 61(4)	25.6	31A(5) 31B(5)	
Disputes Litigation	—	—	—	—	—	25	—	—

Table 1.08: Comparison of JCT 80 and JCT 63

Clause		Comment
JCT 80	JCT 63	
1	*	No interpretation clause in JCT 80
2.1	1(2)	
2.2	*	
2.3	1(2)	
3	*	New provision
4	2	
5	3	
6	4	
7	5	
8	6	
9	7	
10	8	
11	9	
12	10	
13	11	Wider definition of variation, revised valuation rules, and clause 11(6) omitted
14	12/13	
15	13A	Separate VAT agreement no longer required
16	14	
17	15	
18	16	
19	17	
19A	17A	
20	18	
21	19/19A	
22A	20A	
22B	20B	
22C	20C	
23	21	
24	22	A major redraft in JCT 80 relating to both liquidated damages and extensions of time
25	23	
26	24	New procedure regarding claims
27	25	
28	26	Some drafting changes
29	29	
30	30	A major redraft
31	30B	
32	32	
33	33	
34	34	
35	27	Entirely new provisions for nomination
36	28	
37	31	

Note: The arbitration agreement (JCT 63 clause 35) is now found in substantially amended form in JCT 80 clause 41 and article 5. The whole contract has been substantially redrafted.

Clause	JCT 80	JCT 81 With Contractor's Design	IFC 84 Intermediate Form	MW 80 Minor Works Form	JCT 87 Management Form	JCT Fixed Fee Form	ACA 2	GC/Works/1
BY EMPLOYER								
Contractor wholly suspends the work	O	O	O	O*	O	O	O	
Contractor fails to proceed regularly and diligently with the works	O	O	O	O*	O	O	O	
Contractor does not comply with instruction re defective work, etc	O	O	O		O	O	O	O
Contractor assigns without consent	O	O	O		O	O	O	
Contractor becomes insolvent, etc	●	●	●	O*	O	●		O*
Contractor corrupt	O^{2}*	O^{2}*	O^{2}*	O^{2}*	O			O*
Contractor otherwise in breach of contract							O	
At the employer's discretion						O		O*
BY CONTRACTOR								
Non-payment	O	O	O	O	O	O	O	
Obstruction by employer	O*		O	O	O	O	O	
Delay in works for specified period due to:								
Force majeure						O*		
Damage by insurance contingencies						O*		
Civil commotion						O*		
Certain AIs	O*	O*	O		O	O*		
Late instructions	O*	O*	O		O	O*		
Delay by employer's men	O*	O*	O		O	O*		
Opening up and testing	O*	O*			O	O*		
Planning approval		O*						
Failure to give access			O		O			
Employer's breach				O				
Employer becomes insolvent, etc	O^{1}		O*	O*		O*		

Table 1.09: Comparison of Determination Clauses in Standard Forms – (continued)

Clause	JCT 80	JCT 81 With Contractor's Design	IFC 84 Intermediate Form	MW 80 Minor Works Form	JCT 87 Management Form	JCT Fixed Fee Form	ACA 2	GC/Works/1
BY EITHER PARTY								
Damage to existing works due to insurance contingencies	O*	O*	O*			O*		
Outbreak of hostilities	O*	O*				O*		
Suspension of work for a specified period due to:								
Force majeure	O		O*		O		O*	
Damage by insurance contingencies	O		O*		O		O*	
Civil commotion	O		O*		O			
War, etc							O*	

KEY
1 – Not applicable to local authorities
2 – Only applicable to local authorities
* – Notice not required before determination forthwith
● – Automatic determination

Table 1.10: Suggested Uses of Alternative Clauses in the ACA2 Form

TYPE OF PROJECT	Architect's drawings	Contractor's dwgs and details	Full extras	Limited extras	With quantities	Without quantities	General damages	Liquidated damages	Employer's damages	Employer's insurance	Contractor's insurance	Sectional completion	Single completion	Adjudication or arbitration
One-off private dwelling	O		O			O	O			O		O	O	
Housing estate (private)	O	O		O	O		O			O	O		O	
Housing estate (public)	O	O	O		O			O		O		O		O
Housing association	O	O		O	O			O		O		O	O	
New office for owner-occupier	O			O		O	O			O		O	O	
New office for development	O	O		O	O			O		O		O	O	
Refurbished office for owner-occupier	O			O	O			O	O		O		O	
Refurbished office for development	O	O		O	O			O	O			O	O	
New factory for owner-occupier	O			O		O	O			O	O		O	
New factory for development	O	O		O	O			O	O			O	O	
Refurbished factory for owner-occupier	O			O	O		O		O				O	
Refurbished factory for development								O	O				O	
New warehouse for owner-occupier	O	O		O		O	O			O		O	O	
New warehouse for development	O	O	O		O			O		O		O	O	
Refurbished warehouse for owner-occupier	O			O	O		O		O		O		O	
Refurbished warehouse for development	O	O		O	O			O		O		O	O	
New hotel	O	O	O		O			O		O		O	O	
Refurbished hotel	O			O	O			O	O			O	O	
New hospital	O		O		O			O	O		O		O	
Hospital, refurbished wards	O		O		O			O	O		O		O	
Hospital, technical areas	O	O	O		O			O	O		O			
New laboratories	O		O		O		O			O	O		O	
Refurbished laboratories	O	O	O		O			O	O		O		O	
Refurbished local authority dwellings	O				O	O		O	O		O		O	

41

2: The JCT Standard Form of Building Contract (JCT 80)

2.01 Introduction

The JCT Standard Form of Building Contract 1980 (JCT 80) replaced an earlier version of the form, last published in 1963. It has been amended from time to time, the latest amendment (No 8) being issued in April 1989. JCT 80 has many advantages over its predecessor and is probably one of the most widely used standard form contracts in the construction industry.

It is a lump sum contract and the JCT has given little guidance on its use. Primarily, it is designed for use in larger and more complex projects and it must be used where the employer wishes to make use of nominated sub-contractors or nominated suppliers, since none of the other JCT forms makes provision for these specialists. It should be used where there are building services installations of a complex nature or, indeed, where there is other specialist work of a complex sort.

The JCT Practice Note 20 *Deciding on the appropriate form of JCT Main Contract* was revised in July 1984, and emphasises that the price range of the works is not conclusive as to the choice of form. Where bills of quantities are required the employer has an effective choice between JCT 80, with Quantities edition and the Intermediate Form (IFC 84) using bills of quantities, although in fact many architects have used the Minor Works Agreement with bills quite successfully.

It is the JCT's view that "the use of bills of quantities is generally necessary for work estimated to have a contract value of £100,000 or more (at 1984 prices)" and that it may be desirable to use quantities below this figure "if the Works are complex".

JCT 80 is itself a long and complex document (summarised in **Table 2.01**) and currently exists in six variants:

- Local Authorities With Quantities
- Local Authorities Without Quantities
- Local Authorities With Approximate Quantities
- Private With Quantities
- Private Without Quantities
- Private With Approximate Quantities.

The differences between the local authorities and private editions are minimal and cater for the difference between local authority and private practice. The versions with and without quantities are differentiated almost entirely by the presence of a bill of quantities or specification as a contract document. The version with approximate quantities is suitable where adequately detailed contract documents cannot be prepared. A lump sum cannot be quoted and the tender sum is merely indicative of the final figure. All work is completely remeasured and priced on the basis of the rates set out in the bills of approximate quantities which replace the full and detailed bills of quantities in the With Quantities version.

The employer can, of course, amend the contract to suit his own requirements, but among other things, the effect of extensive amendments could be to negate the status of the form as a negotiated document.

The JCT produces a number of documents intended to be used with JCT 80:

- The Standard Form of Nominated Sub-contract Tender and Agreement (NSC/1)
- The Standard Form of Tender for a Nominated Sub-contractor (NSC/1a)
- The Standard Form of Employer/Nominated Sub-contractor Agreement (NSC/2)
- The Standard Form of Employer/Nominated Sub-contractor Agreement where NSC/1 has not been used (NSC/2a)
- The Standard Form of Nominated Instruction (NSC/3) and (NSC/3a)
- The Standard Form of Nominated Sub-contract (NSC/4)
- The Standard Form of Nominated Sub-contract where NSC/1 has not been used (NSC/4a)

- The Standard Form of Tender by a Nominated Supplier (TNS/1)
- The Sectional Completion Supplement when it is desired to complete the works in sections
- Fluctuation clauses (clauses 38, 39 and 40).

JCT 80 is extremely comprehensive, but it has been criticised for its length and the complexity of its provisions, notably the provisions for nomination. The previous edition (JCT 63) has had much adverse judicial comment, not all of which has been taken into account in JCT 80. However, JCT 80 is well-known and regularly updated.

2.02 Contractor's Obligations

The contractor's basic obligation is stated in clause 2.1. It is to "carry out and complete the works" in accordance with the contract documents. The contract documents are:
- *The standard form with quantities*
  Drawings
  Bills of quantities (which specify the quality and quantity of the works)
- *The standard form without quantities*
  Drawings
  Specifications or Schedule of Work
- *The standard form with approximate quantities*
  Drawings
  Bills of approximate quantities (which specify the quality and the approximate quantity of the works).

The contractor is to use "materials and workmanship of the quality and standards therein specified, provided that where and to the extent that approval of the quality of materials or of the standards of workmanship is a matter for the opinion of the Architect... such quality and standards shall be to the reasonable satisfaction of the Architect". This proviso is of considerable importance at the final certificate stage (clause 30.9.1.1). Moreover, clause 8.2.2 stipulates that the architect must express his dissatisfaction with such work within a reasonable time from its execution. This could lead to difficulties if properly executed work becomes unsatisfactory before practical completion, such as finishes becoming scratched or chipped. In practice, the fewer items left to the approval of the architect, the better.
Clause 2.2.1 contains the crucial proviso that nothing contained in the contract bills can override or modify the printed conditions. This provision is directly contrary to the normal rule of the interpretation of contracts, which is that written or typed documents are taken in preference to printed ones where there is a conflict but it has been shown to be effective in the courts.

2.03 Contract Documentation and Information

Clause 5.1 provides for the signed or sealed contract documents to be kept by the employer (the architect in the private edition), but they must be available to the contractor for inspection at all reasonable times. The contractor must be provided with a certified copy of the documents immediately after execution, together with two further copies of the contract drawings and unpriced bills of quantities.

The architect is responsible for providing the contractor with two copies of "such further drawings or details as are reasonably necessary" either to amplify the contract drawings or to enable the contractor to carry out and complete the works in accordance with the conditions (clause 5.4). This obligation, like the obligation in clause 5.3.1.1 to provide the contractor with two copies of "descriptive schedules or other like documents", is not dependent upon the contractor's application. It should be noted, however, that the contractor must apply at the appropriate time if he expects to take advantage of the provisions of clauses 25.4.6 and 26.2.1 relating to extensions of time and financial claims for loss/or expense.

The contractor must provide the architect with two copies of his master programme. The contract does not stipulate any particular form of the programme and it appears that, unless the architect states something to the contrary in the bills or specification, it can be in any form of the contractor's own choice. Although the requirement for a master programme is an optional one, it should not be deleted. The master programme is important. When a master programme is provided, clauses 25.3.1 and 33.1.3 oblige the contractor to update it within 14 days of a decision by the architect fixing a later completion date under the extension of time provisions.

Clause 5.3.1.3 of the Without Quantities version requires the contractor to provide a schedule of rates to enable the valuation of variations to take place.

2.04 Commencement and Completion

Clause 23.1 stipulates that possession of the site must be given to the contractor on the due date and he must immediately proceed "regularly and diligently" with the works in order to complete them *on or before* the completion date stated in the appendix. The contractor is entitled to complete before the completion date set out in the appendix, but is not obliged to do so. It follows that if he produces a programme showing an earlier completion date, the architect is not bound to provide him with drawings and other information so as to enable him to achieve early completion since it is only the contractual date which is significant: *Glenlion Construction Ltd* v *The Guinness Trust* (1988) 11 ConLR 126. The employer may defer the giving of possession of the site to the contractor for up to six weeks if the appendix is completed appropriately.

If completion is delayed beyond the completion date or any extended date, the contractor is liable to pay liquidated damages and the employer has the option of deducting them from monies due to to become due (ie from certificates), or of recovering them as a debt (clause 24). The architect's certificate of non-completion is a pre-requisite before any deduction can take place. Whether or not to deduct is solely a matter for the employer's discretion, but he must notify the contractor of his intention to do so before the issue of the final certificate.

The architect has the power to postpone any *work* to be executed under the contract and the contractor may then claim an extension of time under clause 25.4.5.1 and loss and/or expense under clause 26.2.5. The architect has no power to order acceleration of the works. If this is desired to be done, both employer and contractor must agree and proper payment must be made.

When the architect is of the opinion that practical completion has been achieved, he must issue a certificate to that effect (clause 17.1). Clause 18 provides for the situation which might arise if the employer, with the contractor's consent, takes possession of part of the works. The architect must issue a certificate stating an approximate value for that part of the works, practical completion is deemed to have taken place, for the part only, on the date of possession by the employer and insurance and liquidated damages provision must be proportionately reduced.

2.05   Extensions of Time

Grounds for extension of time are covered by clause 25.4; (termed "relevant events"). A number of events are listed which are the fault or responsibility of the employer or the architect, such as failure to give access to the site in due time, deferment of possession or late instructions. The remainder of the items are matters which are beyond the control of both parties such as *force majeure*, exceptionally adverse weather conditions and shortages of labour or materials which could not reasonably be foreseen. In order for the clause to operate:

- It must become reasonably apparent to the contractor that completion of the works is likely to be delayed; *and*
- The contractor must notify the architect in writing immediately specifying the cause of the delay and, in the contractor's opinion, the relevant event; *and*
- In respect of each relevant event the contractor must give:
  – Particulars of its effects
  – An estimate of delay in completion; *and*
- If the contractor's written notice includes a reference to a nominated sub-contractor, he must receive a copy of the notice from the contractor; *and*
- The contractor must update the particulars and estimate as required by the architect.

The giving of the appropriate notices and information in good time is not a condition precedent to the granting of an extension of time by the architect. It is clearly necessary that the architect gives an appropriate extension of time whenever the cause of the delay is an act or default of the employer or architect, otherwise the completion date may become unenforceable and the employer would lose his right to deduct liquidated damages. In exercising his functions under clause 25, the architect owes a duty to both the contractor and the employer to make an appropriate extension for delay caused by relevant events: see *London Borough of Merton* v *Stanley Hugh Leach Ltd* (1985) 32 BLR 51.

If the architect is of the opinion that any of the events in the contractor's notice is a relevant event and that the completion of the works will be delayed thereby, he must grant an extension of time in writing to the contractor and fix a new completion date. He must notify the contractor in writing where his decision is not to fix a later date as a new completion date. The architect has 12 weeks from receipt of "notice and of reasonably sufficient particulars and estimate" in which to give his award, if this is reasonably practicable. If the completion date occurs within the 12-week period, the architect must give his award "not later than the Completion Date". The extension of time must be "fair and reasonable" and it may take into account any variations requiring an omission issued after any previous award of extension of time.

The award of an extension is subject to the important proviso that the contractor must "use constantly his best endeavours to prevent delay in the progress of the Works" and he must "do all that may reasonably be required to the satisfaction of the architect ... to proceed with the Works." This proviso probably does not require the contractor to incur substantial additional expenditure (clause 25.3.4).

Subsequent awards may fix a date earlier than the date previously fixed to take account of instructions requiring the omission of work or obligations under clause 13 provided that the instructions were issued after the previous award. Under no circumstances can the architect fix a completion date earlier than the date stated in the appendix.

Clause 25.3.3 requires that, after the completion date, if this occurs before the date of practical completion, the architect may, and no later than 12 weeks after the date of practical completion, must:

- Fix a later completion date; *or*
- Fix an earlier completion date; *or*
- Confirm the completion date already fixed.

He must do this in writing and he is entitled to take into account:

- Any of the relevant events whether notified by the contractor or not
- Any omissions to the work since the last award.

The wording of the clause now leaves no doubt that the review can take account of employer's or architect's acts or defaults after the contractual completion date is past.

2.06 Architect's Instructions

Clause 4 empowers the architect to issue instructions. Although clause 4.3.1 states that "All instructions ... shall be issued in writing", clause 4.3.2 gives detailed provisions regarding the procedure to be adopted if the architect purports to issue oral instructions. Either the architect or the contractor may confirm the instruction in writing. The contractor must comply forthwith with written instructions except that he need not comply immediately if:

- The instruction requires a variation under clause 13.1.2 (restrictions to access, hours, etc)
- He requests the architect to name the empowering clause.

Failure to comply forthwith for any other reasons can be dealt with by the architect under clause 4.1.2. If the contractor fails to comply after the operation of a 7-day notification procedure, the employer may employ others to do the work at the contractor's expense.

Instructions requiring the "alteration or modification of the design, quality or quantity of the Works" or "the addition, alteration or omission of any obligations or restrictions imposed by the Employer in the Contract Bills" are referred to as *variations*. The definition and valuation of variations is covered in clause 13. The basis of valuation is the prices contained in the bills of quantities, schedule of rates or bills of approximate quantities as appropriate (unless the contractor has tendered for the work under the provisions of clause 35.2). If it would not be reasonable to use these prices, either a fair valuation may be made or the variations can be priced on a daywork basis. Clause 13.4.1 stipulates that the valuation of variations must be carried out by the quantity surveyor.

2.07 Contractor's Claims

The contractor's contractual right to loss and/or expense is chiefly contained in clause 26. The contractor may claim "direct loss and/or expense" because the employer has deferred giving possession of the site or if "the regular progress of the Works or any part thereof has been or is likely to be . . . materially affected" due to any of the matters noted in the clause, and he has made written application to the architect stating "that he has incurred or is likely to incur direct loss and/or expense . . . for which he would not be reimbursed" under any other clause. The matters generally fall into the category of acts or defaults of the employer or the architect. The architect is not empowered to deal with all breaches of contract under this clause. He can only deal with the matters expressly stated such as late instructions, postponement and the employer's failure to give access in due time.

The contractor is entitled to be reimbursed in interim certificates immediately following ascertainment or partial ascertainment (clause 3) provided that he:

- Gives written notice to the architect as soon as it becomes apparent that regular progress has been or is likely to become affected, *and*
- States that he has or is likely to incur loss and/or expense in carrying out the contract, for which he would not be reimbursed under any other provision of the contract, because regular progress of the works has been or is likely to be substantially affected by one or more of the matters in clause 26.2, *and*
- Supplies, on request, information to enable the architect to form an opinion, *and*
- Supplies, on request, whatever details are reasonably necessary to enable ascertainment to take place.

If the contractor fails to submit written particulars or fails to submit them "as soon as it has become . . . reasonably . . . apparent to him that the regular progress of the Works or of any part thereof has been or was likely to be affected", the architect is entitled to reject the claim, though the contractor's common law rights are preserved.

It is the architect's function to decide the validity of the claim. He may carry out the ascertainment himself or instruct the quantity surveyor to do so. His failure to do so is a breach of contract for which the employer is liable in damages: *Croudace Ltd* v *London Borough of Lambeth* (1986) 6 ConLR 70.

An architect who acts unfairly towards the contractor in certifying, granting extensions of time, dealing with loss and expense claims and so on, may be liable to the contractor direct but the case of *Pacific Associates Inc* v *Baxter* (1988) CILL 460 suggests that the liability is very limited. The provisions of this clause are without prejudice to the contractor's common law remedies (clause 26.6). The contractor is not bound to invoke the clause and may prefer to rely on his common law rights.

2.08 Certificates and Payment

The procedure for payment is contained at length in clause 30. Certificates must be issued to the employer with a duplicate copy immediately to the contractor (clause 5.8). Clause 30.1.3 stipulates that interim certificates must be issued as stated in the appendix, normally monthly, up to practical completion and thereafter as necessary. The architect may, but need not, require the quantity surveyor to carry out a valuation not more than 7 days before the date of the interim certificate. The employer must pay within 14 days of the date of the interim certificate. Failure to pay is a ground for determination under clause 28.1.1.

In the private editions, retention monies must be deposited by the employer in a special bank account (clause 30.5.3).

Within six months after practical completion, the contractor must submit all documents to the architect for the purpose of final adjustment of the contract sum. Within three months of receipt, the architect or the quantity surveyor must prepare a statement of all adjustments and ascertainments of loss and/or expense. The architect must forthwith send a copy of the statement and ascertainment to the contractor. The architect must issue his final certificate not later than two months from the latest of the following:

- Completion of making good of defects under clause 17
- End of the defects liability period
- The date the architect sent the statement and ascertainment to the contractor.

Before the issue of the final certificate, the architect must do two things:
- Supply the contractor with a copy of the finally adjusted contract sum (clause 30.6.1)
- Issue an interim certificate not less than 28 days before the issue of the final certificate including the amounts of all sub-contract sums for nominated sub-contractors as finally adjusted.

The employer has 14 days in which to honour the final certificate.

The final certificate is conclusive evidence:
- That where quality and standards are to be to the satisfaction of the architect, they are to his satisfaction
- All the provisions of the contract requiring adjustment of the contract sum have been complied with
- That all due extensions of time have been given
- That reimbursement of loss and/or expense is in final settlement of all contractor's claims in respect of clause 26 matters *unless* either party commences arbitration or other proceedings within 21 days after the issue of the final certificate.

Although limited, the conclusiveness provides valuable protection for the employer against certain late claims. Clause 30.10 makes clear that no other certificate has any degree of conclusiveness.

2.09 Sub-Contractors and Employer's Licensees

The contractor may not sub-let without the architect's consent (clause 19.2), but he must not withhold his consent unreasonably. Such sub-contractors are termed domestic sub-contractors. They can also arise if the architect names not less than three persons in the contract bills (or specification) for the contractor's selection (clause 19.3).

The contract provides for the nomination of sub-contractors in a very long and complex clause (clause 35). It sets out procedures for nomination, payment, extensions of time and renomination. There are no less than eight basic ways in which a sub-contractor can be nominated. The architect can use a prime cost sum or he can name a sub-contractor in one of four ways in each case:

- In the contract bills (or specification)
- In an architect's instruction regarding the expenditure of a provisional sum
- In an architect's instruction requiring additional work similar in kind to work which the contract bills (or specification) provided for nomination
- By agreement between contractor and architect on behalf of the employer.

Two procedures are laid down for nomination: the basic method and the alternative method. The basic method has the great advantage of ensuring agreement between all the parties before nomination takes place, but its complexity has proved too daunting for many architects. The main provisions are:

- The proposed nominated sub-contractor is asked by the architect to tender (NSC/1) and enter into a collateral agreement with the employer (NSC/2). The architect must send the completed tender, a copy of the agreement NSC/2 and a preliminary notice of nomination "instructing the contractor forthwith to settle with the proposed sub-contractor" any particular conditions in schedule 2 of NSC/1 which remain to be agreed. The contractor has 10 days from receipt of the notice to reach agreement. If he fails, the architect must issue whatever instructions are necessary. If the contractor reaches agreement with the nominee, he must send a copy of the completed NSC/1 to the architect. The architect must then nominate the sub-contractor (NSC/3)
- The alternative method is somewhat simpler: Tender NSC/1 is not used. The architect may invite tenders in any form he chooses, but the use of the optional Tender NSC/1a is recommended. The employer must enter into agreement (NSC/2a) with the proposed nominated sub-contractor, unless the tender has been requested on the basis that NSC/2a will not be used, which is not a wise thing to do. Without any attempt to agree the matters contained in schedule 2 of NSC/1, the architect issues a nomination instruction to the contractor, ideally using nomination instruction NSC/3a, with a copy of the successful tender. The contractor must then enter into an agreement (NSC/4a) with the nominated sub-contractor.

The contractor has the right of reasonable objection to the nomination. In the case of the basic method, he must do so no later than the date on which he returns tender NSC/1 to the architect; in the case of the alternative method, not later than 7 days from receipt of the nomination instruction from the architect. It is clear that the alternative method is more likely to lead to disputes and it should only be used in the most straightforward cases.

Clause 35.13 sets out the procedure for payment. Sub-contract amounts are to be included in interim certificates and the contractor and nominated sub-contractor must be notified. If NSC/2 or NSC/2a is in operation, failure by the contractor to pay the nominated sub-contractor results in the employer paying direct and deducting the appropriate amount from the next certificate due to the main contractor. If NSC/2 or NSC/2a is not used, this procedure is discretionary.

The contractor may grant an extension of time to the nominated sub-contractor, with the consent of the architect. If the architect is satisfied that all allowable extensions have been given, he must issue his certificate in accordance with clause 35.15 if the nominated sub-contractor fails to complete by the completion or any extended date for the sub-contract works. The architect's certificate is also required when practical completion of the sub-contract works has been achieved (clause 35.16).

If the nominated sub-contractor fails (eg becomes insolvent), the architect is under a duty to renominate.

There are two important points to note with regard to nominated sub-contractors:

- The contractor has no design responsibility for their work, whether or not the nominated sub-contractor has such responsibility (clause 35.21)
- If the nominated sub-contractor is successful in limiting his liability under clause 2.3 of NSC/4 or NSC/4a, the main contractor's liability is similarly limited (clause 35.22).

Work not forming part of the contract may be carried out by the employer's own contractors *either:*

- If the contract documents so provide, *or*
- If the contractor agrees; he must not unreasonably withhold his agreement (clause 29).

Any resultant disruption or delay to the progress of the works may form the basis for a claim under clauses 25.4 (extension of time) or 26.2.4 (loss and/or expense). It should be noted that this provision (clause 29) cannot be used to take work away from the contractor and allocate it to others. A statutory body may be regarded as an employer's licensee if employed by the employer not in pursuance of its statutory duties. If employed by the contractor in similar circumstances, it ranks as a domestic sub-contractor.

Clause 10 obliges the contractor to employ a competent person-in-charge constantly on the works. There is no similar provision as regards workmen, but the architect has power, under clause 8.5, to order the dismissal from site of persons employed upon the works provided he does not do so unreasonably or vexatiously. Clearly incompetence would be a reasonable ground for dismissal under this clause.

2.10 Statutory Obligations

The contractor must comply with relevant statutes and regulations and give all statutory notices (clauses 6.1.1). He must also pay all fees and charges and indemnify the employer against liability in this respect (clause 6.2). He is however, entitled to have the amounts added to the contract sum unless:

- They arise for work or goods by a local authority or statutory undertaker in a nominated capacity, *or*
- They are priced in the contract bills; *or*
- They are included in the contract bills as a provisional sum.

The contractor has an obligation to give the architect written notification if he finds any divergence between statutory requirements and all or any of the contract documents or architect's instructions. It is thought that the contractor does not have an obligation to search for divergences, but it can be argued that he should find any diverges as a matter of course if he is carrying out his general obligations correctly. On receipt of a notice from the contractor, or if the architect discovers the divergence himself, his duty is to issue instructions within 7 days of receiving the notice or otherwise discovering the divergence. Clause 6.1.3 goes on to make clear that if the works are varied, the variation must be valued in accordance with clause 13.2. Provided that the contractor complies with these provisions, he cannot be held liable by the employer if the works do not comply, to the extent notified, with statutory requirements. The contractor's own liabilities and duties in complying are not affected, ie although the employer cannot take action against the contractor in respect of non-compliance, a public authority can take action, eg by launching a criminal prosecution for breach of building regulations.

Clause 6.1.4 makes provision for emergency compliance. The contractor is to supply only such limited works and materials as is necessary to secure immediate compliance and he must inform the architect forthwith, not necessarily in writing although written confirmation is clearly desirable. If the contractor observes the requirements of this sub-clause, he is entitled to have the work done and materials supplied treated as a variation under clause 13.2.

2.11 Injury, Damage and Insurance

The insurance and indemnity provisions are contained in clauses 20, 21 and 22. They were extensively revised in November 1986. The contractor must insure against and indemnify the employer against all claims arising from personal injury or death due to the carrying out of the works. He is similarly responsible in respect of injury or damage to property, where it is due to his negligence, omission, default or breach of statutory duty. He also assumes responsibility for his servants or agents and "any person employed or engaged upon or in connection with the works or any part thereof, his servants or agents or any other person who may properly be on the site, upon or in connection with the works or any part thereof his servants or agents".

This responsibility does not extend to the employer or those for whom he is responsible or local authorities or statutory undertakers (and their employees) who are carrying out statutory work. Nonetheless, it is a very wide provision.

"Property" covered by clause 20.2 excludes the works themselves, and site materials, up to the date of issue of the certificate of practical completion or determination of the contractor's employment. The sum to be insured is to be not less than the amount stated in the appendix. Policies and premium receipts must be produced at the employer's reasonable request and, if the contractor defaults, the employer is entitled to take out the necessary insurance himself and deduct the appropriate amount from monies due to the contractor.

Provision is made for the contractor to insure against the employer's liability for damage to adjacent property due to collapse, heave, subsidence etc, and if this is required it is to be stated in the appendix, together with a limit of indemnity. The contractor only obtains this insurance if and when so instructed by the architect. The employer approves the insurers and the policy is deposited with him. There is provision for the employer to insure himself in case the contractor defaults (clause 21.2.4).

There are alternative works insurance clauses:
- A new building which the contractor must insure (clause 22A)
- A new building which the employer must insure (clause 22B)
- Work to an existing structure which the employer must insure (clause 22C).

The risks for which works insurance is required have been widened to include impact, subsidence, theft and vandalism, and the policy under clause 22A or 22B must be a joint names policy, ie one which includes both contractor and employer as the insured, and cover is to be for the full reinstatement value of the works plus the percentage, if any, stated in the appendix to cover professional fees. Insurance for loss or damage to existing structures and their contents and insurance for loss or damage to the works are treated by clause 22C. The employer is to take out an appropriate joint names policy. If clause 22C insurance is maintained and loss or damage occurs either party may, within 28 days of the occurrence, determine the contractor's employment if it is just and equitable to do so. This is to provide for the situation which might arise if, for example, a major part of an existing building was damaged and proposed alterations were clearly out of the question. Either party has the right to seek arbitration as to whether the determination is just and equitable within 7 days and the dispute is arbitrable immediately.

Clause 22D gives the employer the option to require the contractor to arrange for insurance to compensate the employer for the amount of liquidated damages which he cannot recover because of an extension of time granted under clause 25.4.3 because of loss or damage to the works caused by the occurrence of the specified perils. The employer must state in the appendix that he may require this insurance, and then require the contractor to effect it as soon as the contract is entered into.

2.12 Determination

Clauses 27, 28 and 28A provide for determination of the contractor's employment. Three situations are envisaged:
- Determination by the employer (clause 27)
- Determination by the contractor (clause 28)
- Determination by either party (clause 28A)

Among the reasons for which the employer may determine are total suspension of the works before completion without reasonable cause, failure of the contractor to proceed regularly and diligently and his refusal to remove defective work or goods and the work being materially affected thereby. The contractor may determine if he does not receive payment properly due, if the employer obstructs the issue of any certificate or if substantial suspension of the works is caused for a period named in the appendix by a series of events listed in clause 28.1.3, such as late architect's instructions.

The employer must first issue a default notice and allow 7 days for remedial measures to begin before issuing a notice determining the contractor's employment, except in the case of corruption. The contractor is only obliged to follow this procedure in respect of overdue payment. The contract determines automatically in the case of the contractor's insolvency; the employer's insolvency results in automatic determination only in the private edition.

Quite apart from the normal provisions for payment after determination, the party who determines can claim loss and/or expense. In the contractor's case it may include loss of anticipated profit for the whole of the contract. The common law rights of both parties are unaffected.

Clause 28A enables either party to determine the contractor's employment for "neutral" events such as *force majeure* and loss or damage to the works caused by insured risks which result in substantial suspension of the works for the period stated in the appendix. Determination is by notice, and the payments to be made by the employer to the contractor do not include, "any direct loss and/or damage caused to the contractor".

2.13 Disputes

The procedure for the settlement of disputes is contained in article 5 and clause 41. Article 5 briefly states that the method of settling any disputes or differences – except those relating to VAT or the statutory tax deduction scheme – is to be by arbitration. The detailed provisions relating to the appointment and powers of the arbitrator are found in clause 41, which incorporates the JCT Arbitration Rules, first published on 18 July 1988.

The arbitrator is to be appointed by agreement between the parties or failing agreement by either the President or a Vice-President of the RIBA, the RICS or the Chartered Institute of Arbitrators, as specified in the appendix entry. Clause 41.2.1 usefully provides that if a reference has already been made in a related matter involving a nominated sub-contractor or nominated supplier the two disputes may be effectively joined under the same arbitrator, ie the arbitrator already appointed. Either party has the power to require the dispute to be referred to a different arbitrator if he "reasonably considers that the arbitrator appointed to determine the related dispute is not appropriately qualified to determine the dispute or difference under this contract".

Under clause 41.6 the parties agree at the time of entering into the contract that questions of law arising in the course of the reference to arbitration or out of the award are to be determined by the High Court under the Arbitration Act 1979.

The arbitrator is given wide powers by clause 41.4. He may order rectification of the contract, direct measurements and valuations, ascertain and award any sum which ought to have been included in any certificate and "open up, review and revise any certificate, opinion, decision . . . requirement or notice . . . as if no such certificate etc, had been given". This confers upon the arbitrator more extensive powers than those enjoyed by the High Court, which is not empowered to open up, review and revise the architect's certificates, opinions and decisions: *Northern Regional Health Authority* v *Derek Crouch Construction Co Ltd* [1984] 2 ALL ER 175, CA.

Normally a reference to arbitration cannot be opened before practical completion, termination or abandonment of the works unless both the employer (or architect on his behalf) and the contractor give written consent to immediate arbitration. Immediate arbitration is available in the following cases:

- The identity of the architect or the quantity surveyor (articles 3 and 4)
- Whether an instruction is empowered by the contract
- Whether a certificate has been improperly withheld
- Whether a certificate is in accordance with the contract
- Whether or not a determination under clause 22.4.3.1 (insurance) is just and equitable
- Whether an objection is reasonable in regard to clause 4.1 (instructions), clause 8.4 (testing etc), clause 18.1 (partial possession) or clause 23.3.2 (use or occupation by employer)
- Disputes or differences with regard to clause 25 (extensions of time), clause 32 (hostilities) and clause 33 (war damage).

The arbitrator's award is final and binding (subject of course to the Arbitration Acts 1950 and 1979) and the right of the parties to appeal on or refer questions of law to the High Court (clause 4.1.6).

The JCT Arbitration Rules 1988, which are incorporated by reference into the contract, provide a speedy method of settling disputes during the currency of the works. The Rules provide strict time-scales and a choice of three procedures, and their correct application should do much to still the criticism of the arbitral process.

Table 2.01:   Contents of JCT 80 Summarised

Clause	Comment
1	Interpretation, definitions etc
1.1	Method of reference to clauses
1.2	Articles, etc to be read as a whole
1.3	Definitions
1.4	Contractor's responsibility
2	Contractor's obligations
2.1	Contract documents
2.2	.1 Contract bills – relation to articles, conditions and appendix
2.2	.2 Preparation of contract bills – errors in preparation, etc
2.3	Discrepancies in or divergences between documents
3	Contract sum – additions or deductions – adjustment – interim certificates
4	Architect's/contract administrator's instructions
4.1	Compliance with architect's/contract administrator's instructions
4.2	Provisions empowering instructions
4.3	.1 Instructions to be in writing
4.3	.2 Procedure if instructions given otherwise than in writing
5	Contract documents – other documents – issue of certificates
5.1	Custody of contract bills and contract drawings
5.2	Copies of documents
5.3	Descriptive schedules, etc – master programme of contractor
5.4	Drawings or details
5.5	Availability of certain documents
5.6	Return of drawings, etc
5.7	Limits to use of documents
5.8	Issue of architect's/contract administrator's certificates
6	Statutory obligations, notices, fees and charges
6.1	Statutory requirements
6.2	Fees or charges
6.3	Exclusion of provisions on domestic and nominated sub-contractors
7	Levels and setting out of the works
8	Materials, goods and workmanship to conform to description, testing and inspection
8.1	Kinds and standards
8.2	Vouchers – materials and goods
8.3	Inspection – tests
8.4	Removal from the site – work, materials or goods
8.5	Exclusion from the works of persons employed thereon
9	Royalties and patent rights
9.1	Treatment of royalties, etc – indemnity to employer
9.2	Architect's/contract administrator's instructions – treatment of royalties, etc
10	Person-in-charge
11	Access for architect/contract administrator to the works
12	Clerk of works

Table 2.01: Contents of JCT 80 Summarised – (continued)

Clause	Comment
13	Variations and provisional sums
13.1	Definition of variation
13.2	Instructions requiring a variation
13.3	Instructions on provisional sums
13.4	Valuation of variations and provisional sum work and work covered by an Approximate Quantity
13.5	Valuation rules
13.6	Contractor's right to be present at measurement
13.7	Valuations – addition to or deduction from contract sum
14	Contract sum
14.1	Quality and quantity of work included in contract sum
14.2	Contract sum – only adjusted under the conditions – errors in computation
15	Value added tax – supplemental provisions
15.1	Definitions – VAT agreement
15.2	Contract sum – exclusive of VAT
15.3	Possible exemption from VAT
16	Materials and goods unfixed or off-site
16.1	Unfixed materials and goods – on site
16.2	Unfixed materials and goods – off-site
17	Practical completion and defects liability
17.1	Certificate of practical completion
17.2	Defects, shrinkages or other faults
17.3	Defects, etc – architect's/contract administrator's instructions
17.4	Certificate of completion of making good defects
17.5	Damage by frost
18	Partial possession by employer
18.1	Employer's wish – contractor's consent
	.1 Practical completion – relevant part
	.2 Defects, etc – relevant part
	.3 Insurance – relevant part
	.4 Liquidated damages – relevant part
19	Assignment and sub-contracts
19.1	Assignment
19.2	Sub-letting – domestic sub-contractors – architect's/contract administrator's consent
19.3	Sub-letting – list in contract bills
19.4	Sub-letting – determination of employment of domestic sub-contractor
19.5	Nominated sub-contractors
20	Injury to persons and property and indemnity to employer
20.1	Liability of contractor – personal injury or death – indemnity to employer
20.2	Liability of contractor – injury or damage to property – indemnity to employer
20.3	Injury or damage to property – exclusion of the works and site materials
21	Insurance against injury to persons and property
21.1	Contractor's insurance – personal injury or death – injury or damage to property

Table 2.01: Contents of JCT 80 Summarised – (continued)

Clause	Comment
21.2	Insurance – liability etc of employer
21.3	Excepted risks
22	Insurance of the works
22.1	Insurance of the works – alternative clauses
22.2	Definitions
22.3	Nominated and Domestic sub-contractors – benefit of Joint Names Policies – Specified Perils
22A	Erection of new building – all risks insurance of the works by the contractor
22A.1	New buildings – contractor to take out and maintain a joint names policy for all risks insurance
22A.2	Single policy – insurers approved by employer – failure by contractor to insure
22A.3	Use of annual policy maintained by contractor – alternative to use of clause 22A.2
22A.4	Loss or damage to works – insurance claims – contractor's obligation – use of insurance monies
22B	Erection of new building – all risks insurance of the works by the employer
22B.1	New buildings – employer to take out and maintain a joint names policy for all risks insurance
22B.2	[Number not used]
22B.3	Loss or damage to works – insurance claims – contractor's obligations – payment by employer
22C	Insurance of existing structures – insurance of works in or extensions to existing structures
22C.1	Existing structures and contents – specified perils – employer to take out and maintain joint names policy
22C.2	Works in or extensions to existing structures – all risks insurance – employer to take out and maintain joint names policy
22C.3	[Number not used]
22C.4	Loss or damage to works – insurance claims – contractor's obligations – payment by employer
22D	Insurance for employer's loss of liquidated damages – clause 25.4.3
23	Date of possession, completion and postponement
23.1	Date of possession – progress to completion date
23.2	Architect's/contract administrator's instructions – postponement
23.3	Possession by contractor – use or occupation by employer
24	Damages for non-completion
24.1	Certificate of architect/contract administrator
24.2	Payment or allowance of liquidated damages
25	Extension of time
25.1	Interpretation of delay, etc
25.2	Notice by contractor of delay to progress
25.3	Fixing completion date
25.4	Relevant events

Table 2.01: Contents of JCT 80 Summarised – (continued)

Clause	Comment
26	Loss and expense caused by matters materially affecting regular progress of the works
26.1	Matters materially affecting regular progress of the works – direct loss and/or expense
26.2	List of matters
26.3	Relevance of certain extensions of completion date
26.4	Nominated sub-contractors – matters materially affecting regular progress of the sub-contract works – direct loss and/or expense
26.5	Amounts ascertained – added to contract sum
26.6	Reservation of rights and remedies of contractor
27	Determination by employer – default by contractor
27.1	Default by contractor
27.2	Contractor becoming bankrupt, etc
27.3	Corruption
27.4	Determination of employment of contractor – rights and duties of employer and contractor
28	Determination by contractor
28.1	Acts, etc giving ground for determination of employment by contractor
28.2	Determination of employment by contractor – rights and duties of employer and contractor
28A	Determination by employer or contractor
29	Works by employer or persons employed or engaged by employer
29.1	Information in contract bills
29.2	Information not in contract bills
30	Certificates and payments
30.1	Interim certificates and valuations
30.2	Ascertainment of amounts due in interim certificates
30.3	Off-site materials or goods
30.4	Retention – rules for ascertainment
30.5	Rules on treatment of retention
30.6	.1 Final adjustment of contract sum – documents from contractor – final valuations under clause 13
	.2 Items included in adjustment of contract sum
	.3 Computation of adjusted contract sum – contractor to receive copy
30.7	Interim certificate – final adjustment or ascertainment of nominated sub-contract sums
30.8	Issue of final certificate
30.9	Effect of final certificate
30.10	Effect of certificates other than final certificate
31	Finance (No 2) Act 1975 – statutory tax deduction scheme
31.1	Definitions
31.2	Whether employer a "contractor"
31.3	Provision of evidence – tax certificate
31.4	Uncertificated contractor obtains tax certificate – expiry of tax certificate – cancellation of tax certificate
31.5	Vouchers

Table 2.01: Contents of JCT 80 Summarised – (continued)

Clause	Comment
31.6	Statutory deduction – direct cost of materials
31.7	Correction of errors
31.8	Relation to other clauses
31.9	Application of arbitration agreement
32	Outbreak of hostilities
32.1	Notice of determination of the contractor's employment
32.2	Protective work, etc
32.3	Payment
33	War damage
33.1	Effect of war damage
33.2	Relation with clause 32
33.3	Use of compensation for war damage
33.4	Definition of war damage
34	Antiquities
34.1	Effect of find of antiquities
34.2	Architect's/contract administrator's instructions on antiquities found
34.3	Direct loss and/or expense
35	Nominated sub-contractors
	General
35.1	Definition of a nominated sub-contractor
35.2	Contractor's tender for works otherwise reserved for a nominated sub-contractor
35.3	Documents relating to nominated sub-contractors
	Procedure for nomination of a sub-contractor
35.4	Contractor's right of reasonable objection to proposed sub-contractor
35.5	Use of tender NSC/1 – circumstances where tender NSC/1 is not used
35.6	Limit on nomination
35.7	Architect's/contract administrator's preliminary action prior to nomination of a proposed sub-contractor – duty of contractor
35.8	Contractor and proposed sub-contractor – failure to agree – contractor's and architect's/contract administrator's duty
35.9	Proposed sub-contractor – withdrawal of offer
35.10	Receipt of completed tender – issue of nomination instruction by architect/contract administrator
35.11	Tender NSC/1 and agreement NSC/2 not used – use of agreement NSC/2a
35.12	Sub-contract NSC/4a
35.13	Payment of nominated sub-contractor
35.13 and	.1 Architect/supervising officer – .2 direction as to interim payment for nominated sub-contractor
35.13 to	.3 Direct payment of nominated .5 sub-contractor
35.14 and	.1 Extension of period or periods .2 for completion of nominated sub-contract work
35.15 and	.1 Failure to complete nominated .2 sub-contract works
35.16	Practical completion of nominated sub-contract works
35.17 to .19	Final payment of nominated sub-contractors

Table 2.01:   Contents of JCT 80 Summarised – (continued)

Clause	Comment
35.18	Defects in nominated sub-contract works after final payment of nominated sub-contractor – before issue of the final certificate
35.19	Final payment – saving provisions
35.20	Position of employer in relation to Nominated sub-contractor
35.21	Clause 2 of agreement NSC/2 or clause 1 of agreement NSC/2a – position of contractor
35.22	Restrictions in contracts of sale, etc – limitation of liability of nominated sub-contractors
35.23	Position where proposed nomination does not proceed further
35.24	Circumstances where re-nomination necessary
35.25	Determination of employment of nominated sub-contractor
35.26	Architect's/contract administrator's instructions
36	Nominated suppliers
36.1	Definition of nominated supplier
36.2	Architect's/contract administrator's instructions
36.3	Ascertainment of costs to be set against prime cost sum
36.4	Sale contract provisions – architect's/contract administrator's right to nominate supplier
36.5	Contract of sale – restriction, limitation or exclusion of liability
37	Choice of fluctuation provisions – entry in appendix *Note: clauses 38, 39 and 40 are published separately*
38	Contribution, levy and tax fluctuations
38.1	.1 Deemed calculation of contract sum – types and rates of contribution etc
	.2 Increases or decreases in rates of contribution – payment or allowance
	.3 Persons employed on site other than
and	.4 "workpeople"
	.5 Refunds and premiums
to	.7
	.8 Contracted-out employment
	.9 Meaning of contribution, etc
38.2	.1 Materials – duties and taxes
and	.2
38.3	Fluctuations – work sub-let – Domestic sub-contractors
38.4	to .6 Provisions relating to clause 38
	.1 Written notice by contractor
	.2 Timing and effect of written notices
	.3 Agreement – quantity surveyor and contractor
	.4 Fluctuations added to or deducted from contract sum
	.5 Evidence and computations by contractor
	.6 No alteration to contractor's profit
	.7 Position where contractor in default over completion
38.5	Work, etc to which clauses 38.1 to .3 are not applicable
38.6	Definitions for use with clause 38
38.7	Percentage addition to fluctuation payments or allowances
39	Labour and materials cost and tax fluctuations
39.1	.1 Deemed calculation of contract sum – rates of wages, etc
	.2 Increases or decreases in rates of wages, etc – payment or allowance
	.3 and .4 Persons employed on site other than "workpeople"

Table 2.01: Contents of JCT 80 Summarised – (continued)

Clause		Comment
		.5 and .6 Workpeople – wage-fixing body – reimbursement of fares, etc
39.2		.1 to .8 Contributions, levies and taxes
39.3		.1 to .3 Materials, goods, electricity and fuels
39.4		Fluctuations – work sub-let – domestic sub-contractors
39.4		.1 Sub-let work – incorporation of provisions to like effect
39.4		.2 Sub-let work – fluctuations – payment to or allowance by the contractor
39.5	to	.7 Provisions relating to clause 39
		.1 Written notice by contractor
		.2 Timing and effect of written notices
		.3 Agreement – quantity surveyor and contractor
		.4 Fluctuations added to or deducted from contract sum
		.5 Evidence and computations by contractor
		.6 No alteration to contractor's profit
		.7 Position where contractor in default over completion
39.6		Work, etc to which clauses 39.1 to .4 not applicable
39.7		Definitions for use with clause 39
39.8		Percentage addition to fluctuation payments or allowances
40		Use of price adjustment formulae
40.1		Adjustment of contract sum – price adjustment formulae for building contracts – formula rules
40.2		Amendment to clause 30 – interim valuations and payment
40.3		Fluctuations – articles manufactured outside the United Kingdom
40.4		.1 Nominated sub-contractors
		.2 domestic sub-contractors
40.5		Power to agree – quantity surveyor and contractor
40.6		Position where monthly bulletins are delayed, etc
40.7		Formula adjustment – failure to complete
41		Settlement of disputes – Arbitration
		Appendix
		Supplement provisions (the VAT agreement)

Table 2.02: JCT 80 – Time Chart

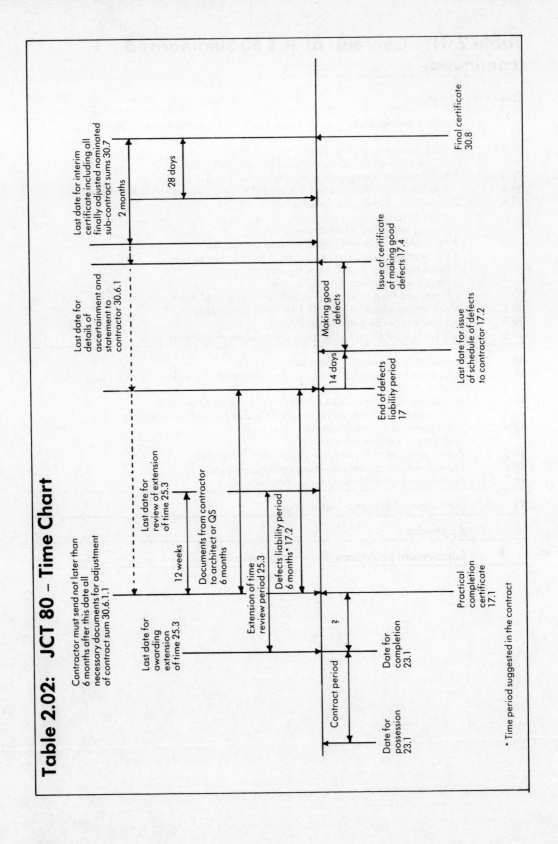

Table 2.03: Architect's Powers under JCT 80

Clause	Power	Comment
4.1.2	Issue written notice requiring compliance with instructions	Within 7 days employer may employ and pay others to do the work
4.3.2	Dissent from an oral instruction	Dissent must be in writing within 7 days of receipt of confirmation
4.3.2.1	Confirm an oral instruction	If confirmed in writing within 7 days of giving, contractor need not confirm and instruction takes effect from date of confirmation
4.3.2.2	Confirm an oral instruction	If otherwise than under clause 4.3.2 or 4.3.2.1, may be done in writing at any time up to the issue of the final certificate and deemed to have taken effect on the date given orally
5.6	Request the contractor to return all drawings, details, descriptive schedules and other documents of a like nature which bear the architect's name	Upon final payment under clause 30.8
7	Instruct the contractor not to amend setting out errors	The contract sum must be adjusted accordingly
8.2	Request the contractor to provide vouchers	To prove that the materials and goods comply with clause 8.1: "shall so far as procurable be of the respective kinds and standards described in the Contract Bills"
8.3	Instruct the contractor to open up for inspection or carry out tests	The costs + costs of making good must be added to the contract sum unless provided for in the contract bills or unless the inspection or test shows that the work or goods are not in accordance with the contract
8.4.1	Instruct the contractor to remove from site work or goods	Not in accordance with the contract
8.4.2	Allow such work to remain	After consulting contractor and with employer's agreement must be confirmed in writing to contractor An appropriate deduction is to be made from the contract sum
8.4.3	Issue reasonably necessary instructions re: variation following 8.4.1 instruction	After consulting contractor No addition is to be made to contract sum and no extension of time given
8.4.4	Issue reasonable instructions to open up work or carry out tests to establish to architect's satisfaction the likelihood of further similar non-compliance	After having due regard to the code of practice appended to the conditions

Table 2.03: Architect's Powers under JCT 80 – (continued)

Clause	Power	Comment
8.5	Instruct the contract to exclude from the works any person employed thereon	Instruction must not be given unreasonable or vexatiously "Person" may include a firm or body corporate
11	Access to the works, workshops or other places of the contractor where work is being prepared for this contract	At all reasonable times
12	Confirm clerk of works' direction	Must be done within 2 working days of issue of direction
13.2	Issue instructions requiring a variation or sanction un-authorised variations made by the contractor	No variation required or sanctioned by the architect will vitiate the contract
13.4.1	Approve agreement between contractor and nominated sub-contractor that valuation of variations to the sub-contract works shall be other than in accordance with the relevant provisions of NSC/4 or NSC/4a	
13.5.4	Verify vouchers specifying time, workmen's names, plant and materials employed on the work	Vouchers must be presented not later than the end of the week following that in which the work has been executed Relates to daywork
16.1	Consent to removal of goods and materials, unfixed, from the site	Must be in writing and must not be unreasonably withheld
17.2	Instruct that defects, etc in the schedule of defects are not to be made good	The contract sum must be adjusted
17.3	Issue instructions requiring any defects, etc appearing during the defects liability period to be made good Instruct that defects, etc appearing within the defects liability period are not to be made good	Contractor must comply within a reasonable time Instructions must not be issued after the later of: Delivery of schedule of defects 14 days from end of defects liability period The contract sum must be adjusted
17.5	Certify that frost damage appearing after practical completion is due to injury which	Otherwise, the contractor is not liable for the cost of making good such frost damage

Table 2.03: Architect's Powers under JCT 80 – (continued)

Clause	Power	Comment
	took place before practical completion	
19.2	Consent to subletting	Consent must not be unreasonably withheld
21.2	Issue instruction to contractor to take out insurance against employer's liabilities	If it is stated in appendix that the insurance may be required and the employer does so require
23.2	Issue instructions in regard to the postponement of any work to be executed under the contract provisions	
25.2.3	Require the contractor to give further written notices to keep particulars and estimates up to date	Contractor must send a copy to any nominated subcontractor who received a copy of any written notice under clause 25.2.1.2
25.3.2	Fix a completion date earlier than that previously fixed under clause 25	If it is fair and reasonable having regard to instructions requiring omission of work since extension of time was last made. The architect may never fix a completion date earlier than that in the appendix
25.3.3	Review extensions of time granted and fix a new completion date or confirm existing	May be carried out at any time after completion date if this occurs before practical completion, but no later than 12 weeks after practical completion
25.3.4.2	Require the contractor to proceed with the works to the architect's satisfaction	The contractor cannot be made to incur additional expenditure without reimbursement
25.4.12	Agree ingress or egress to or from the site	
26.1.2	Require the contractor to submit information in support of his application for loss and/or expense	To enable the architect to form an opinion
26.1.3	Require the contractor to submit details of loss and/or expense	To enable the architect to carry out ascertainment
27.1.4	Serve a default notice on the contractor	If the contractor: Suspends the work without reasonable cause: or Fails to proceed regularly and diligently: or Refuses or persistently neglects to remove defective work, etc and thereby the works are materially affected: or If he fails to comply with the provisions of clauses 19 or 19A (LA edition only)

Table 2.03: Architect's Powers under JCT 80 – (continued)

Clause	Power	Comment
27.4.3	Require the contractor to remove from the works temporary buildings, etc belonging to or hired by him	If the contractor does not comply within a reasonable time, the employer may remove and sell them. The contractor must not remove them before receipt of architect's instruction
30.1.2	Instruct the quantity surveyor to carry out interim valuations	If the architect considers it necessary for ascertainment of amount due in interim certificate
30.3	Include the value of off-site goods and materials in any interim certificate	Provided that: Materials are intended for incorporation Nothing remains to be done to them They have been set apart and marked with employer's name and destination Provision is made for passing of property if ordered by contractor or sub-contractor They are in accordance with the contract Contractor provides proof of passing of property Contractor provides proof of insurance
30.6.1.1	Instruct that all documents necessary for adjustment of contract sum be sent to quantity surveyor	
32.2	Issue instructions requiring protective work or continuation of work up to specified point of stoppage	Within 14 days after notice of determination issued under clause 32.1
33.1.2	Issue instructions requiring the contractor to remove and/or dispose of debris, etc and execute specified protective work	If the works sustain war damage as defined in clause 33.4
35.2.1	Receive tenders from the contractor	For works otherwise reserved for a nominated sub-contractor
35.5.2	Issue an instruction substituting provisions of clauses 35.11 and 35.12 for NSC/1 and NSC/2 or vice versa	Treated as a variation under clause 13.2 May not be issued if architect has issued preliminary notice of nomination under clause 35.7.1 or nomination under clause 35.11 for the part of the work for which a sub-contractor will be nominated unless the nomination does not proceed (clause 35.23) or re-nomination is necessary (clause 35.24)

Table 2.03: Architect's Powers under JCT 80 – (continued)

Clause	Power	Comment
35.17	Issue an interim certificate including the amount of the relevant sub-contract sum or ascertained final sub-contract sum	Where NSC/2 or NSC/2a has been entered into: *and* Clause 5 of NSC/2 or clause 4 of NSC/2a are not amended: *and* Sub-contract remedial work has been carried out: *and* The architect has received all documents for final adjustment or computation: *and* Practical completion of the sub-contract works has been achieved

Table 2.04: Architect's Duties under JCT 80

Clause	Duty	Comment
2.3	Issue instructions in regard to discrepancies or divergence in contract bills, instructions (except those requiring a variation) or drawings, etc issued under clauses 5.3.1.1, 5.4 and 7	If the contractor notifies in writing
3	Take amounts into account in the computation of the next interim certificate following whole or partial ascertainment	As soon as amounts are ascertained which are to be added or deducted from or dealt with by adjustment of the contract sum
4.2	Forthwith comply with contractor's request to specify in writing the empowering clause for an instruction	On receipt of written specification, the contractor may: Refer the matter to arbitration: or Comply with the instruction
4.3.1	Issue all instructions in writing	
5.2	Provide the contractor, without charge, with: certified copy of the contract documents 2 copies of contract drawings 2 copies of unpriced bills of quantities	Immediately after the execution of the contract
5.3.1	Provide the contractor, without charge, with 2 copies of descriptive schedules or other like documents necessary to carry out the works	As soon as possible after the execution of the contract unless already provided
5.4	Provide the contractor, without charge, with 2 copies of such further drawings, etc reasonably necessary to explain and amplify the contract drawings or to enable the contractor to carry out and complete the works in accordance with the conditions	From time to time as necessary
5.7	Preserve the confidentiality of the rates or prices in the contract bills	
5.8	Issue certificates to the employer and duplicates to the contractor	Except where specifically provided otherwise
6.1.3	Issue instructions regarding divergence between statutory requirements and contract documents or variation instructions	If contractor submits written notice or If the architect otherwise discovers Instruction must be issued within 7 days and contractor is entitled to payment as for a variation

Table 2.04:   Architect's Duties under JCT 80 – (continued)

Clause	Duty	Comment
7	Determine levels which may be required and provide accurately dimensioned drawings	The contractor is responsible for setting out the works
8.2.2	Express dissatisfaction within a reasonable time from execution of unsatisfactory work	In respect of materials, goods or workmanship to be to the reasonable satisfaction of architect
13.3.1	Issue instructions regarding the expenditure of provisional sums in the contract bills	
13.3.2	Issue instructions regarding the expenditure of provisional sums in a sub-contract	
17.1	Certify practical completion	When the architect is of the opinion that it has been achieved
17.2	Deliver a schedule of defects to the contractor specifying defects, etc which appear during the defects liability period	Not later that 14 days after the end of the defects liability period The defects must be due to defect, etc due to materials or workmanship not in accordance with the contract or frost before practical completion
17.4	Certify making good of defects	When the architect is of the opinion that defects, etc he required to be made good have been so
18.1.1	Issue to contractor on behalf of employer a written statement identifying part taken into possession	If, before practical completion, the employer with contractor's consent takes possession of part of the works
18.1.3	Certify making good of defects	When the architect is of the opinion that defects, etc in the relevant part which he required to be made good have been so
22D.1	Either inform contractor that insurance is not required or instruct him to obtain quotation Instruct contractor whether or not employer wishes quotation to be accepted	If appendix states liquidated damages insurance may be required Instruction must not be unreasonably withheld or delayed
24.1	Issue a certificate	If the contractor fails to complete the works by the completion date
25.3.1	Give the contractor, in writing, a fair and reasonable extension of time	If it is reasonably apparent that progress is being delayed; *and* The contractor has given all required notices; *and* The delaying events are relevant events: *and* Completion of the works is likely to be delayed

Table 2.04: Architect's Duties under JCT 80 – (continued)

Clause	Duty	Comment
	Notify contractor in writing	beyond completion date. New date must be fixed not later than 12 weeks from receipt of notices or before completion date whichever is the earlier If it is not fair and reasonable to fix a later date notice must be given not later than 12 weeks from receipt of notices etc or before completion date whichever is the earlier
25.3.3	Review extensions of time granted and fix new completion date or confirm existing date	Contractor's notification is not required Must be carried out no later than 12 weeks after practical completion
26.1	Ascertain or instruct the quantity surveyor to ascertain the amount of loss and/or expense incurred by the contractor	If the contractor applies in writing as soon as it becomes apparent that the regular progress has been or is likely to become affected; and He responds to the architect's requests for information and details of loss and/or expense to enable the architect to form an opinion and carry out ascertainment
26.3	State in writing to the contractor what extension of time has been made in respect of related events under clause 25	If and to the extent necessary for ascertainment
26.4.1	Ascertain or instruct the quantity surveyor to ascertain the amount of loss and/or expense incurred by a nominated sub-contractor	If the contractor passes to the architect a copy of the nominated sub-contractor's application properly made under clause 13.1 of NSC/4 or NSC/4a and The architect is of the opinion that the regular progress of the sub-contract works has been or is likely to be affected
26.4.2	State in writing to the contractor with a copy to the sub-contractor what extension of time has been made in respect of related events under clause 25 of the main contract and clause 11 of sub-contract NSC/4 or NSC/4a as applicable	If and to the extent necessary for ascertainment of the sub-contract loss and/or expense
30.1.1.1	Issue interim certificates stating the amount due to the contractor from the employer according to the rules contained in clause 30.2	At the frequency stated in the appendix but not less than 1 calendar month, to practical completion. Thereafter, as and when further amounts are ascertained as due and when the certificate of making good defects is issued
30.5.2	Prepare or instruct the quantity surveyor to prepare a statement showing the contractor's and	At the date of each interim certificate

Table 2.04: Architect's Duties under JCT 80 – (continued)

Clause	Duty	Comment
	each nominated sub-contractor's retention deducted; *and* Issue it to the employer, contractor and each applicable nominated sub-contractor	
30.6.1.2	Ascertain or cause the quantity surveyor to ascertain, any loss and/or expense under appropriate clauses Forthwith send copy of ascertainment and statement of adjustments to be made to the contract sum to the contractor and relevant extract to each nominated sub-contractor	If the contractor has sent to the architect or quantity surveyor all necessary documents for adjusting the contract sum and not later than 3 months thereafter
30.7	Issue an interim certificate to include finally adjusted sub-contract sum amounts	Not less than 28 days before the issue of the final certificate
30.8	Issue the final certificate	Within 2 months from the latest of: ● The end of the defects liability period; or ● Issue of making good defects certificate; or ● Date ascertainment and statement sent to contractor under clause 30.6.1.2
34.2	Issue instructions regarding antiquities	On receipt of the contractor's notice
34.3.1	Acertain loss and/or expense in connection with antiquities	If the contractor's compliance with architect's instructions has involved the contractor in loss and/or expense for which he will not be reimbursed under any other provision of the contract
34.3.2	State in writing to the contractor what extension of time has been made in respect of the relevant event in clause 25.4.5.1	If and to the extent necessary for ascertainment
35.7.1	Send completed NSC/1, NSC/2 and preliminary notice of nomination to the contractor instructing him to settle particular conditions of schedule 2 of NSC/1	If the basic method of nomination is used
35.10.2	Forthwith issue a nomination instruction to the contractor and a copy to the sub-contractor	If the contractor has settled particular conditions of schedule 2 of NSC/1 and sent completed NSC/1 to the architect
35.11.2	Issue a nomination instruction to the contractor and a copy to the sub-contractor	If the alternative method of nomination is used

Table 2.04:   Architect's Duties under JCT 80 – (continued)

Clause	Duty	Comment
35.13.1	Direct the contractor as to the amount of each interim or final payment to nominated sub-contractors included in each interim certificate. Compute the amounts in accordance with the provisions of the relevant sub-contracts Forthwith inform each nominated sub-contractor of the amounts	On the issue of each interim certificate
35.13.5.2	Issue a certificate stating that the contractor has failed to pro-vide reasonable proof of payment of nominated sub-contractors and stating the amount concerned	If he has so failed; *and* If NSC/2 or NSC/2a is in operation; *or* If the employer so directs Copy to nominated sub-contractors concerned
35.14.2	Operate the relevant provisions of NSC/4 or NSC/4a with regard to written consent to a sub-contract extension of time	If contractor and nominated sub-contractor send notification and request
35.15.1	Certify sub-contractor's failure to complete sub-contract works within the specified or any extended period	If: Nominated sub-contractor so fails; *and* Contractor sends notification to architect with copy to nominated sub-contractor; *and* The architect is satisfied that clause 35.14 has been properly applied Certificate must be issued not later than 2 months from the date of the contractor's notification
35.16	Issue certificate of practical completion of the sub-contract works	When the architect is of the opinion that practical completion has been achieved
35.17	Issue an interim certificate including the amount of the relevant sub-contract sum or ascertained final sub-contract sum	Where NSC/2 or NSC/2a has been entered into *and* clause 5 of NSC/2 or clause 4 of NSC 2a are not amended; *and* sub-contract remedial work has been carried out; *and* the architect has received all documents for final adjustment or computation; *and* 12 months have elapsed since practical com-pletion; *and* the certificate has not been issued already
35.18.1	Issue an instruction nominating a person to carry out the sub-contract rectification works	If the original sub-contractor fails to rectify any defect, etc which: Appears before the issue of the final certificate;

Table 2.04: Architect's Duties under JCT 80 – (continued)

Clause	Duty	Comment
		and He is bound to remedy Clause 35 provisions will apply to the new nomination
35.23	Issue an instruction omitting work intended to be the subject of nomination; *or* Select another person to be nominated	If: Contractor makes reasonable objection to the proposed sub-contractor; *or* Proposed sub-contractor does not agree particular conditions in schedule 2 of NSC/1 (where used) within reasonable time; *or* Proposed sub-contractor does not enter into NSC/4a (where used) within a reasonable time
35.24.6.1	Instruct the contractor to give default notice to sub-contractor	If the contractor notifies that sub-contractor has defaulted in respect of clause 29.1.1 to 1.4 of NSC/4 or NSC/4a; *and* Has passed sub-contractor's comments on the same to the architect; *and* The architect considers sub-contractor is in default The architect may instruct that a further instruction is required before the contractor may determine the sub-contractor's employment
35.24.6.3	Make such further nomination as may be necessary	If the contractor notifies that the sub-contractor's employment has been determined Contractor must have opportunity to agree new sub-contract price if determination is in accordance with clause 29.1.3 of NSC/4 or NSC/4a
35.24.7	Make such further nomination as may be necessary	If the nominated sub-contract becomes bankrupt, etc Duty may be postponed if receiver or manager may continue the sub-contract without prejudicing the interests of employer, contractor or any other sub-contractor
35.24.8.1	Make such further nomination as may be necessary	If the nominated sub-contractor determines his own employment under clause 30 of NSC/4 or NSC/4a Any extra costs may be deducted from the contractor by the employer
35.24.8.2	Make such further nomination as may be necessary	After architect has exercised his powers under clauses 7 or 8.4 or 17.2 or 17.3
35.24.10	Make all further nominations of sub-contractors within a reasonable time	

Table 2.04: Architect's Duties under JCT 80 – (continued)

Clause	Duty	Comment
35.26	Direct the contractor as to any amount included in interim certificate in respect of work done or goods supplied (clause 29.4 of sub-contract)	If determination occurs under clause 29 of NSC/4 or NSC/4a
36.2	Issue instructions to nominate a supplier	If a prime cost sum is included in the contract bills or arises under clause 36.1
36.3.2	Add expense to the contract sum	If architect is of the opinion that it has been incurred by contractor in obtaining goods from nominated supplier; and it would not be reimbursed under any other clause of the contract
36.4	To nominate as a supplier only such person as will enter into a contract in the terms laid down in this clause	Unless otherwise agreed with the contractor

Table 2.05:   Contractor's Powers under JCT 80

Clause	Power	Comment
4.1.1	Not to comply with instruction under clause 13.2	If and to the extent that he makes reasonable objection in writing
4.2	Request the architect to specify in writing the empowering provision in the contract	On receipt of what purports to be an architect's instruction
5.1	Inspect the contract drawings and bills at any reasonable times	They are to remain in the custody of the employer (the architect in the private edition)
13.4.2	Agree with the nominated sub-contractor that the valuation of variations shall not be in accordance with the relevant provisions of NSC/4 or NSC/4a	With the approval of the architect
18.1	Consent to the employer taking possession of part of the works before practical completion	The architect must thereupon issue a written statement identifying the part and giving the date taken into possession. Defects liability period for the part starts on the date of possession Liquidated damages are to be reduced by the appropriate amount. Insured value is to be reduced by an appropriate amount
19.1	Assign the contract	With the employer's consent
19.3.2.1	Add additional persons to the list of named persons	With the employer's consent at any time prior to the execution of a binding sub-contract
19.3.2.2	Add other persons to the list of named persons	If the employer agrees (agreement must not be unreasonably withheld) otherwise the contractor must carry out the work himself or sub-let with the architect's consent. This clause operates if the list of named persons falls below 3
21.1.1.2	Choose a greater sum than that stated in the appendix	In respect of personal injury or death, or injury or damage to property insurance
22B.2	Require employer to produce policy receipts Insure all work executed against all rists, perils and have the premium amount added to the contract sum	If the employer fails to produce policy receipts on request (applies only to private edition)
22C.3	Require employer to produce policy receipts to show that policies under clauses 22C.1 and 22C.2 have been taken out Insure existing structures against specified perils and the works against all risks, perils and have the premium amount added to	If the employer fails to produce policy receipts on request (applies only to private edition)

Table 2.05: Contractor's Powers under JCT 80 – (continued)

Clause	Power	Comment
	the contract sum. Also has right of inspection and entry to existing structures for the purpose of inventory	
22C.4.3.1	Determine his employment	Within 28 days of occurrence of clause 22C.4 loss or damage. It must be just and equitable to do so; *and* 7 days notice must be given during which time either party may request arbitration
22D.1	Require information from the employer, via the architect	To obtain quotation under this clause
23.3.2	Consent to the employer using or occupying the site or works before the issue of practical completion certificate	If insurers confirm that insurance will not be prejudiced, consent must not be unreasonably withheld
26.1	Make written application to the architect for loss and/or expense	Must be made as soon as it becomes apparent that regular progress of the work is likely to be materially affected; *and* he must respond to architect's request for reasonable further information
28.1.1	Serve a default notice on the employer	If he does not pay the contractor the amounts properly due on any certificate within 14 days of issue of the certificate
28.1	Forthwith determine his employment under the contract	If: The employer does not comply with the default notice under clause 28.1.1 within 7 days; *and* The employer interferes with or obstructs any certificate; *or* The carrying out of substantially the whole of the works is suspended for a period stated in the appendix by reason of: ● Architect's instructions under clauses 2.3, 13.2 or 23.2; *or* ● Late instructions; *or* ● Employer's failure to give access ● Employer's men; *or* ● Opening up or testing; *or* ● The employer becomes bankrupt etc (applicable only to private edition)
28A.1	Forthwith determine his employment under the contract	If the carrying out of substantially the whole of the works is suspended for a period named in the appendix by reason of: ● *Force majeure* ● Loss by specified perils ● Civil commotion

Table 2.05:   Contractor's Powers under JCT 80 – (continued)

Clause	Power	Comment
29.2	Consent to execution of work not forming part of the contract by employer's men	If the information is not included in the contract bills. Consent must not be unreasonably withheld
32.1	Determine his employment under the contract	If 28 days has elapsed from the date of general mobilisation; and practical completion has not occurred (unless war damage has been sustained)
32.2	Abandon protective work ordered by the architect	If prevented from completing within 3 months for reasons beyond his control
35.2.1	Tender for work intended to be the subject of nomination	If he normally carries out such work; and If the items are set out in the appendix; and If the architect agrees Employer has the right to reject any tender Contractor must not sub-let such items without the architect's consent
35.4.1	Make reasonable objection to a proposed sub-contractor	No such person may be nominated
35.24.5.3	Agree the price to be charged by a substituted sub-contractor	After the original nominated sub-contractor has had his employment determined
36.4	Agree to the nomination as supplier of a person who will not enter into a contract of sale in accordance with the terms set out in this clause	
36.5.2	Refuse to enter into a contract with a nominated supplier	Until the architect has specifically approved in writing any restrictions, limitations or exclusions upon the liability of the supplier and included in the contract of sale
41.2.2	Require the dispute to be referred to a different arbitrator	If he reasonably considers the arbitrator appointed to determine a related dispute is not appropriately qualified to determine the dispute under this contract

Table 2.06: Contractor's Duties under JCT 80

Clause	Duty	Comment
2.1	Carry out and complete the works in accordance with the contract documents	If approval of materials and workmanship are to be for the architect's opinion, they are to be to his reasonable satisfaction
2.3	Immediately give written notice to the architect	If he finds discrepancy or divergence between: Contract drawings Contract bills Architect's instruction other than a variation Information issued by the architect in accordance with clauses 5.3.1.1, 5.4 or 7
4.1.1	Forthwith comply with architect's instructions	If they are expressly empowered by the contract, unless requiring a variation under clause 13.2; *and* the contractor makes reasonable objection
4.1.2	Comply with architect's written notice	If the contractor does not comply within 7 days, the employer may employ and pay others to do the work
4.3.2	Confirm in writing to the architect within 7 days	If the architect purports to issue an oral instruction If he does not dissent within 7 days, it takes effect forthwith
5.3.1.2	Provide the architect without charge with 2 copies of the master programme Provide 2 further copies of revisions and amendments to take account of any decision of the architect	As soon as possible after the execution of the contract unless already provided Within 14 days of any decision by the architect under clause 25.3.1 or clause 33.1.3
5.5	Keep 1 copy of: Contract drawings Unpriced bills of quantities Descriptive schedules, etc Drawings and details referred to in clause 5.4 Master programme upon the works	To be available to the architect or his representative at all reasonable times
5.6	Forthwith return all drawings, etc which bear the name of the architect	Upon final payment under clause 30.8 and if so requested by the architect
5.7	To use all contract and contractual documents only for the purposes of the contract	
6.1.1	Comply with and give all notices required by statutory requirements	

Table 2.06: Contractor's Duties under JCT 80 – (continued)

Clause	Duty	Comment
6.1.2	Immediately give the architect a written notice	If he finds any divergence between statutory requirements documents referred to in clause 2.3 and a clause 13.2 variation instruction
6.1.4.1	Supply such limited materials and workmanship as reasonably necessary	If the contractor has to comply with statutory requirements as an emergency measure
6.1.4.2	Forthwith inform the architect	Of the emergency and the steps being taken
6.2	Pay and indemnify the employer against statutory charges	The amount to be added to the contract sum unless they: ● Are for work or materials by local authorities or statutory undertakers not in pursuance of their statutory duties ● Are priced in the contract bills ● Are included as provisional sums in the bills
7	Set out the works	Architect must provide levels and accurately dimensioned drawings Contractor must correct errors at his own cost unless architect, with employer's consent, instructs otherwise when an appropriate deduction must be made from the contract sum
8.1.1	Provide materials and goods of kinds and standards described in the contract bills or to reasonable satisfaction of architect	Only so far as procurable
8.1.2	Provide workmanship to standards described in contract bills or appropriate to works or to reasonable satisfaction of the architect	To extent not so described
8.2	Provide vouchers to prove that goods, etc comply with clause 8.1	If the architect so requests
8.4.2	Immediately consult with any relevant nominated sub-contractor	If architect consults contractor regarding allowing non-conforming work to remain
8.4.3	Immediately consult with any relevant nominated sub-contractor	If architect consults contractor regarding the issue of a variation with no addition to the contract sum after operating clause 8.4.1 or 8.4.2
9.1	Indemnify the employer against all claims, etc due to infringement of patent rights	If work, etc is described in the contract bills and royalties may be payable, it is deemed to have been included in the contract sum Not applicable if the work is the subject of an architect's instruction

Table 2.06: Contractor's Duties under JCT 80 – (continued)

Clause	Duty	Comment
10	Constantly keep a competent person-in-charge upon the works	Instructions or directions given to him are deemed to have been given to the contractor
11	Give access to the architect and his representatives to the works and workshops and by a term in the sub-contract give a similar right in respect of sub-contract works and do all things reasonably necessary to make such rights effective	At all reasonable times
12	Give every reasonable facility to enable the clerk of works to carry out his duties	
16.1	Not to allow unfixed goods, etc intended for the works to be removed therefrom	Unless the architect gives his written consent If goods, etc have become the property of the employer, the contractor remains responsible for loss or damage
16.2	Not to allow off-site goods, etc to be removed except for use on the works	If the contractor has been paid for them and property has passed to the employer
17.2	Make good defects in the schedule of defects within a reasonable time	Defects must: ● Have appeared within the defects liability period ● Be due to materials or workmanship not in accordance with the contract or frost occurring before practical completion ● Be notified not later than 14 days after the end of the defects liability period
17.3	Make good defects, etc in architect's instructions	As above Architect may issue such instructions whenever he considers it necessary but not later than the delivery of the schedule of defects
17.5	Make good damage by frost appearing after practical completion	If the architect certifies that it is due to injury taking place before practical completion
18.1.4	Reduce the value insured under clause 22A (if applicable)	If the employer has taken possession of part of the works with the contractor's consent
19.3.1	Select a sub-contractor from the list of not less than 3 persons to be a domestic sub-contractor	If included in the contract bills
20.1	Indemnify the employer against any claim in respect of personal injury or death	Arising out of the carrying out of the contract unless and to the extent due to employer's act or neglect

Table 2.06: Contractor's Duties under JCT 80 – (continued)

Clause	Duty	Comment
20.2	Indemnify the employer against any claim, etc in respect of injury or damage to real or personal property	Must arise out of the carrying out of the contract and be due to contractor's negligence, etc
21.1.1.1	Maintain insurance against personal injury or death and damage to real or personal property	
21.1.2	Produce evidence of insurance and the policies and premium receipts	If so required by the employer On any occasion required by the employer provided the request is not unreasonable or vexatious
21.2	Maintain insurances in joint names against claims against employer due to collapse etc, of property other than the works Policies and receipts must be placed with the employer	If it is stated in the appendix that such insurance may be required and the architect so instructs Employer must approve insurers. Premium amounts must be added to the contract sum
22.3.1	Ensure that the joint names policies referred to in clause 22A.1 or 22A.3 *either* ● provide for recognition of each nominated sub-contractor as an insured *or* ● include insurers' waiver of rights of subrogration	If clause 22A applies in respect of specified perils
22A.1	Take out and maintain all risks insurance in joint names against loss or damage to the works and unfixed goods	Excludes temporary buildings, etc owned or hired by the contractor or any sub-contractor
22A.2	Policies and receipts must be placed with the employer	Employer must approve insurers
22A.4.1	Give written notice to architect and employer	Upon discovering loss or damage caused by risks covered by the joint names policy in clause 22A.1 or 22A.2 or 22A.3
22A.4.3	With due diligence restore damaged works etc, dispose of debris and carry out and complete the works	After an insurance claim under clause 22A.1 or 22A.2 or 22A.3 and any inspection required by the insurers
22A.4.4	Authorise insurers to pay insurance monies to employer	Acting also on behalf of sub-contractors recognised pursuant to clause 22.3

Table 2.06: Contractor's Duties under JCT 80 – (continued)

Clause	Duty	Comment
22B.3.1	Forthwith give notice to architect and employer in writing stating extent, nature and location of damage	On discovering damage caused by risks covered by joint names policy in clause 22B.1
22B.3.3	With due diligence restore damaged works etc, dispose of debris and carry out and complete the works	After an insurance claim under clause 22B.1 and any inspection required by the insurers
22B.3.4	Authorise insurers to pay insurance monies to employer	Acting also on behalf of sub-contractors recognised pursuant to clause 22.3
22C.4	Forthwith give notice to architect and employer in writing stating extent, nature and location of damage	On discovering damage caused by risks covered by joint names policy in clause 22C.2
22C.4.2	Authorise insurers to pay insurance monies to employer	Acting also on behalf of sub-contractors recognised pursuant to clause 22.3
22C.4.4.1	With due diligence reinstate or make good loss or damage and carry out and complete the work	After an insurance claim under clause 22C.2 and any inspection by insurers if contractor's employment is not determined
22D.1	Send quotation to the architect Forthwith take out and maintain the relevant policy and send to architect for deposit with employer with premium receipts	If appendix states that liquidated damages insurance may be required and the architect has so instructed If so instructed by the architect
23.3.2	Notify insurers under clause 22A or 22B or 22C.2 and 22C.4 and obtain confirmation that use or occupation will not prejudice insurance	Before giving consent to use or occupation
24.2.1	Pay liquidated damages to the employer	If the employer requires in writing not later than the final certificate; and Provided that the architect has issued his certificate in accordance with clause 24.1
25.2.1	Forthwith give written notice to the architect of material circumstances including cause of delay and relevant events Forthwith send a copy of the notice to the nominated sub-contractor	If it becomes apparent that progress of the works is or is likely to be delayed. Note that the contractor must do this even if he does not intend to claim any extension of time If the notice makes reference to such sub-contractor

Table 2.06: Contractor's Duties under JCT 80 – (continued)

Clause	Duty	Comment
25.2.2	For every relevant event included in the notice, give the expected effects and estimate delay	At the time of the notice or as soon as possible thereafter
	Send a copy to the nominated sub-contractor	If he has had a copy of a clause 25.2.1 notice
25.2.3	Give further written notices to the architect keeping up to date the particulars and estimate	If reasonably necessary or if the architect so requires
	A copy must be sent to the nominated sub-contractor	If he has had a copy of the clause 25.2.1.2 notice
25.3.4.1	Constantly use his best endeavours to prevent delay in the progress of the works and prevent delay beyond the completion date	
25.3.4.2	Do all that the architect may reasonably require to proceed with the works	
26.1.1	Make application to the architect as soon as it becomes apparent that regular progress is or is likely to be affected	If he wishes to claim loss and/or expense under clause 26
26.1.2	Submit such information as will enable the architect to form an opinion	As above, if the architect so requests
26.1.3	Submit details of loss and/or expense as is reasonably necessary for ascertainment	As above
26.4.1	Pass to the architect a copy of any written application by a nominated sub-contractor	
27.1.4	Comply with default notice from employer	
27.4.3	Remove from the works any temporary buildings, etc	After the employer has determined and as and when required to do so by the architect
27.4.4	Allow or pay to the employer direct loss and/or expense after determination	To be taken into account when the architect makes a final certification of monies after determination
28.2.1	Remove from site all temporary buildings etc, and give facilities to sub-contractors to do the same	With reasonable dispatch and with due precautions to prevent injury, death or damage

Clause	Duty	Comment
29.1	Permit the execution of work by the employer or his employees, etc	Provided: The work does not form part of the contract The contract bills provide sufficient information to enable the contractor to carry out and complete the works
30.6.1.1	Send to the architect all documents necessary to adjust the contract sum	Before or within a reasonable time after practical completion
31.3	Either: Provide evidence to the employer of entitlement to payment without statutory deduction; or Inform employer in writing, copy to architect, that he is not entitled to be paid without deduction	Not later than 21 days: Before first contractual payment; or After the employer has become a "contractor"
31.4.1	Inform employer if he gets tax certificate	If previously not entitled to payment without deduction Deduction not made thereafter
31.4.2	Provide evidence to employer of entitlement to payment without statutory deduction Inform the employer in writing of cessation of entitlement after expiry of certificate	If tax certificate expires before final payment due. Contractor must take action at least 28 days before expiry If not satisfied, employer will make deduction
31.4.3	Immediately write to employer	If tax certificate is cancelled
32.2	Comply with instructions after determination	If issued within 14 days after determination under clause 32.1
33.1.3	Reinstate war damage and carry out and complete the works	If war damage sustained
34.1	Leave antiquities undisturbed Take all necessary steps to preserve Inform the architect or clerk of works	
35.2.1	Not to sublet to a domestic sub-contractor	If his tender for nominated sub-contract work is accepted
35.7.2	Forthwith agree particular conditions in schedule 2 of NSC/1	After receipt of preliminary notice of nominations
35.8	Write to architect if unable to agree as above within 10 days	Architect must issue any necessary instructions

Table 2.06: Contractor's Duties under JCT 80 – (continued)

Clause	Duty	Comment
	and give reasons *and* continue to attempt agreement	
35.9	Inform architect in writing and take no further action pending instructions	If proposed nominated sub-contractor notifies withdrawal
35.10.1	Send completed NSC/1 to architect	When agreement reached with proposed nominated sub-contractor
35.12	Conclude a sub-contract on NSC/4a	Within 14 days of nomination instruction
35.13.2	Discharge interim payments to nominated sub-contractors	As directed by architect
35.13.3	Provide reasonable proof of discharge to nominated sub-contractors	Before any interim or final certificate other than the first
35.14.1	Request the architect's consent to extension of time for nominated sub-contractors	Contractor must operate the relevant provisions of sub-contract
35.18.1	Pay or allow the employer difference between amount recovered and price of substituted sub-contractor	If original sub-contractor fails to rectify defects, etc; *and* Architect has nominated a substitute sub-contractor; *and* Employer has tried to recover the price from the original sub-contractor; *and* The contractor has agreed the price of the substituted sub-contractor
35.19.1	Responsible for loss or damage to the works	Covers work, for which a final payment has been made to a nominated sub-contractor, up to practical completion or possession
35.24.4.2	Inform the architect whether the sub-contractor's employment has been determined	Either: After a notice given on the architect's instruction; or After a further instruction from the architect Only if the sub-contractor has defaulted on any sub-contract clause 29.1.1 to 1.4 matter
35.25	Only determine a nominated sub-contract if the architect so instructs	
41.1	Give written notice to the employer	If the contractor requires a dispute to be referred to arbitration
41.8	Together with the employer, forthwith appoint another arbitrator	If the arbitrator ceases to act

Table 2.07: Employer's Powers under JCT 80

Clause	Power	Comment
4.1.2	Employ and pay others and deduct cost from contractor	If contractor fails to comply with architect's notice regarding instruction
12	Appoint a clerk of works	His duties are purely that of inspector on behalf of the employer, under the direction of the architect
13.4.1	Agree the valuation of variations otherwise than in accordance with clause 13.5	Contractor must also agree
18.1	Take possession of part of the works	With the contractor's consent
19.1.1	Assign the contract	With the contractor's consent
19.1.2	Assign to any transferee or lessee the right to bring proceedings in the employer's name or enforce any contractual terms made for the employer's benefit	If employer transfers leasehold or freehold interest of grants a leasehold interest in the whole of the works
	The assignee is estopped from disputing enforceable ageements reached between employer and contractor related to the contract	If made period to the date of the assignment
19.3.2.1	Add additional persons to the list of named persons	With the contractor's consent at any time prior to the execution of a binding sub-contract
19.3.2.2	Add other persons to the list of named persons	If the contractor agrees (which must not be unreasonably withheld) otherwise the contractor must carry out the work himself or sub-let with the architect's consent
		This clause operates if the list of named persons falls below 3
21.1.2	Require documentary evidence of insurance	
21.1.3	Insure and deduct premium amounts from monies due to contractor or recover them as a debt	If contractor fails to insure against personal injury or death or injury to real or personal property
21.2.2	Approve insurers	In regard to insurance against damage to property other than the works – employer's liability
21.2.4	Take out insurance against damage to property other than the works	If the contractor fails to insure
22A.2	Approve insurers	In regard to insurance against all risks to be taken out by contractor
	Insure against all risks and	If the contractor fails to insure

Table 2.07: Employer's Powers under JCT 80 – (continued)

Clause	Power	Comment
	deduct sums from monies due or recover them as a debt	
22A.3.1	Inspect documentary evidence or the policy	If the contractor maintains a policy independently of his obligations under the contract and it is in joint names
22C.4.3.1	Determine the contractor's employment	Within 28 days of occurrence of clause 22C.4 loss or damage It must be just and equitable to do so; and 7 days notice must be given during which time either party may request arbitration
22D.1	Require the contractor to accept the quotation in respect of liquidated damages insurance	Architect must so instruct
23.1.2	Defer giving of possession for not more than 6 weeks	Where clause 23.1.2 is stated in the appendix to apply
23.3.2	Use or occupy the site or the works before issue of practical completion certificate	With contractor's written consent
24.2.1	In writing require the contractor to pay or allow liquidated damages for the period between the completion date and practical completion, or Recover the liquidated damages as a debt	If the architect has issued a certificate under clause 24.1 and The employer acts before the date of the final certificate
27.1	Forthwith determine the contractor's employment under the contract	If the contractor continues a default for 14 days after receipt of a default notice from the architect under this clause; or If the contractor repeats the default at any time thereafter Notice of determination must be given within 10 days after the continuance or repetition
27.2	Reinstate the contractor's employment	If the contractor, his liquidator etc, agree after automatic determination due to bankruptcy, etc
27.3	Forthwith determine the contractor's employment under the contract	If the contractor has committed a corrupt act
27.4.1	Employ and pay other persons to carry out and complete the works	After the employer has determined the contractor's employment The other persons or the employer have the right to enter the site and use all temporary plant, etc belonging to the contractor

Table 2.07: Employer's Powers under JCT 80 – (continued)

Clause	Power	Comment
27.4.2.1	Require the contractor to assign him without payment the benefit of any agreement for goods or work	Must be done within 14 days of the date of determination and the sub-contractors or suppliers have the right of reasonable objection to any further assignment by the employer Does not apply if determination was for bankruptcy, etc
27.4.2.2	Pay any supplier or sub-contractor for goods or work	If not already paid by the contractor. Money so paid may be deducted from contractor. Does not apply in case of bankruptcy, etc
28A.1	Forthwith determine the contractor's employment under the contract	If the carrying out of substantially the whole of the works is suspended for a period named in the appendix by reason of: ● *Force majeure* ● Loss by specified perils ● Civil commotion
29.1	Carry out or employ others to carry out work	If the work does not form part of the contract *and* the contract bills contain enough information to enable the contractor to carry out and complete the works in accordance with the contract
29.2	Carry out or employ others to carry out work	If the work does not form part of the contract; *and* The contract bills do not provide sufficient information; *but* The contractor agrees
30.1.1.2	Make deductions from money due under any interim certificate	If the right exists under the provisions of the contract and even though retention money is held in trust
30.4.1	Deduct and retain retention money in accordance with the percentage specified in the appendix	Clause 30.2 specifies what amounts are and are not subject to retention Half the retention held must be released in the interim certificate following practical completion, the other half must be released in the interim certificate following the issue of the making good of defects certificate
32.1	Determine the contractor's employment under the contract forthwith	If 28 days have elapsed from the date of general mobilisation *and* Practical completion has not occurred (unless war damage has been sustained)
35.11.1	Approve a sub-contract tender on the basis that NSC/2a will not be entered into	

Table 2.07: Employer's Powers under JCT 80 – (continued)

Clause	Power	Comment
35.13.5.1	Pay nominated sub-contractors direct if contractor fails to pay in accordance with the architect's direction of amounts included in any interim certificate	Obligatory if NSC/2 or NSC/2a have been entered into
35.24.7	Deduct the difference between the original nominated sub-contract and the substituted sub-contractor's price or recover the difference as a debt	If the employment of the original nominated sub-contractor has been determined and a substituted sub-contractor has been appointed
41.2.2	Require the dispute to be referred to a different arbitrator	If he reasonably considers the arbitrator appointed to determine a related dispute is not appropriately qualified to determine the dispute under this contract

Table 2.08: Employer's Duties under JCT 80

Clause	Duty	Comment
5.1	Retain custody of the contract drawings and contract bills	Local authority editions only
5.7	Preserve the confidentiality of the rates and prices in the contract bills	
22.3.1	Ensure that the joint names policies referred to in clause 22B.1 or 22C.1 and 22C.2 *either*: ● provide for recognition of each nominated sub-contractor as an insured; *or* ● include insurers' waiver of rights of subrogation	If clause 22B or clause 22C applies In respect of specified perils
22A.4.4	Pay insurance monies received to the contractor	By instalments under architect's certificate
22B.1	Maintain insurance against all risks Produce premium receipts to the contractor on request	In joint names Private edition only
22C.1	Maintain insurance against specified perils for existing structures	In joint names
22C.2	Maintain insurance against all risks for the works of alteration or extension	In joint names
22C.3	Produce premium receipts to the contractor on request	Only applicable to private editions
23.3.2	Notify insurers under clause 22A or 22B or 22C.2 and 22C.4 and obtain confirmation that use or occupation will not prejudice insurance	
24.2.2	Repay amounts of liquidated damages deducted from or paid by the contractor	If the architect fixes a later completion date after the issue of a clause 24.1 certificate
28.1.1	Comply with default notice from contractor	
28.2.2	Pay the contractor: Total value of work completed at the date of determination Total value of work begun but not completed at the date of determination	After the contractor has determined his employment under the contract

Table 2.08: Employer's Duties under JCT 80 – (continued)

Clause	Duty	Comment
	Any direct loss and/or expense Cost of materials ordered for the works for which the contractor has paid or is legally bound to pay	Goods become the property of the employer
	Reasonable cost of removal of temporary plant etc, from site Any direct loss and/or damage caused to the contractor or to the sub-contractor by the determination after taking into account amounts previously paid	This may include the contractor's loss of expected profit
28.2	Notify the contractor in writing which parts of the amount are payable to the nominated sub-contractors Notify the nominated sub-contractors which parts are payable to them	On payment under clause 28.2.2
30.1.1.1	Pay the contractor the amounts shown on interim certificates within 14 days of the date of issue	The employer may make any deductions empowered by the contract provisions
30.1.1.3	Give written notification to the contractor of his reason	If he exercises his right to deduct from money due
30.5.3	Pay retention money into separate bank account identified as retention held on trust Certify the fact to the architect with copy to the contractor	If: The employer deducts retention; *and* The contractor or any nominated sub-contractor so requests The employer is said to be entitled to the full beneficial interest in interest accruing, but the matter is thought to be debatable This clause is only applicable to the private editions
30.5.4	Notify the contractor of amount of deduction from contractor's retention or nominated sub-contractor's retention under the sub-contract	If the employer deducts money due to him from retention money
31.2.2	Notify the contractor	If the employer becomes a "contractor" for the purposes of the Finance (No 2) Act 1975; *and* The words "if a 'contractor' " have been deleted from the appendix
31.3.2	Give written notification to the contractor that he intends to make the statutory deduction	If he is not satisfied with the evidence submitted by the contractor that he is entitled to be paid without statutory deduction

Table 2.08: Employer's Duties under JCT 80 – (continued)

Clause	Duty	Comment
	from payments due under the contract	
31.5	Promptly pass all vouchers submitted by the contractor, to the Inland Revenue	If the employer is a "contractor"
31.6.1	Notify the contractor in writing	If he considers that the Act requires him to make statutory deduction from payment due to be made
	Require the contractor's statement of the amount to be included representing direct cost, to contractor or any other person, of materials used in carrying out the works	Not later than 7 days before each future payment becomes due (or within 10 days of the notification above, if that would be later)
31.7	Repay to, or deduct from, payments to contractor to correct errors	If an error has occurred, unless there is a contrary statutory obligation
32.3	Pay the contractor the value of protective work, etc instructed by the architect	If: 14 days has elapsed since determination has occurred following outbreak of hostilities; or Protective works are required by the architect The contractor is also entitled to be paid as though he had determined under clause 28 except that he is not entitled to any direct loss and/or damage caused by the determination
35.11.1	Enter into NSC/2a with proposed sub-contractor	If nomination is being carried out under the alternative method unless the tender has been requested, submitted and approved on the basis that NSC/2a will not be entered into
35.13.5	Pay nominated sub-contractors direct if contractor fails to pay in accordance with the architect's direction of amounts included in any interim certificate	If NSC/4 or NSC/4a have been entered into
	Pay available amounts *pro rata* to amounts remaining undischarged by the contractor; or Adopt some other method of appointment as the employer thinks fair and reasonable	If 2 or more nominated sub-contractors have to be paid and insufficient amounts remain due to the contractor
35.18.1.2	Take reasonable steps to recover a sum, equal to the price of the substituted sub-contractor, from the original sub-contractor	If: The original sub-contractor has been paid the whole of the sub-contract sum; *and* He has failed to remedy defects he is bound to remedy; *and* A substituted sub-contractor has been appointed

Table 2.08: Employer's Duties under JCT 80 – (continued)

Clause	Duty	Comment
41.1	Give written notice to the contractor	If the employer requires a dispute to be referred to arbitration
41.8	Together with the contractor, forthwith appoint another arbitrator	If the arbitrator ceases to act

Table 2.09:   Clauses that May Give Rise to Claims under JCT 80

Clause	Event	Type
2.2.2.2	Departure from SMM or error in description, etc	C
2.3	Discrepancy between any two or more of: ● Drawings ● Bills of quantities ● Architect's instructions (except variations)	C
3	Failure to take ascertainment into account in next interim certificate	CL
4.1.1	Additions, omissions, alterations in goods, workmanship, order of work	C
4.1.2	Employer employs others to do work without proper procedure	CL
4.3	Instructions by employer, oral instructions by architect	CL
5.2	Failure to provide correct documents	CL
5.3	Documents purporting to impose obligations beyond contract documents	CL
5.4	Failure to provide information as necessary	C or CL
5.8	Failure to send duplicate copies of certificates to contractor	CL
6.1	Divergence between statutory requirements and contract documents etc in clause 2.3	C
6.2	Statutory fees etc	C
7	Failure to provide levels or accurately dimensioned drawings for setting out	CL
8.1	Materials, goods or workmanship not procurable	C
8.3	Opening up or testing of work etc found to be in accordance with the contract	C

Table 2.09: Clauses that May Give Rise to Claims under JCT 80 – (continued)

Clause	Event	Type
8.4	Wrongly worded instruction or failure to have regard to Code of Practice	CL
8.5	Unreasonable or vexatious instructions	CL
9.2	Royalties and patent rights	C
12	Clerk of works exceeding contractual duties	CL
13.1.3	Nomination of sub-contractor to do work priced by the contractor	CL
13.2	Variations	C
13.3	Expenditure of provisional sums	C
13.4	Failure to value	CL
13.5.1–5	Failure to follow valuation rules	CL
13.5.6	Valuations not otherwise included	C
13.6	Contractor not given opportunity to be present at time of measurement	CL
13.7	Failure to give effect to a valuation	CL
15	Recovery of VAT or loss of input tax	C
17.1	Failure to issue certificate of practical completion	CL
17.2	Failure to deliver a schedule of defects	CL
17.3	Late instructions to make good defects	CL
17.4	Failure to issue certificate of making good defects	CL
17.5	Wrongful instruction to make good frost damage	C
18.1	Possession without contractor's consent	CL

Table 2.09: Clauses that May Give Rise to Claims under JCT 80 – (continued)

Clause	Event	Type
18.1.1	Failure to issue certificate of partial possession	CL
18.1.2	Failure to give effect to all the results of the certificate	CL
18.1.3	Failure to issue certificate of making good defects	CL
18.1.5	Failure to reduce liquidated damages correctly or at all	CL
19.1	Assignment by employer without consent	CL
19.2	Unreasonably withholding consent to sub-letting	CL
21.2	Special insurances, effects of Special insurances	CL C
22A.4.2	Accepted insurance claims	C
22B.3.5	Restoration of damaged work	C
22C.4.4.2	Restoration of damaged work	C
23.1.1	Failure to give possession on due date if no deferment	CL
23.2	Postponement of work	C
24.2.2	Repayment of liquidated damages	C
25	Architect not carrying out his duties	CL
26	Loss and/or expense	C
27.1	Invalid determination	CL
28.2	Payment after determination	C
29	Work by employer	C
30	Certificates Failure to observe rules Interest on retention	C CL CL
31	Failure to observe requirements of this clause	CL

Table 2.09: Clauses that May Give Rise to Claims under JCT 80 – (continued)

Clause	Event	Type
32	Invalid determination	CL
32.3	Payment for protective work	C
33.1	Making good war damage	C
34.3	Loss and/or expense regarding antiquities	C
35	Nominated sub-contractors	CL
36	Nominated suppliers	CL
38–40	Fluctuations	C

KEY
C = Contractual claim   Contractual claims are usually dealt with by the architect

CL = Common Law claim   Common law claims are usually dealt with by the employer

Table 2.10: Certificates to be Issued by the Architect under JCT 80

Clause	Certificate
17.1	Practical completion
17.4	Making good of defects
18.1.3	Making good of defects when partial possession has taken place
22A.4.4	Payment of insurance money
24.1	Contractor's failure to complete on the due date
27.4.4	Expenses properly incurred by employer on determination of contract by employer
30.1.1.1	Interim certificates
30.7	Interim certificate including finally adjusted sub-contract sums
30.8	Final certificate
35.15.1	Delay by nominated sub-contractor
35.16	Practical completion of nominated sub-contract works

Table 2.11:   Architect's Instructions Empowered by JCT 80

Clause	Instruction
2.2.2.2	To correct errors in contract bills
2.3	In regard to discrepancy in or divergence between contract documents
6.1.3	In relation to divergence between statutory requirements and all or any of the contract documents or any variation instruction
7	That errors in setting out are not to be amended
8.3	To open up for inspection or carry out testing
8.4.1	Removal from site of work, materials or goods
8.4.3	Reasonably necessary variation after defective work
8.4.4	Reasonably necessary to open up and establish likelihood of non-compliance
8.5	Requiring the exclusion from site of any person employed thereon
12	To confirm directions of the clerk of works
13.2	Requiring or sanctioning a variation
13.3	Expenditure of provisional sums included in the contract bills or in a sub-contract
17.2	Schedule of defects
17.3	Requiring defects etc, to be made good
21.2	To take out insurance against employer's liabilities
22C.4.4.2	Requiring the removal and disposal of any debris after loss and damage
22D.1	To obtain and accept liquidated damages insurance
23.2	Postponing work
32.2	Requiring the execution of protective work or continuation of work up to a specified point of stoppage after determination on the outbreak of hostilities
33.1.2	Requiring removal and disposal of debris and execution of protective work after war damage
34.2	Regarding antiquities, including excavation, examination or removal by third parties
35.5.2	Substituting NSC/1 and NSC/2 for clauses 35.11 and 35.12 or *vice versa*
35.10.2	Nominating a sub-contractor
35.11.2	Nominating a sub-contractor
35.23	Omitting work or selecting another person if proposed nomination does not proceed
35.24.4.1	That the contractor give a default notice to the sub-contractor
36.2	To nominate a supplier

Table 2.12: Adjustment of Contract Sum under JCT 80

Clause	Adjustment
2.2.2.2	Errors in bills
2.3	Discrepancy in contract documents
3	Contract sum adjustments
6.1.3	Divergence between contract documents and requirements of statutory authorities
6.1.4.3	Emergency in complying with statutory requirements
6.2	Fees legally demandable under Act of Parliament etc
7	Levels and setting out
8.3	Opening up the works and testing
9.2	Royalties and patent rights
13	Variations
17.2, 17.3	Defects, shrinkages and other faults
21.2.3	Insurance payments under clause 21.2 by the contractor
22B.2	Contractor insuring if employer defaults
22C.3	Contractor insuring if employer defaults
26.5	Loss and/or expense
28.2.2.2	Work begun but not completed at date of determination
30.6	Final adjustment of contract sum
32.3	Works required after outbreak of hostilities
33.1.4	Removal of debris and protective work after war damage
34.3.3	Loss and/or expense due to antiquities
35.24.7	Renomination of sub-contractor
36.3.2	Expense in obtaining goods from a nominated supplier
38, 39, 40	Fluctuations

Table 2.13: Arbitrator's Powers under JCT 80 and JCT Arbitration Rules 1988

Power	Source of Authority
To rectify the contract	
To direct measurements and valuations to determine the rights of the parties	
To ascertain and award any sum which ought to have been the subject of or included in any certificate	Clause 41.4 These are the express powers conferred on the arbitrator by the parties
To open up, review, and revise any certificate, opinion, decision requirement or notice	
To determine all matters in dispute which shall be submitted to him *de novo*	JCT Arbitration Rules, rule 12
To take legal or technical advice	
To give directions for protecting, storing or disposing of property	
To order security for costs and or his fees or expenses	
To proceed *ex parte*, subject to notice	
To tax costs if not agreed	
To direct affidavit evidence	
To order production, inspection and copies of documents	
To take evidence on oath	Arbitraction Act 1950 s 12(1)
To order disclosure and inspection of documents	1950 Act, s 12(1)
To do all other things required for determining facts or law, including the power to make procedural orders	1950 Act, s 12(1)
To apply to the High Court for additional and default powers if a party fails to comply with his orders	1950 Act, s 12(6) and 1979 Act, s 5
To make interim and final awards	1950 Act, ss 13 and 14
To order specific performance where appropriate	1950 Act, s 15
To award costs and to tax and settle their amount	1950 Act, s 18
To award interest	1950 Act, s 20, as amended

Flowchart 2.14:   Architect's Instructions

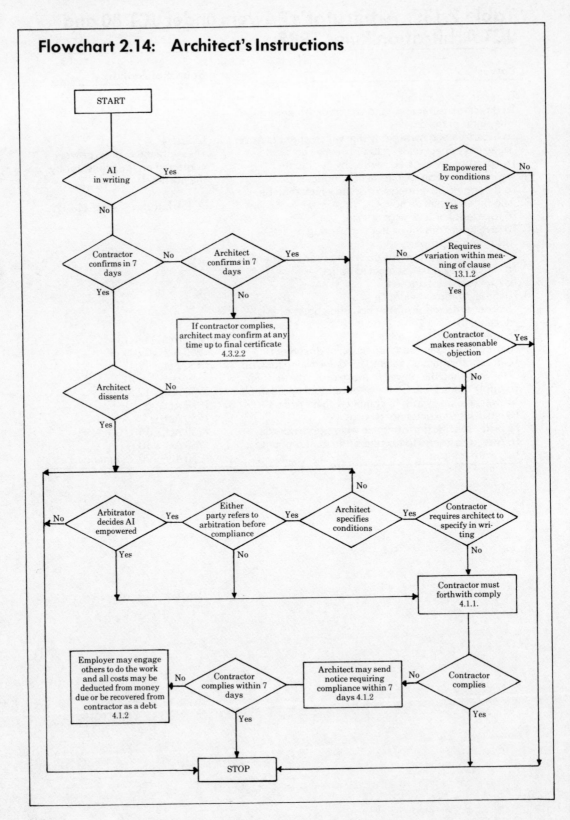

Flowchart 2.15:   Valuation of Variations

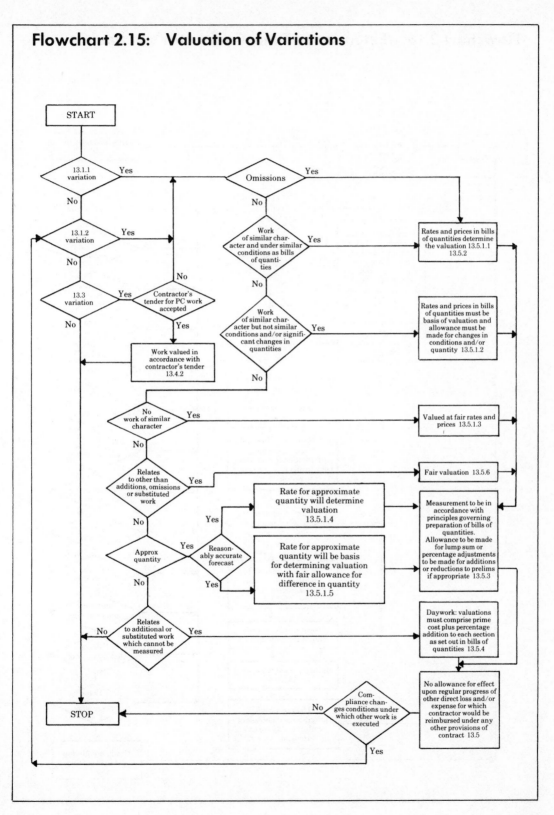

Flowchart 2.16:   Extension of Time: Contractor's Duties

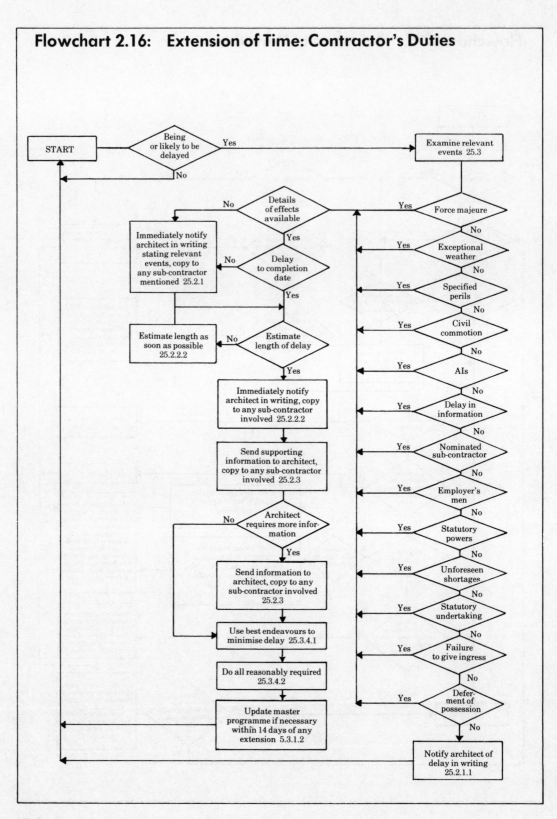

Flowchart 2.17:   Extension of Time: Architect's Duties

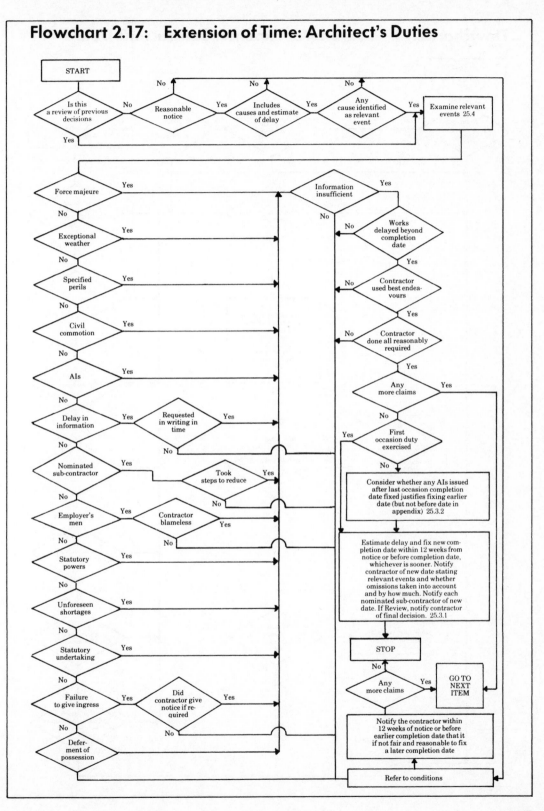

START

Is this a review of previous decisions — No → Reasonable notice — Yes → Includes causes and estimate of delay — Yes → Any cause identified as relevant event — Yes → Examine relevant events 25.4

No (from Reasonable notice) ↑ No (from Includes causes and estimate of delay) ↑ No (from Any cause identified as relevant event) ↑

Yes (from Is this a review of previous decisions)

Force majeure — Yes
No
Exceptional weather — Yes
No
Specified perils — Yes
No
Civil commotion — Yes
No
AIs — Yes
No
Delay in information — Yes → Requested in writing in time — Yes
No / No
Nominated sub-contractor — Yes → Took steps to reduce — Yes
No / No
Employer's men — Yes → Contractor blameless — Yes
No / No
Statutory powers — Yes
No
Unforeseen shortages — Yes
No
Statutory undertaking — Yes
No
Failure to give ingress — Yes → Did contractor give notice if required — Yes
No / No
Deferment of possession

Information insufficient — Yes
No
Works delayed beyond completion date — No
Yes
Contractor used best endeavours — No
Yes
Contractor done all reasonably required — No
Yes
Any more claims — Yes
No
First occasion duty exercised — Yes
No

Consider whether any AIs issued after last occasion completion date fixed justifies fixing earlier date (but not before date in appendix) 25.3.2

Estimate delay and fix new completion date within 12 weeks from notice or before completion date, whichever is sooner. Notify contractor of new date stating relevant events and whether omissions taken into account and by how much. Notify each nominated sub-contractor of new date. If Review, notify contractor of final decision. 25.3.1

STOP
No
Any more claims — Yes → GO TO NEXT ITEM

Notify the contractor within 12 weeks of notice or before earlier completion date that it if not fair and reasonable to fix a later completion date

Refer to conditions

107

Flowchart 2.18: Loss and/or Expense: Contractor's Duties

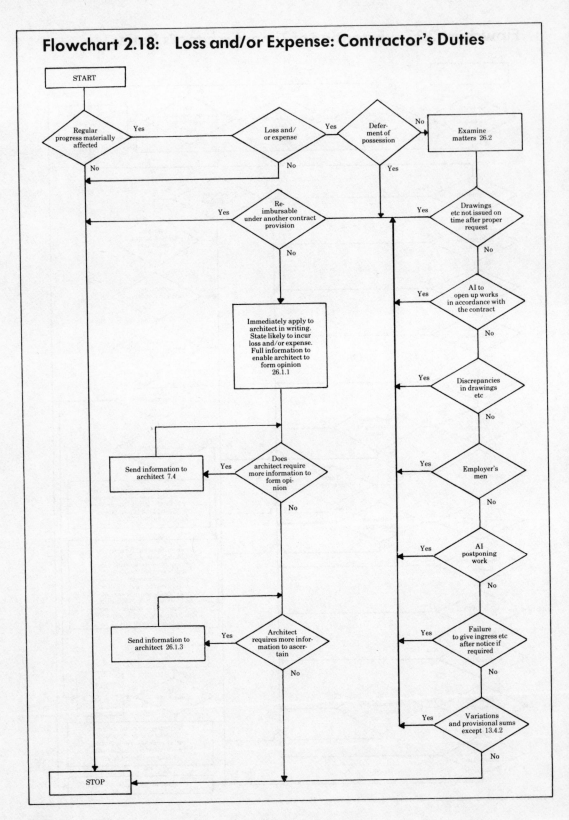

START

Regular progress materially affected — Yes

Loss and/or expense — Yes

Deferment of possession — No → Examine matters 26.2

No (Regular progress)

No (Loss and/or expense)

Yes (Deferment of possession)

Reimbursable under another contract provision — Yes

Drawings etc not issued on time after proper request — Yes

No (Reimbursable)

No (Drawings)

AI to open up works in accordance with the contract — Yes

Immediately apply to architect in writing. State likely to incur loss and/or expense. Full information to enable architect to form opinion 26.1.1

No (AI to open up works)

Discrepancies in drawings etc — Yes

No (Discrepancies)

Send information to architect 7.4 — Yes ← Does architect require more information to form opinion

Employer's men — Yes

No (Does architect require more information)

No (Employer's men)

AI postponing work — Yes

No (AI postponing work)

Send information to architect 26.1.3 — Yes ← Architect requires more information to ascertain

Failure to give ingress etc after notice if required — Yes

No (Architect requires more information)

No (Failure to give ingress)

Variations and provisional sums except 13.4.2 — Yes

No (Variations)

STOP

108

Flowchart 2.19: Loss and/or Expense: Architect's Duties

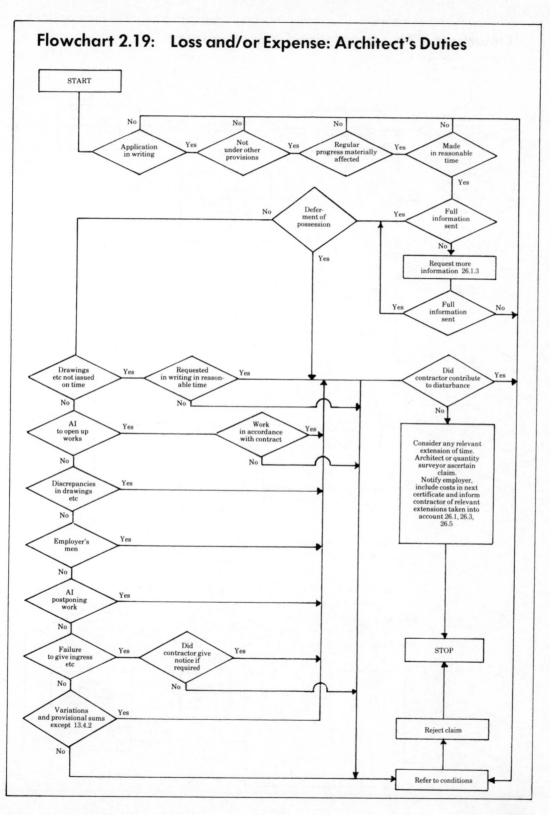

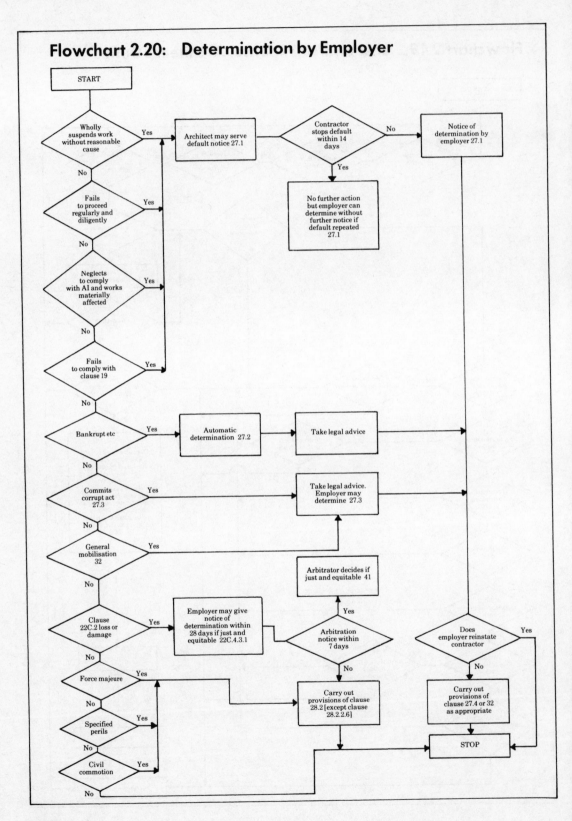

Flowchart 2.20:   Determination by Employer

START

Wholly suspends work without reasonable cause — Yes → Architect may serve default notice 27.1 → Contractor stops default within 14 days — No → Notice of determination by employer 27.1

Contractor stops default within 14 days — Yes → No further action but employer can determine without further notice if default repeated 27.1

Fails to proceed regularly and diligently — Yes

Neglects to comply with AI and works materially affected — Yes

Fails to comply with clause 19 — Yes

Bankrupt etc — Yes → Automatic determination 27.2 → Take legal advice

Commits corrupt act 27.3 — Yes → Take legal advice. Employer may determine 27.3

General mobilisation 32 — Yes

Arbitrator decides if just and equitable 41

Clause 22C.2 loss or damage — Yes → Employer may give notice of determination within 28 days if just and equitable 22C.4.3.1 → Arbitration notice within 7 days — Yes

Arbitration notice within 7 days — No

Does employer reinstate contractor — Yes

Does employer reinstate contractor — No → Carry out provisions of clause 27.4 or 32 as appropriate

Force majeure — Yes

Specified perils — Yes → Carry out provisions of clause 28.2 [except clause 28.2.2.6]

Civil commotion — Yes

No → STOP

110

Flowchart 2.21: Determination by Contractor

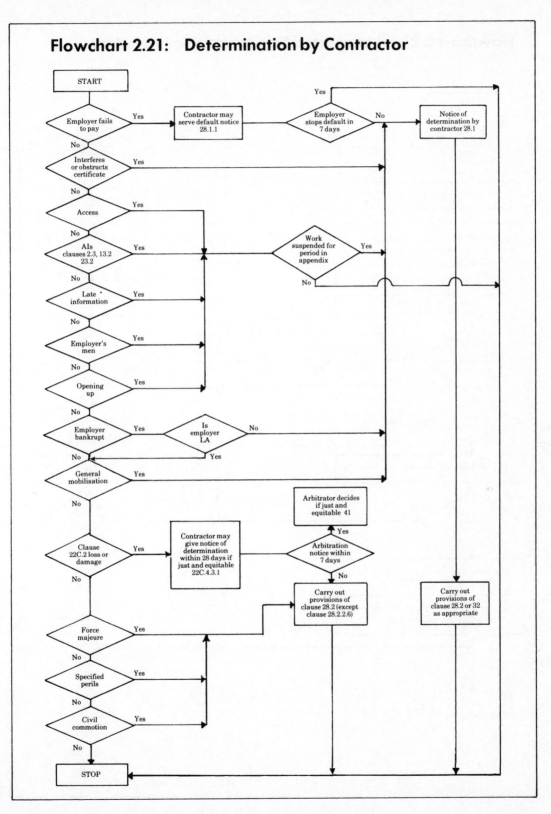

Flowchart 2.22: Nominated Sub-contractor Procedure

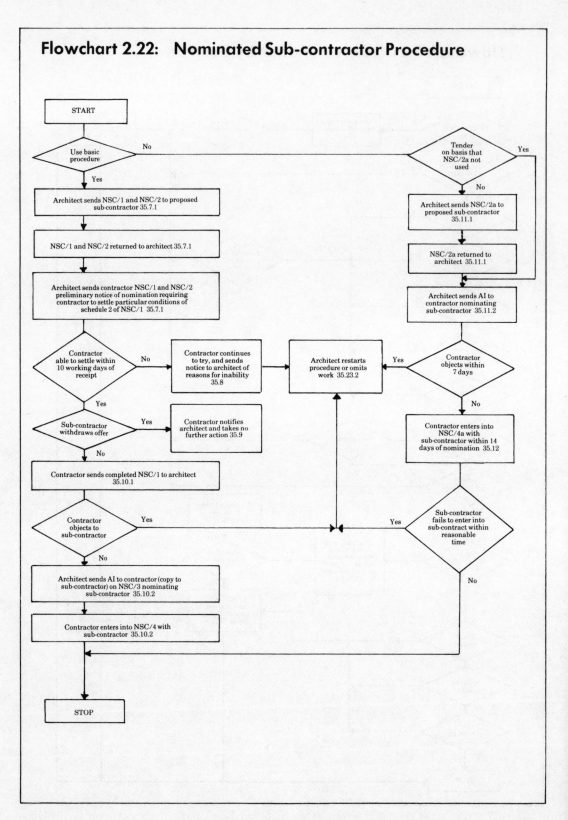

START

Use basic procedure — No → Tender on basis that NSC/2a not used — Yes

Yes

Architect sends NSC/1 and NSC/2 to proposed sub-contractor 35.7.1

NSC/1 and NSC/2 returned to architect 35.7.1

Architect sends contractor NSC/1 and NSC/2 preliminary notice of nomination requiring contractor to settle particular conditions of schedule 2 of NSC/1 35.7.1

Contractor able to settle within 10 working days of receipt — No → Contractor continues to try, and sends notice to architect of reasons for inability 35.8 → Architect restarts procedure or omits work 35.23.2

Yes

Sub-contractor withdraws offer — Yes → Contractor notifies architect and takes no further action 35.9

No

Contractor sends completed NSC/1 to architect 35.10.1

Contractor objects to sub-contractor — Yes →

No

Architect sends AI to contractor (copy to sub-contractor) on NSC/3 nominating sub-contractor 35.10.2

Contractor enters into NSC/4 with sub-contractor 35.10.2

STOP

Tender on basis that NSC/2a not used — No

Architect sends NSC/2a to proposed sub-contractor 35.11.1

NSC/2a returned to architect 35.11.1

Architect sends AI to contractor nominating sub-contractor 35.11.2

Contractor objects within 7 days — Yes → Architect restarts procedure or omits work 35.23.2

No

Contractor enters into NSC/4a with sub-contractor within 14 days of nomination 35.12

Sub-contractor fails to enter into sub-contract within reasonable time — Yes →

No

112

Flowchart 2.23: Determination and Renomination of Sub-contractors

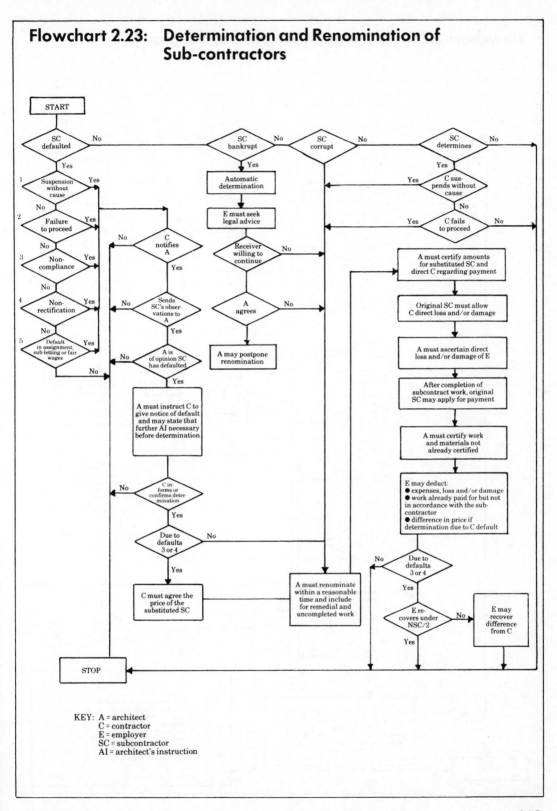

KEY: A = architect
C = contractor
E = employer
SC = subcontractor
AI = architect's instruction

Flowchart 2.24: Arbitration (Article 5 and Clause 41)

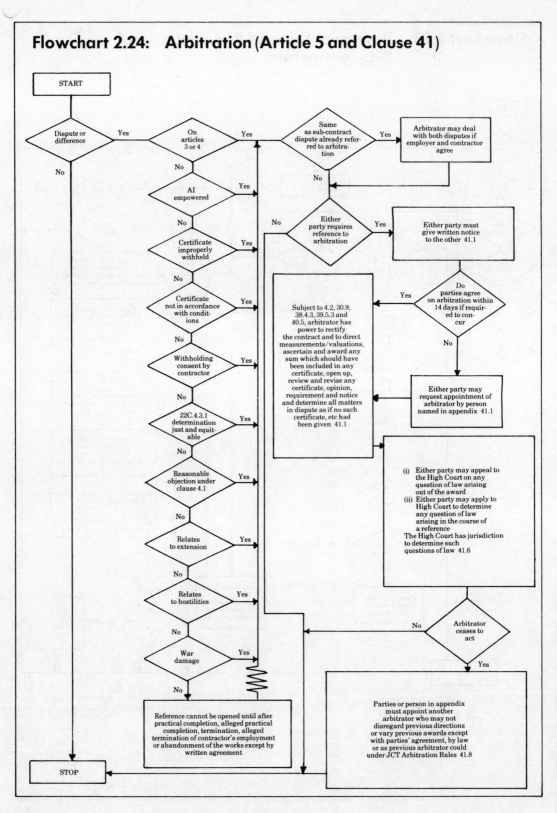

START

Dispute or difference — Yes → On articles 3 or 4 — Yes → Same as sub-contract dispute already referred to arbitration — Yes → Arbitrator may deal with both disputes if employer and contractor agree

No (Dispute or difference) → STOP

On articles 3 or 4 — No → AI empowered — Yes

AI empowered — No → Certificate improperly withheld — Yes

Certificate improperly withheld — No → Certificate not in accordance with conditions — Yes

Certificate not in accordance with conditions — No → Withholding consent by contractor — Yes

Withholding consent by contractor — No → 22C.4.3.1 determination just and equitable — Yes

22C.4.3.1 determination just and equitable — No → Reasonable objection under clause 4.1 — Yes

Reasonable objection under clause 4.1 — No → Relates to extension — Yes

Relates to extension — No → Relates to hostilities — Yes

Relates to hostilities — No → War damage — Yes

War damage — No → Reference cannot be opened until after practical completion, alleged practical completion, termination, alleged termination of contractor's employment or abandonment of the works except by written agreement

Same as sub-contract dispute already referred to arbitration — No → Either party requires reference to arbitration — No

Either party requires reference to arbitration — Yes → Either party must give written notice to the other 41.1

Either party must give written notice to the other 41.1 → Do parties agree on arbitration within 14 days if required to concur

Do parties agree on arbitration within 14 days if required to concur — Yes → Subject to 4.2, 30.9, 38.4.3, 39.5.3 and 40.5, arbitrator has power to rectify the contract and to direct measurements/valuations, ascertain and award any sum which should have been included in any certificate, open up, review and revise any certificate, opinion, requirement and notice and determine all matters in dispute as if no such certificate, etc had been given 41.1

Do parties agree on arbitration within 14 days if required to concur — No → Either party may request appointment of arbitrator by person named in appendix 41.1

(i) Either party may appeal to the High Court on any question of law arising out of the award
(ii) Either party may apply to High Court to determine any question of law arising in the course of a reference
The High Court has jurisdiction to determine such questions of law 41.6

Arbitrator ceases to act — No → (back to flow)

Arbitrator ceases to act — Yes → Parties or person in appendix must appoint another arbitrator who may not disregard previous directions or vary previous awards except with parties' agreement, by law or as previous arbitrator could under JCT Arbitration Rules 41.8

STOP

3: The JCT Intermediate Form of Contract (IFC 84)

3.01   Introduction

The JCT Intermediate Form of Building Contract for works of simple content (IFC 84) is a hybrid form more akin to JCT 80 in wording and detail than to MW 80 although its structure follows the MW 80 pattern. It has been amended five times, the last occasion being April 1989. The supporting Practice Notes advise on its use. A JCT Tender and Agreement (NAM/T) and supporting sub-contract conditions (NAM/SC) are issued for use when the facility for naming sub-contractors under clause 3 is used. RIBA and CASEC have published a Form of Agreement for use in such cases, its effect being to create a collateral contract between the employer and the named person.

IFC 84 is intended for use on contracts up to £280,000 in value (at 1987 prices) where the work is:

- Of simple content
- Without complex service installations
- Adequately specified or specified and billed.

Practice Note 20 suggests a maximum contract period of 12 months but clearly contract period and contract value are not deciding factors.

The most notable features are:

- "Naming" of sub-contractors
- Provision for the architect to issue instructions regarding failure of work and the inspection of similar work
- No restriction on arbitration during the progress of the works.

This was the first of the JCT series to introduce deferment of possession of the site.

The contents are summarised in **Table 3.01.**

3.02   Contractor's Obligations

The contractor's basic obligation (clause 1.1) is to "carry out and complete the works in accordance with the contract documents". These are the contract drawings and *either* a specification *or* schedules of work or bills of quantities. Where quality or standards are matters for the architect's opinion they are to be to his reasonable satisfaction. The conclusiveness of the final certificate in this regard (clause 4.7) suggests that the wise architect will leave nothing to his approval or satisfaction.

Much of the remainder of clause 1 deals with administrative and related matters – quality and quantity of work, priority of documents and so on – and these provisions largely mirror those of JCT 80. Certificates issued by the architect go to the employer, with a duplicate to the contractor (clause 1.9).

3.03   Contract Documentation and Information

The documentation is intended to be extemely flexible. There are four possible combinations which can form the contract documents. They are the *contract drawings* together with:

- The specification priced by the contractor, *or*
- The schedules of work priced by the contractor, *or*
- The bills of quantities priced by the contractor, *or*
- The specification and the sum the contractor requires for carrying out the works.

In the last case, the contractor is required to supply either a contract sum analysis or a schedule of rates on which the contract sum is based. Note that these last two documents are not contract documents under the provisions of the contract although there would appear to be every reason why they should be. It is suggested that a suitable amendment should be made to rectify this situation which might otherwise cause serious problems in practice.

Clause 1.7 requires the architect to provide the contractor with two copies of further drawings and details such "as are reasonably necessary to enable" him to carry out and complete the works in accordance with the conditions. There is no requirement for the contractor to make any application for the additional information and failure to provide it at the right time would render the employer liable (through the architect) to the contractor for breach of contract. It should be noted that this obligation is unaffected by the provisions of clauses 2.4.7 or 4.12.1 relating to extension of time and financial claims respectively.

The usual JCT provision that the printed conditions must take precedence over the other contract documents appears in clause 1.3. The contractor's programme is not mentioned, but the prudent architect will include a requirement for a programme to be drawn up in accordance with his own preference. This can most easily be done by inserting such a requirement in the specification or bills.

3.04   Commencement and Completion

The contractor is to be given possession of the site on the date stated in the appendix (clause 2.1). The contract gives the employer the right to defer giving possession "for a time not exceeding the period stated in the Appendix calculated from the Date of Possession". This period is stated not to exceed 6 weeks although there appears to be no reason why a longer period should not be chosen. It will have obvious repercussions on the tender price. The exercise of the power to defer giving possession will entitle the contractor to an extension of time *and* to payment for loss and/or expense. This is clearly preferable to the situation which would prevail if this power did not exist when the contractor could bring a claim at common law for breach of contract for the employer's failure to give possession.

Once possession of the site is given to him, the contractor must commence work and proceed regularly and diligently and complete the works "on or before" the original or extended completion date. If the contractor fails to so complete the works by the due date then the architect must issue a certificate of non-completion (clause 2.6). There is specific provision for the architect to issue a written cancellation of that certificate and issue another certificate should any extension of time be granted after the issue of the original certificate. This important provision is not found in JCT 80. The certificate of non-completion is a precondition to the deduction of liquidated damages.

Under clause 2.7 the employer has a contractual right to deduct liquidated damages at the specified rate provided:

- The architect has issued a certificate of non-completion; *and*
- The employer has required liquidated damages by written notice to the contractor not later than the date of the final certificate.

Provision is made (clause 2.8) for the repayment of liquidated damages should further extensions of time be granted, but note that the contractor has no contractual or other right to interest on sums repaid.

The provisions on practical completion (clause 2.9) and defects liability (clause 2.10) reflect those of JCT 80, though phrased more succinctly. The contractor is required to make good at his own expense "defects, shrinkages or other faults" which appear during the defects liability period "and which are due to materials or workmanship not in accordance with the contract or frost occurring before practical completion". With the employer's consent the architect may decide that the defects be made good other than by the contractor. In that case the contract sum will be reduced appropriately. The clause appears to give the architect power to order making good at any time *during* and up to 14 days after the end of the defects liability period.

The consequences of practical completion are:

- Contractor's insurance liability under clause 6.3A ends
- His liability for liquidated damages ends
- Half the retention percentage becomes due for release within 14 days
- The period for providing all documents for adjustment of the contract sum (clause 4.5)
- The period of final review of extensions of time commences (clauses 2.3)
- The defects liability period begins (clause 2.10).

3.05   Extensions of Time

Clause 2.3 deals with extensions of time.

For the clause to operate:

- It must become reasonably apparent to the contractor that progress of the works is being or is likely to be delayed
- The contractor must forthwith give written notice of the cause of the delay to the architect
- If required by the architect the contractor must provide such further information as is reasonably necessary to enable the architect to discharge his functions under the clause.

If the architect is of the opinion that the completion of the works is likely to be or has been delayed by one of the specified events he must grant in writing a fair and reasonable extension of time for completion. This he must do "so soon as he is able to *estimate* the length of delay".

Failure to grant an extension may result in the contract completion date becoming unenforceable and the employer losing his right to liquidated damages.

The contractor's written notice is not a precondition to the grant of an extension of time because at any time up to 12 weeks after practical completion the architect may grant an extension of time "whether upon reviewing a previous decision or otherwise and whether or not the contractor has given notice". Architects must consider this matter so as to preserve the employer's position. The only effect of non-notification by the contractor is that he loses the benefit of an early extension of time. The review after practical completion cannot reduce any extension of time previously granted.

In addition to the architect's power to grant an extension before the date for completion, where certain specified events occur after the original or extended completion date is passed the architect is empowered to grant an extension. The exercise of this power will prevent time for completion becoming at large and preserve the employer's right to liquidated damages.

118

The specified events are:

- Clause 2.4.5   Compliance with architect's instructions about inconsistencies (clause 1.4), variations (clause 3.6), provisional sums (clause 3.8), postponement (clause 3.15), named sub-contractors (subject to limitations: see clause 3.3)
- Clause 2.4.6   Compliance with architect's instructions requiring opening-up for inspection or tests where the results are in the contractor's favour
- Clause 2.4.7   Late instructions or drawings
- Clause 2.4.8   Execution of work not forming part of the contract by the employer or his licensees under clause 3.11 or failure to execute such work
- Clause 2.4.9   Supply or failure to supply by the employer goods and materials which the employer contracted to supply
- Clause 2.4.12   Employer's failure to give any agreed access to or from the site

The extension of time provisions are subject to two provisos:

- The contractor must constantly use his best endeavours to prevent delay, eg by reprogramming as necessary, but not by funding acceleration measures
- The contractor must do all that the architect may reasonably require to proceed with the works; but he is not required to expend substantial sums of money to meet this obligation.

The events giving rise to a claim for extension of time (clause 2.4) are essentially the same as those in JCT 80 except:

- Non-availability of labour or materials is an *optional* ground which will apply only where so stated in the appendix
- The exercise of statutory powers by the UK government is not an event giving rise to an extension of time, nor is delay by nominated sub-contractors, since there are none under IFC 84.

3.06 Architect's Instructions

Architect's instructions must be issued in writing (clause 3.5.1) and the contractor must forthwith comply with them, provided they are empowered by the contract. The contractor need not comply if the instruction relates to the "imposition by the employer of any obligations or restrictions or the addition to or alteration or omission of any such obligations or restrictions so imposed or imposed by the employer in the Specification/Schedules of Work/Contract Bills in regard to" access, limitation of working space or hours or the execution or completion of work in a specific order, provided he makes a reasonable objection to the architect. The objection must be in writing.

The contractor can request clarification of the empowering clause in the case of any instruction. The architect must respond immediately to any such written request from the contractor, specifying the clause on which he relies. The contractor then has a choice of either complying – when the instruction will be deemed to be empowered by the conditions whether or not this is the case – or of referring the matter to arbitration.

Should the contractor fail to comply with any instruction, the architect has power to issue a notice requiring compliance. Should the contractor fail to comply for seven days after receipt of the architect's notice, the employer (not the architect) may employ and pay others to do the work involved and deduct the costs involved from sums otherwise due to the contractor.

Interestingly and importantly there is no provision for the issue of oral instructions. All instructions must be in writing and the form makes no provision for what is to happen should they be issued orally. Presumably the contractor can ignore them. Possibly if oral instructions were given and acted upon, the contractor might be able to recover any costs involved by way of an action at common law. The architect must ensure that his instructions are given in writing as the contract requires if problems are to be avoided.

Clause 3.13 deals with failure of work, whether this is due to the fault of the contractor or that of any sub-contractor. When a failure is discovered, the contractor must state in writing to the architect the action which he will take *immediately* – at no cost to the employer – to ensure that there is no similar failure in work already executed or in goods or materials supplied.

If the architect:

- Has not received a statement from the contractor within 7 days of discovery of the failure; *or*
- Is dissatisfied with the contractor's proposed action; *or*
- Is unable to wait for the contractor's proposals because of considerations of safety or statutory obligation;

he may instruct the contractor to open up any work for inspection or to arrange for any test to establish that there is no similar failure and to make good in consequence. This is to be done at no cost to the employer and the contractor is bound forthwith to comply with any such architect's instruction.

The contractor has a right to object to compliance. The right must be exercised within 10 days of receipt of the architect's instruction and the objection must be a reasoned and written statement. The architect then has 7 days from receipt of the contractor's written objection in which to consider the matter. He may withdraw the instruction or else modify it to meet the contractor's objection. If he does not do so, the dispute is referred to arbitration automatically. The arbitrator will then decide what amount of money (if any) should be paid to the contractor in respect of his compliance with the instruction, as well as granting any appropriate extension of time. Note that the provision is so worded as to enable a sub-contractor who is involved to be joined in these arbitration proceedings.

Variations are defined in and covered by clause 3.6. These provisions are broadly similar to those of JCT 80. Variations are to be valued by the quantity surveyor on the basis of a priced document (specification, schedules of work, bills of quantities, contract sum analysis or schedule of rates), or a fair valuation or daywork rates as appropriate.

3.07 Contractor's Claims

The direct loss and/or expense provisions (money claims) are set out in clauses 4.11 and 4.12. They are broadly similar to those of JCT 80, clause 26. Should the contractor wish to claim for loss and/or expense he must:

- Make written application to the architect within a reasonable time of it becoming apparent that he has incurred or is likely to incur the loss and/or expense because of one or more of the specified matters. The application need not be in any specific form and the cases of *Croudace Ltd* v *London Borough of Lambeth* (1986) 6 ConLR 70 and *Rees & Kirby Ltd* v *Swansea Corporation* (1985) 5 ConLR 11 suggest that the time requirement may be interpreted generously
- Submit supporting information to the architect or quantity surveyor as reasonably required by them. This does not envisage a "moneyed-out" claim but, of course, the architect is entitled to ask for back-up information to support the heads of claim. Figures cannot be plucked out of the air.

If the architect forms the opinion that the contractor either has incurred or is likely to incur direct loss and/or expense as claimed by him – and the sum must not be reimbursable under any other contract provision – then he must either himself ascertain the amount of the direct loss and/or expense or instruct the quantity surveyor to do so. Clearly, the architect's failure to meet this duty is a breach of contract for which the employer may be liable in damages: *Croudace Ltd* v *London Borough of Lambeth* (1986) 6 ConLR 70. The architect *may* be liable to the contractor direct in very special circumstances, although this liability is very limited: *Pacific Associates Inc* v *Baxter* (1988) CILL 460, where the Court of Appeal ruled that it is generally not just and reasonable to superimpose duties beyond those freely agreed in the contractual structure.

3.08 Certificates and Payment

Clause 4 contains detailed provisions for certification by the architect of monthly interim and final payments. It also deals with the effect of the final certificate.

The scheme of payments is 95% of the value of work properly executed and of materials on site (97½% on practical completion) and, at the discretion of the architect, the value of any off-site goods and materials. The monthly interim payments will include 100% of sums payable in respect of disturbance payments, insurance monies, statutory fees and so forth, insofar as these have been ascertained. The retention percentage is treated as trust money except where the employer is a local authority.

The contractor must provide the architect with the information needed for the computation of the final adjusted contract sum within six months of practical completion, and the quantity surveyor is to prepare a statement of all the final valuations of variations. A copy of the computations of the adjusted contract sum is then sent to the contractor within three months of receipt of the information required from the contractor.

The architect has 28 days from the sending of these final computations to the contractor or the issue of the certificate of making good defects whichever is the later, in which to issue the final certificate. The employer has a further 28 days from the date of that certificate in which to pay. The final certificate is a significant document. Subject to certain qualifications, it is expressed to be conclusive evidence that:

- Where quality of materials and standards of workmanship are to be to the reasonable satisfaction of the architect, they are to such satisfaction
- Any necessary effect has been given to all the contract terms which require an adjustment to be made to the contract sum
- All due extensions of time have been given
- Reimbursement of loss and/or expense is in final settlement of all contractor's claims in respect of clause 4.12 matters.

The qualifications are:

- Where proceedings have been commenced before or within 28 days after the issue of the final certificate. That certificate is not then conclusive as to those matters to which the proceedings relate
- Accidental inclusion or exclusion of any item
- Mathematical error.

There is a choice of fluctuations provisions: contributions, levy and tax fluctuations or, where there are bills, the alternative and more popular method of formula adjustment. These provisions are akin to their JCT 80 counterparts.

3.09 Sub-Contractors and Employer's Licensees

Clause 3 is the longest and most complex in the form. There is the usual prohibition against assignment of the contract without the consent of the other party (clause 3.1). The only practical effect of this sub-clause is to prevent either party assigning his contractual rights, since as a matter of general law the party cannot assign his contractual duties.

The contractor must seek the architect's written consent before sub-letting any part of the works unless the sub-contractor involved is one who is named under clause 3.3. The architect may not withhold his consent unreasonably. Any resulting sub-contract must contain specified minimum terms:

- Provision for its immediate determination should the main contractor's employment under the main contract be determined
- Provision designed to ensure that the sub-contractor's unfixed materials and goods which have been paid for by the employer in main contract certificates shall become the employer's property on payment. The effectiveness of such provisions is open to doubt under the general law.

Named sub-contractors are a concept peculiar to the Intermediate Form and can come into existence under the provisions of clause 3.3. This sub-clause enables the employer to name persons to carry out work priced in the contract documents or included in a provisional sum. There is no corresponding provision for naming suppliers. Unfortunately, it has to be said that these provisions are both complicated and unclear.

A named sub-contractor can arise in two ways:

- Where work is included in the contract documents to be priced by the contractor but executed by a person named as a sub-contractor: clause 3.3.1
- Where work is included in an architect's instruction as to the expenditure of a provisional sum and a person is named to carry it out.

Different procedures apply in each case. Where the named person is heralded in the contract documents, the contractor is obliged to enter into a sub-contract with him "not later than 21 days after entering into this contract" using section III of the form of tender and agreement [NAM/T] which incorporates the special sub-contract conditions.

If the contractor is "unable to enter into a sub-contract in accordance with the particulars given" he must inform the architect immediately. His notification must detail the "particulars" which have prevented the sub-contract being made. Presumably the "particulars" referred to are details as to programme and otherwise contained in the sub-contractor's completed tender NAM/T.

Provided the architect is reasonably satisfied that the specified particulars have caused the problem he must issue an instruction. This instruction can:

- Change the particulars so as to remove the impediment; *or*
- Omit the work; *or*
- Omit the work from the contract documents and substitute a provisional sum.

Where the work is omitted entirely, the employer may get someone else to do it, subject to the provisions of clause 3.11, discussed below. Both in that case and where the instruction changes the particulars, it is to be valued as a variation.

Assuming the contractor is able to sub-contract as required, he must notify the architect of the date when he entered into the sub-contract. At any time before the date so notified – but not after – the architect may decide to have the work carried out by someone else and so instruct the contractor. In that case, a provisional sum is substituted and the matter is dealt with accordingly.

Clause 3.3.2 covers the alternative method, namely where a named sub-contractor arises through a provisional sum. A PS instruction may require work to be executed by a named person. The instruction must describe the work to be done and include all the particulars of the named person's tender (NAM/T section I and II). Form NAM/T is itself a complicated document but essentially comprises the named person's tender. In this case the contractor has a right to make reasonable objection to the person named.

The contract is silent about what a reasonable objection is, but reasonable grounds for objection might be:

- Financial instability of person named
- Named person's programme is incompatible with contractor's programme
- Bad past experiences on other projects.

Objection must be made within 14 days of the issue of the architect's instruction. The contract says nothing about what is to happen if the contractor does make an objection which is regarded as reasonable. In that case, presumably the architect must omit the work or name someone else.

Re-naming is clearly not a rapid process. The architect has no power to grant an extension of time except perhaps on the basis set out by Parker LJ in *Rhuddlan Borough Council* v *Fairclough Building Ltd* (1985) 3 ConLR 38:

"If there is a *lacuna* in the contractual machinery, as there appears to be, it might, as it seems to us, possibly be filled by an implied term, that if the nomination were accepted, an appropriate extension would be granted".

The administrative burden on the architect is considerable if this procedure is used. In either mode, it is desirable (if not essential) that the employer be advised to enter into the supporting RIBA/CASEC Form of Agreement, which is in effect a collateral contract between employer and named person, so enabling the employer to take direct action if the specialist defaults. However, in view of *Greater Nottingham Co-operative Society* v *Cementation Piling and Foundation Ltd* (1988) CILL 404, it appears that ESA/1 requires amendment so as to make the specialist liable if he fails to exercise reasonable care and skill in the execution of the sub-contract works.

Clause 3.7 exempts the contractor from liability to the employer "whether or not" the named person is responsible to him, for any failure by the specialist in three important areas:

- Sub-contract design undertaken by him
- Selection of kinds of materials and goods for the sub-contract works undertaken by him
- Satisfaction of any performance specification or requirement so undertaken.

It is important to note the blanket exemption given to the contractor by clause 3.7. He "shall not be responsible to the employer ... for anything to which the above terms relate, nor, through the contractor, shall the person so named or any other sub-contractor be so responsible".

Clauses 3.3.3 to 3.3.6 cover the problems caused by a named sub-contractor's default or failure. The contractor must advise the architect "as soon as is reasonably practicable" of any events likely to lead to a determination of the named person's employment. If the named person's employment is determined before the sub-contract works are completed, the contractor must notify the architect in writing, setting out the circumstances.

The architect must then issue necessary instructions. These may either:

- Name another person to execute the work or the outstanding balance of the work (the contractor has a right of reasonable objection to the substitute); *or*
- Instruct the contractor to make his own arrangements for the execution of the work (in this case the contractor may sub-let with consent under clause 3.2); *or*
- Omit the work remaining to be done.

What happens next depends on whether the work was included in the contract documents or arose through a provisional sum instruction.

- Where the named person was heralded in the contract documents "except to the extent that (the) instruction was issued by reason of some default of the contractor", *if another person is named* the instruction may give rise to an extension of time but not to a money claim. The contract sum is to be adjusted by the amount of any increase or reduction in the substitute sub-contractor's price for the work not carried out by the failed sub-contractor. Any amount included in the new price for the repair of the defective work is to be excluded from this adjustment
- Where the architect's instruction either omits the work or requires the contractor to make his own arrangements for it, the instruction ranks as a variation and gives rise to a claim for extension of time and for direct loss and/or expense: clause 3.3.5
- Where the named contractor arose through a PS instruction then, whatever the nature of the architect's instruction following failure, it gives rise to a claim for extension of time and for direct loss and/or expense. It also ranks for payment as a further instruction under a provisional sum. Once again this is subject to the sensible proviso that the contractor shall not benefit from his own default: clause 3.3.5
- If the sub-contractor's employment is determined otherwise than under 27.1 or 27.2 of NAM/SC, the provisions only apply insofar as they result in a reduction in cost and no extension or disturbance is allowed.

Interestingly, where there is a failure on the part of a named sub-contractor, the contractor is bound "to take such reasonable action as is necessary" to recover the following sums from the defaulter:

- Any additional amount that the employer has to pay the contractor as a result of the architect's instructions following the failure
- An amount equal to any liquidated damages which the employer would have been able to deduct had the extension of time provisions not had to be operated consequent on the failure.

The contractor is not bound to take legal or arbitral proceedings unless the employer agrees to indemnify him against legal costs reasonably incurred, and so the "reasonable steps" he is bound to take will be minimal. However, if he fails to take any reasonable steps, he must repay the employer equivalent sums. Any sums recovered by the contractor must be accounted for to the employer: clause 3.3.6.

Local authorities and statutory undertakers such as British Telecom, Water Boards, and so on, carrying out work under their statutory obligations cannot be named sub-contractors (clause 3.3.8). They may, of course, in an appropriate case be employer's licensees under clause 3.11, which parallels the provision in JCT 80, clause 29, and provides an exception to the principle that the contractor is in sole charge of the works.

As in the case of other JCT contracts, there is a provision (clause 3.4) requiring the contractor to keep a competent person on site in charge of the works "at all reasonable times". When an architect's instruction is given to that person, it is deemed to have been given to the contractor.

3.10 Statutory Obligations

The terms of clause 5.1 oblige the contractor both to comply with and give statutory notices and also to comply with the relevant statutory requirements, eg the provisions of the Building Act 1984 and the Building Regulations made under it. The contractor must also pay the associated fees and charges, but these are to be added to the contract sum unless required by the contract documents to be included in it.

Clause 5.2 requires the contractor to notify the architect in writing of any divergence from statutory requirements, eg a variation required through compliance with the building regulations. Unlike the corresponding provision in JCT 80 there is no express statement of the status of any instruction issued as a result, except as regards emergency compliance with statutory requirements, when the limited work and materials supplied by the contractor are to be treated as a variation. This is subject to two provisos:

- The contractor must have notified the architect of the emergency and the steps he is taking; *and*
- The emergency arose because of a divergence between those requirements and the contract documents or any instruction or document issued by the architect under clauses 1.7 (further drawings or details), 3.5 (architect's instructions) or 3.9 (levels).

The remainder of clause 5 deals – by reference to supplemental conditions – with value added tax (clause 5.5) and the statutory tax deduction scheme (clause 5.6).

3.11 Injury, Damage and Insurance

The indemnity and insurance provisions in clause 6 were completely revised in November 1986. They are identical to those of JCT 80 and follow the wording of JCT 80 almost exactly. Provision is made for the level of insurance cover to be specified in the contract documents and the appendix. The advice of a competent insurance broker is essential if the employer's interests are to be properly protected.

The works insurance clauses provide for joint names insurance against "all risks" to new building:

- If the contractor insures (6.3A)
- If the employer insures (6.3B).

In the case of works in, or extensions to, existing structures (6.3C), the insurance must be taken out by the employer in joint names:

- Against "specified perils" in respect of existing works
- Against "all risks" in respect of the new works.

As in JCT 80 there is provision for the employer to require insurance against the loss of liquidated damages for the specified period on account of loss or damage to the works by one of the "specified perils".

If the works are damaged by one of the insured risks, the contractor must notify the architect and the employer forthwith. After any inspection required by the insurers, the contractor must commence reinstatement. The exception is in relation to existing buildings. If it is just and equitable to do so, either party may determine the contractor's employment.

3.12 Determination

The determination provisions are modelled on those of JCT 80. As in JCT 80 the common law rights of the parties are preserved, so that either of them may use common law remedies as a method of terminating the contractual relationship. Indeed, under IFC 84 as under other JCT forms it is not the contract which is terminated, but merely the employment of the contractor under it. Determination of employment is the last resort and these provisions should never be invoked without seeking competent legal advice.

Determination by employer

Under clause 7.1 the employer may bring the contractor's employment under the contract to an end in the event of certain specified defaults on the contractor's part. These defaults are if the contractor:

- Wholly suspends the carrying out of the works before completion; the suspension must be without reasonable cause
- Fails to proceed regularly and diligently with the works
- Refuses or neglects to comply with a written notice from the architect requiring removal of defective work or improper materials. The works must be *materially affected* by the contractor's refusal or neglect
- Fails to comply with the contract provisions about assignment and sub-letting (clause 3.2) or named persons (clause 3.3).

Provision is made for a default notice to be served on the contractor by registered post or recorded delivery. This must specify the default. If the contractor continues the default for 14 days after receipt of the notice – or repeats the default at any time thereafter – the employer (*not* the architect) may determine the contractor's employment under the contract forthwith. This is effected by serving notice on the contractor by registered post or recorded delivery. The termination notice must not be given unreasonably or vexatiously. Clauses 7.2 and 7.3 cover determination of the contractor's employment for insolvency or corrupt acts respectively. This last ground is available only where the employer is a local authority. Unlike clause 7.1 defaults, no preliminary notice is required. In the case of insolvency – though not all the events listed are in fact true insolvency – the determination is said to be automatic, while in the second case it simply requires service of notice of determination.

Clause 7.4 sets out the consequences of determination and is expressed to be "without prejudice to any arbitration or proceedings in which the validity of the determination is in issue". It governs the rights of the parties after determination and "so long as the contractor's employment has not been reinstated or continued". The contractor must:

- Give up possession of the site
- Remove from the works any temporary buildings, plant, etc belonging to or hired by him, as and when so instructed by the architect.

Should the contractor fail to do this within a reasonable time, the employer is empowered to remove and sell the contractor's property, holding the nett proceeds to the contractor's credit.

The employer may:

- Employ and pay others to complete the works
- Enter on the works
- Use all temporary buildings, plant, etc
- Purchase all materials and goods necessary for the completion contract.

The employer is not bound to make any further payment to the contractor until after completion. He would be unwise to do so. When the works are completed, the architect – with the quantity surveyor's assistance – must draw up an account for the employer. This must show the amount of:

- Expenses and direct loss and/or damage caused to the employer by the determination (including foreseeable economic loss) and including the cost of the completion contract
- The amound paid to the contractor before determination.

The difference between these two amounts will be the sum payable by the contractor to the employer or by the employer to the contractor, as appropriate.

Determination by contractor

Clause 7.5 entitles the contractor to end his employment under the contract for certain specified defaults by the employer, the procedure being the same as under clause 7.1. The grounds giving rise to determination are:

- Employer's failure to pay amounts properly due to the contractor on interim or final certificates
- Employer's interference with or obstruction of *any* certificate
- Suspension of the carrying out of the whole or substantially the whole of the works for a continuous period of 1 month due to architect's instructions under

clause 1.4 (inconsistencies), clause 3.6 (variations) or clause 3.15 (post-ponement) unless caused by the default of the contractor, his servants or agents or any person employed on the works other than the employer, his men or a statutory body in pursuance of its statutory obligations

- Late instructions, for which the contractor applied at the proper time
- Failure or delay in executing work by the employer or his licensees or delay in supplying materials which the employer agreed to supply
- Failure by the employer to give any agreed access to the site.

Clause 7.6 has a similar content to clause 7.2 and deals with the employer's insolvency. In this case, determination is not automatic. It is brought about by the contractor serving notice on the employer by registered post or recorded delivery.

Clause 7.7 covers the consequences of determination by the contractor under the foregoing sub-clauses and contains post-determination and financial provisions similar to those which apply on employer determination. Here, however, the contractor is to be paid by the employer and his entitlement includes "any direct loss and/or damage caused to [him] by the determination". This will include the profit on the contract which he would otherwise have earned: *Wraight Ltd* v *P H & T (Holdings) Ltd* (1968) 13 BLR 26.

Determination by either party

Three further grounds which entitle either party to determine the contractor's employment under the contract are specified in clause 7.8. These grounds are:

- *Force majeure*
- Loss or damage to the works caused by clause 6.3 perils, eg fire
- Civil commotion.

These events provide grounds for determination if, as a result, the carrying out of the whole or substantially the whole of the works is suspended for a period of three calendar months. Determination is effected by service of written notice on the other party by registered post or recorded delivery. Service of the notice is subject to the proviso that it must not be given unreasonably or vexatiously, and the contractor is precluded from determining in respect of damage caused by clause 6.3 perils if that event was caused by his negligence or the negligence of those for whom he is vicariously responsible in law.

The post-determination procedures and financial settlement are the same as those under clause 7.7 except that the contractor is not, in this case, entitled to "direct loss and/or damage" caused to him by the determination.

3.13 Disputes

As in the case of other JCT contracts, disputes arising under the contract are to be settled by arbitration. The arbitration agreement is set out in article 5 referring to clause 9, and the following points should be noted:

- An appendix entry must be made to indicate which of the three presidents is to be the appointor in default of agreement. The choice is from the President or a Vice-President of the Royal Institute of British Architects, or of the Royal Institute of Chartered Surveyors or of the Chartered Institute of Arbitrators
- There is no restriction on when the arbitration can be opened up and so arbitration is possible during the running of the contract

- The arbitrator is given extensive express powers, including a power to go behind the architect's certificate, decisions and opinions which is a power which the courts do not possess. He is also expressly empowered to rectify the contract
- The parties agree in advance for matters of law to be determined by the High Court, though the legal effect of this provision is doubtful
- There is an optional joinder provision for related sub-contract disputes
- There is provision for another arbitrator to be appointed if the original arbitrator dies or, for some other reason, ceases to act
- The arbitration is to be conducted in accordance with the JCT Arbitration Rules which were introduced in July 1988.

Table 3.01: Contents of IFC 84 Summarised –

Clause	Comment
1	**Intentions of the parties**
1.1	Contractor's obligations
1.2	Quality and quantity of work
1.3	Priority of contract documents
1.4	Instructions as to inconsistencies, errors or omissions
1.5	Bills of quantities and SMM
1.6	Custody and copies of contract documents
1.7	Further drawings and details
1.8	Limits to use of documents
1.9	Issue of certificates by architect/contract administrator
1.10	Unfixed materials of goods: passing of property etc
1.11	Off-site materials and goods: passing of property etc
2	**Possession and completion**
2.1	Possession and completion dates
2.2	Deferment of possession
2.3	Extension of time
2.4	Events referred to in clause 2.3
2.5	Further delay or extension of time
2.6	Certificate of non-completion
2.7	Liquidated damages for non-completion
2.8	Repayment of liquidated damages
2.9	Practical completion
2.10	Defects liability
3	**Control of the works**
3.1	Assignment
3.2	Sub-contracting
3.3	Named persons as sub-contractors
3.4	Contractor's person-in-charge
3.5	Architect's/contract administrator's instructions
3.6	Variations
3.7	Valuation of variations and PS work
3.8	Instructions to expend provisional sums
3.9	Levels and setting out
3.10	Clerk of works
3.11	Work not forming part of the contract
3.12	Instructions as to inspections-tests
3.13	Instructions following failure of work etc
3.14	Instructions as to removal of work etc
3.15	Instructions as to postponement
4	**Payment**
4.1	Contract sum
4.2	Interim payments
4.3	Interim payment on practical completion
4.4	Interest in percentage withheld
4.5	Computation of adjusted contract sum
4.6	Issue of final certificate
4.7	Effect of final certificate
4.8	Effect of certificates other than final
4.9	Fluctuations
4.10	Fluctuations: named persons
4.11	Disturbance of regular progress
4.12	Matters referred to in clause 4.11

Table 3.01: Contents of IFC 84 Summarised – (continued)

Clause	Comment
5	**Statutory obligations**
5.1	Statutory obligations, notices, fees and charges
5.2	Notice of divergence from statutory requirements
5.3	Extent of contractor's liability for non-compliance
5.4	Emergency compliance
5.5	Value added tax: supplemental condition A
5.6	Statutory tax deduction scheme: supplemental condition B
6	**Injury, damage and insurance**
6.1	Injury to persons and property and indemnity to employer
6.2	Insurance against injury to persons or property
6.3	Insurance of the works – alternative clauses – definitions – sub-contractors – benefit of Joint Names Policy – specified perils
6.3A	Erection of new buildings – All Risks Insurance of the works by the contractor
6.3B	Erection of new builings – All Risks Insurance of the works by the employer
6.3C	Insurance of existing structures – Insurance of works in or extensions to existing structures
6.3D	Insurance for employer's loss of liquidated damages – clause 2.4.3
7	**Determination**
7.1	Determination by employer
7.2	Contractor becoming bankrupt, etc
7.3	Corruption: determination by employer
7.4	Consequences of determination under clauses 7.1-7.3
7.5	Determination by contractor
7.6	Employer becoming bankrupt, etc
7.7	Consequences of determination under clauses 7.5-7.6
7.8	Determination by employer or contractor
7.9	Consequences of determination under clause 7.8
8	**Interpretation**
8.1	References to clauses
8.2	Articles, etc to be read as a whole
8.3	Definitions
8.4	The architect/contract administrator
8.5	Priced specification or priced schedule of work
	Appendix
	Supplemental conditions:
A	Value added tax
B	Statutory tax deduction scheme
C	Contribution, levy and tax fluctuations
D	Use of price adjustment formulae

Note: There is no provision for the employer to take possession of part of the works which is ready for occupation before practical completion of the whole. However, Practice Note IFC/1, appendix, contains a suitable clause (clause 2.11). There is no sectional completion supplement.

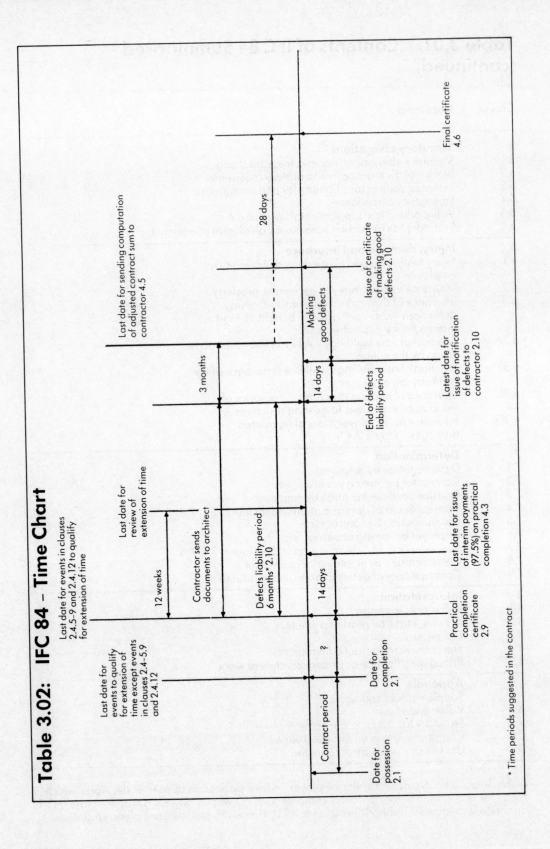

Table 3.02: IFC 84 – Time Chart

Last date for events in clauses 2.4.5–9 and 2.4.12 to qualify for extension of time

Last date for sending computation of adjusted contract sum to contractor 4.5

Last date for events to qualify for extension of time except events in clauses 2.4.5–9 and 2.4.12

Last date for review of extension of time

Contractor sends documents to architect

28 days

Final certificate 4.6

Issue of certificate of making good defects 2.10

Making good defects

3 months

14 days

Latest date for issue of notification of defects to contractor 2.10

End of defects liability period

12 weeks

Defects liability period 6 months* 2.10

14 days

Last date for issue of interim payments (97.5%) on practical completion 4.3

Practical completion certificate 2.9

Date for completion 2.1

Contract period

?

Date for possession 2.1

* Time periods suggested in the contract

132

Table 3.03: Architect's Powers under IFC 84

Clause	Power	Comment
1.10	Consent in writing to removal of unfixed materials or goods delivered to, or placed on or next to, the works	If the contractor's request is for good reason: consent must not be unreasonably withheld
2.3	Review extension of time granted	This is implied and the power should always be exercised in order to preserve the employer's right to liquidated damages if there has been some default for which the employer is legally responsible
	Make in writing a fair and reasonable extension of time for completion even if the contractor has not given notice	He can do this at any time up to 12 weeks after date of practical completion
2.10	Issue instructions that defects etc be made good at the employer's cost	If the employer consents
3.2	Consent to the employment of a sub-contractor	Application from contractor; consent must not be unreasonably withheld
3.3.1	Issue an instruction requiring the named sub-contractor's work to be carried out by another person	This must be done before the contractor notifies the architect of his entering into a named sub-contract
3.3.2	Instruct that particular provisional sum work be carried out by a named person	In an instruction on the expenditure of a provisional sum the instruction must include a description of the work and the relevant tender particulars from NAM/T sections 1 and 2 The contractor has the right of reasonable objections to the named person
3.5.1	Require compliance with an instruction by written notice to the contractor	If contractor fails to comply, others may be employed to carry out the instructions
3.6	Issue variation instructions and sanction in writing any unauthorised variation made by the contractor	The variation ordered must fall within the definition in clause 3.6.1 Variations must be valued by the quantity surveyor if there is no prior agreement between the *employer* and the contractor

Table 3.03: Architect's Powers under IFC 84 – (continued)

Clause	Power	Comment
3.9	Instruct the contractor not to amend setting out errors	If the employer consents: an appropriate deduction must be made from the contract sum
3.12	Issue a written instruction requiring the work to be opened up etc for inspection or testing	Cost to be added to the contract sum unless results show that the work etc is not in accordance with the contract
3.13.2	Withdraw or modify instruction issued under clause 3.13.1	If the contractor objects to compliance within 10 days of receipt of clause 3.13.1 instructions and the architect accepts the contractor's reasons
3.14	Issue written instructions requiring the removal of work, materials or goods not in accordance with the contract	
3.15	Issue instructions on postponement of any work	
4.2.1	Include the value of off-site goods and materials in interim certificates	
4.5	Instruct the contractor to send to the quantity surveyor the documentation needed to adjust the contract sum	
4.11	Require from the contractor information to support the claim as is reasonably necessary to ascertain the amount of direct loss and/or expense	
6.2.4	Issue instructions to contractor to take out insurance against employer's liabilities	If it is stated in appendix that the insurance may be required and the employer does so require

Table 3.04: Architect's Duties under IFC 84

Clause	Duty	Comment
1.4	Issue instructions on inconsistencies, errors or omissions in or between the contract documents, drawings, etc. Value the correction under clause 3.7 if the instructions change the quality or the quantity of work	The power to correct errors in description or quantity applies only to *items*, not to prices
1.6	Provide the contractor with a copy of the contract documents certified on behalf of the employer and two further copies of the contract documents and specification, schedule of work, or bills	
1.7	Give the contractor two copies of further drawings or details necessary to carry out the works properly	
1.8	Not to divulge to third parties or use any of the contract rates for prices except for the purposes of the the contract	
2.3	Make in writing a fair and reasonable extension of time for completion as soon as the contractor is able to estimate the length of delay	It must become apparent that the progress of the works is being or is likely to be delayed; *and* The contractor must give written notice to the architect of the cause of the delay forthwith; *and* The architect must think that completion is likely to be or has been delayed beyond the original or extended completion date; *and* The reasons for delay must be a relevant event, as listed in clause 2.4
2.6	Issue a certificate of non-completion Cancel the clause 2.6 certificate in writing and issue further certificates as necessary	If the contractor fails to complete the works by the date for completion or within the extended period If an extension of time is granted after the former certificate is issued

Table 3.04: Architect's Duties under IFC 84 – (continued)

Clause	Duty	Comment
2.9	Certify the date when practical completion is achieved	When he is of the opinion that this is so
2.10	Certify the discharge of the contractor's defects liability	When he is of the opinion that the contractor has discharged his obligations
3.3.1	Issue instructions changing particulars or omitting the work or substituting a provisional sum	If the contractor cannot sub-contract in accordance with particulars and so informs the architect
3.3.3	Issue the necessary instructions, should employment of the named person be determined before completion of the sub-contract work	The instruction must either: Name another person and describe the work and relevant particulars; or Instruct the contractor to make his own arrangements; or Omit the work
3.5.1	Issue written instructions	
3.5.2	Specify in writing the contract clause empowering the issue of an instruction	On the contractor's written request
3.8	Issue instructions on expenditure of provisional sums	
3.9	Determine levels required for execution of the works and give the contractor the information necessary to enable him to set out the works	The information must include accurately dimensioned drawings
3.13.1	Issue instructions following failure of work, materials or goods	If the architect has either not received the contractor's proposals within seven days of discovery of failure; or He is not satisfied with contractor's proposed actions; or Safety considerations or statutory obligations require urgent action
4.2	Certify interim payments at monthly intervals calculated	This is subject to any agreement between the employer and the contractor on stage payments

Table 3.04: Architect's Duties under IFC 84 – (continued)

Clause	Duty	Comment
	from the date of possession stated in the appendix	Different intervals may be specified in the appendix Interim valuations are to be made by the quantity surveyor whenever the architect considers them to be necessary to ascertain the amount to be certified The amounts to be included are 95% of the total value of work properly executed, including variations, with any appropriate adjustment for fluctuations; *and* materials and goods for incorporation in the works. They latter must have been reasonably and properly, and not prematurely, delivered to the site. They must be adequately protected against the weather and other risks Amount to include 100% of ascertained disturbance claims, fees, insurance premiums and payments etc
4.3	Certify an interim payment to the contractor of 97½% of the total amount to be paid to the contractor	Within 14 days after the certified date of practical completion
4.6	Issue the final certificate	This must be done with 28 days of *sending* the computations of the adjusted contract sum to the contractor or of the date of issue of the clause 2.10 defects liability certificate, whichever is later
4.11	Ascertain or instruct the quantity surveyor to ascertain the amount of direct loss and/or expense incurred or likely to be incurred by the contractor due to the employer's deferment of site possession under clause 2.2 (if applicable) or to regular progress being materially affected by one or more of the matters specified in clause 4.12	If the contractor makes written application within a reasonable time of it becoming apparent; *and* The architect believes that the contractor has incurred or is likely to incur direct loss and/or expense not reimbursable by any other payment under the contract; *and* Supporting information is supplied
6.3D.1	Either inform contractor that insurance is not required or instruct him to obtain quotation Instruct contractor whether or not employer wishes quotation to be accepted	If appendix states liquidated damages insurance may be required Instruction must not be unreasonably withheld or delayed

Table 3.05:   Contractor's Powers under IFC 84

Clause	Power	Comment
1.6	Inspect the contract documents	The power can be exercised at reasonable times, that is, during the employer's normal hours of business
2.1	Consent to the employer using or occupying the site or works before the issue of practical completion certificate	If insurers confirm that insurance will not be prejudiced, consent must not be unreasonably withheld
3.1	Assign the contract	If the employer gives consent in writing
3.2	Sub-contract any part of the works	If the architect consents in writing and subject to clause 3.3 below There are conditions which must be imposed in any ensuing sub-contract
3.5.2	Request the architect to specify in writing which contract clause empowers the instruction Serve written request on the employer to concur in the appointment of an arbitrator	When he receives an instruction If dissatisfied with the architect's reply and not willing to comply
3.7	Agree with the employer the adjustment to the contract sum in respect of variation instructions and of instructions on expenditure of provisional sums	Before the contractor complies with the instruction
3.11	Consent to the carrying out of such works by others	Where employer requests and contract documents do not so provide Consent must not be unreasonably withheld
4.11	Make written application to the architect within a reasonable time	If it becomes apparent that regular progress is being materially affected by one or more of the specified matters or due to deferment of possession of the site by the employer
6.3B	Require the employer to produce for inspection	Only where the employer is not a local authority

Table 3.05: Contractor's Powers under IFC 84 – (continued)

Clause	Power	Comment
	documentary evidence and premium receipts showing the policy is in force	
	Insure in joint names all work executed etc against all risks and have premium added to contract sum	If the employer defaults in taking out or maintaining the policy
6.3C.3	Require employer to produce policy receipts showing that policies under clauses 6.3C.1 and 6.3C.2 have been taken out	Except where the employer is a local authority
	Insure existing structures in joint names and for that purpose enter the premises to make a survey and inventory and insure the works against all risks	If employer defaults
6.3C.4.3	Determine his employment	Within 28 days of occurrence of clause 6.3C.4 loss or damage. It must be just and equitable to do so; *and* 7 days notice must be given during which time either party may request arbitration
6.3D.1	Require information from the employer, via the architect	To otain quotation under this clause
7.5	Serve a default notice on the employer by registered post or recorded delivery specifying the default alleged	If the employer does not pay an amount properly due to contractor or any interim or final certificate; or Interferes with or obstructs the issue of any certificate; or The carrying out of the whole or substantially the whole of the uncompleted works (other than defects liability works) is suspended for a continuous period of one month by reason of: ● Architect's instructions under 1.4 (inconsistencies), 3.6 (variation) or 3.14 (postponement) unless caused by contractor's neglect or default or that of his servants or any person engaged on the works other than the employer or statutory bodies ● Contractor not having received in due time necessary instructions, etc from the architect despite making written application at the right time

Table 3.05: Contractor's Powers under IFC 84 – (continued)

Clause	Power	Comment
	Determine his employment under the contract by written notice served on the employer by registered post or recorded delivery	● Delay in execution of work by employer himself or by others engaged or employed by him or failure to execute such work, or delay or failure in supplying materials, goods that the employer undertook to supply ● Failure by employer to give in due time ingress to or egress from the site if so agreed If the employer continued his default for 14 days after receipt of the default notice or thereafter repeats the same default The notice must not be given unreasonably or vexatiously
7.6	Determine his employment under the contract by written notice served on the employer by registered post or recorded delivery	If the employer becomes bankrupt or is insolvent etc or has a receiver appointed
7.8	Forthwith determine his employment under the contract by written notice served on the employer by registered post or recorded delivery	If the carrying out of the whole or substantially the whole of the uncompleted works (except work required under 2.10 defects liability) is suspended by reason of *force majeure* or Loss or damage to the works occasioned by clause 6.3 perils unless caused by negligence of the contractor or those for whom he is vicariously responsible; or civil commotion

Table 3.06: Contractor's Duties under IFC 84

Clause	Duty	Comment
1.1	Carry out and complete the works in accordance with the contract documents	
1.8	Use the specification, bills, schedules, drawings and details only for the purpose of the contract	
1.11	Use off-site goods and materials that have been paid for by the employer only for the works, and not remove them for any other purpose or permit their removal	
2.1	Begin the works when given possession of site	This is subject to the provisions for extension of time in clause 2.3
	Regularly and diligently proceed with the works and complete them on or before the date for completion specified in the appendix	
	Notify the insurers under clause 6.3A or 6.3B or 6.3C.2 to .4 and obtain confirmation that use or occupation will not prejudice insurance	Before giving consent to use or occupation
	Notify employer of amount of additional premium	If insurers have made the premium a condition of confirmation
	Provide employer with premium receipts	On request
2.3	Notify the architect in writing forthwith of any cause of delay	If it becomes reasonably apparent that progress of the works is being or is likely to be delayed. The duty is in respect of any cause of delay and is not confined to the events specified in clause 2.4
	Constantly use his best endeavours to prevent delay; *and*	The second part of his duty does not require the contractor to spend money
	Do all that may reasonably be required to the architect's satisfaction to proceed with the works	
	Provide the architect with enough information to enable	This is conditional on a request from the architect; and the information must be

Clause	Duty	Comment
	him properly to exercise his duties as regards extensions of time	"reasonably necessary"
2.4.7	Make specific written application to the architect for any necessary instructions, drawings, details or levels	Failure to do so at the right time invalidates any claim for an extension of time on the ground of late instruction
2.7	Pay or allow to the employer liquidated damages at the rate specified in the appendix	If the works are not completed by the specified or extended date for completion; and If the architect has issued a certificate of non-completion under clause 2.6; and If the employer has required liquidated damages in writing not later than the date of the final certificate
2.10	Make good any defects, shrinkages or other faults at no cost to the employer	If the defects etc appear and are notified to the contractor by the architect not later than 14 days after expiry of the defects liability period; and If they are due to materials or workmanship not in accordance with the contract or to frost occurring before practical completion; and If the architect has not instructed otherwise
3.3.1	Enter into a sub-contract using section 3 of NAM/T with any named person, not later than 21 days after entering into the main contract Immediately inform the architect if unable to enter into a sub-contract in accordance with the particulars given in the contract documents and specify which particulars have prevented the execution of the sub-contract Notify the architect of the date of entering into a sub-contract with a named person	The person must be named in the specification, schedule of works or bills
3.3.3	Advise the architect as soon as is reasonably practical of any events that are likely to	

Table 3.06: Contractor's Duties under IFC 84 – (continued)

Clause	Duty	Comment
	lead to the determination of the named person's employment under a sub-contract Notify the architect in writing if the named person's employment is determined before completion of the sub-contract work stating the circumstances	Whether or not the architect has already been advised of events likely to lead to determination
3.3.6 (a)	Take such reasonable action as is necessary to recover from the named sub-contract any additional amount payable as a result of default/failure	Recovery is under clause 27.3.3 of the sub-contract NAM/SC The contractor is not required to commence arbitration proceedings or litigation unless the employer indemnifies him against legal costs
3.3.6 (b)	Account to the employer for amounts recovered	
3.3.6 (d)	Repay to the employer any additional amounts	Only to the extent he has failed in his clause 3.3.6 duty
3.4	Keep a competent person in charge of the works at all reasonable times	
3.5.1	Forthwith carry out all written instructions issued by the architect	Provided the instruction is one that the contract empowers the architect to issue
3.9	Set out the works accurately Amend at his own cost any errors arising from inaccurate setting-out	Architect determines levels and provides contractor with accurately dimensioned drawings to enable this to be done The architect may instruct otherwise with employer's consent
3.11	Permit the execution of work not forming part of the contract to be carried out by the employer or person employed or engaged by him at the same time as the contract works	If contract documents so provide

Table 3.06: Contractor's Duties under IFC 84 – (continued)

Clause	Duty	Comment
3.12	Bear cost of opening up and testing and consenquential costs of making good	If inspection and tests show that materials, goods or works are not in accordance with the contract
3.13.1	State in writing to the architect the immediate action that the contractor proposes to take to establish that there is no similar failure of work, etc	Where such failure is discovered during the carrying out of the works
	Forthwith comply with any architect's instruction requiring opening up for inspection and testing	Unless with 10 days of receipt of the instruction the contractor objects to compliance, stating his reasons in writing Then if within seven days of receipt of the contractor's objection the architect does not withdraw or modify his instruction in writing, the dispute or difference is referred to arbitration
4.5	Not later than 6 months after practical completion provide the architect, or the QS if the architect so instructs, all documents reasonably required for the purposes of adjusting the contract sum	
4.11	Submit to the architect or quantity surveyor such information as is reasonably necessary to ascertain the amount of direct loss and/or expense	
5.1	Comply with, and give all notices required by any statute, statutory instrument rule, order, regulation or bye-law	As applicable to the works
	Pay all fees and charges in respect of the works	The amount of such fees etc is added to the contract sum unless they are required by the specification, schedules of work or contract bills to be included in the contract sum

Table 3.06: Contractor's Duties under IFC 84 – (continued)

Clause	Duty	Comment
5.2	Immediately give to the architect a written notice specifying any divergence between the statutory requirements and contract documents or between such requirements and any architect's instruction	If the contractor finds any divergence
5.4.1	Supply such limited materials and execute such limited work as are reasonably necessary to secure immediate compliance with statutory requirements	In an emergency, for example a dangerous structures notice, and if it is necessary to do this before receipt of an instruction from the architect
5.4.2	Forthwith inform the architect of such emergency compliance	
6.1.1	Indemnify the employer against any expense, liability, loss claim or proceedings whatsoever in respect of personal injury to or death of any person	The claim must arise out of or in the course of or be caused by the carrying out of the works *and* Not be due to any act or neglect of the employer or any person for whom he is responsible
6.1.2	Indemnify the employer against property damage	If the claim arises out of or in the course of or is caused by reason of the carrying out of the works *and* Is due to any negligence, omission or default of the contractor, his servants or agents or that of any sub-contractor, his servants or agents or any other person properly on the works except the employer, his men, local authority or statutory undertaking
6.2.1	Maintain and cause any sub-contractor to maintain necessary insurances in respect of injury to persons or property	The obligation to maintain insurance is without prejudice to the contractor's liability to indemnify the employer
6.2.2	Produce and cause any sub-contractor to produce	When reasonably required to do so by the employer who may (but not unreasonably

Table 3.06: Contractor's Duties under IFC 84 – (continued)

Clause	Duty	Comment
	documentary evidence of insurance cover for the employer's inspection	or vexatiously) require production of the policy or policies and premium receipts
6.2.4	Maintain in joint names of employer and contractor for such amounts of indemnity as are specified in the contract documents Insure against damage to property other than the works caused by collapse, subsidence, etc Deposit with the employer the policy(ies) and premium receipts	If it is stated in the appendix that such insurance may be required and the architect so instructs
6.3A.1	Take out and maintain all risks insurance in joint names against loss or damage to the works and unfixed goods	New buildings – the obligation continues until the date of issue of the certificate of practical completion or date of determination Clause 6.3A.3.1 enables this cover to be by means of the contractor's "all-risks" policy
6.3A.2	Deposit the policy or policies and premium receipt with the employer	
6.3A.4	Give written notice to architect and employer With due diligence restore any work damaged, replace or repair any unfixed goods or materials that have been destroyed or damaged, remove and dispose of debris and proceed with the carrying out and completion of the works	Upon discovering loss or damage caused by risks covered by the joint names policy in clause 6.3A.1 or 6.3A.2 or 6.3A.3 After any inspection by the insurers in respect of any claim under the clause 6.3A.1, 6.3A.2 or 6.3A.3 insurance
6.3A.4.4	Authorise insurers to pay insurance monies to employer	Acting also on behalf of sub-contractors recognised pursuant to clause 6.3.3

Table 3.06: Contractor's Duties under IFC 84 – (continued)

Clause	Duty	Comment
6.3B.3.1	Forthwith notify the architect and the employer of the extent, nature and location of any loss or damage affecting the works or any unfixed materials	The contractor must do this upon discovering the loss or damage. Clause 6.3B covers new buildings where the employer insures against all risks in joint names
6.3B.3.3	With due diligence restore work damaged, replace or repair any unfixed goods or materials that have been destroyed or damaged, remove and dispose of debris and proceed with the carrying out and completion of the works	After any inspection by the insurers in respect of any claim under the clause 6.3B.1 or 6.3B.2 insurance
6.3B.3.4	Authorise insurers to pay insurance monies to employer	Acting also on behalf of sub-contractors recognised pursuant to clause 6.3.3
6.3C.4	Forthwith give written notice to the architect and the employer of the extent, nature and location of any loss or damage	Upon discovering the loss or damage caused by risks covered by joint names policy in clause 6.3C.2 or 6.3C.3
6.3C.4.2	Authorise insurers to pay insurance monies to employer	Acting also on behalf of sub-contractors recognised pursuant to clause 6.3.3
6.3C.4.4	With all due diligence reinstate and make good loss or damage and proceed with the carrying out and completion of the work	If no notice of determination is served or if the arbitrator decides against the notice of determination
6.3D.1	Send quotation to the architect Forthwith take out and maintain the relevant policy, and send to architect for deposit with employer with premium receipts	If appendix states that liquidated damages insurance may be required and the architect has so instructed If so instructed by the architect

Table 3.06:   Contractor's Duties under IFC 84 – (continued)

Clause	Duty	Comment
7.4	Give up possession of the site of the works Remove from the works any temporary buildings, plant, tools, equipment, goods and materials belonging to or hired by the contractor	In the event of determination by the employer under clause 7.1, 7.2 or 7.3 As and when so instructed in writing by the architect
7.7	Remove from the site with all reasonable dispatch all his temporary buildings, plant, tools, equipment, goods and materials, and give facilities to his sub-contractor to do the same	Where the contractor determines his own employment
7.9	Remove from site with all reasonable dispatch all his temporary buildings, etc and give facilities to his sub-contractors to do the same	
9.1	Give written notice to the employer	If the contractor requires a dispute to be referred to arbitration
9.7	Together with the employer, forthwith appoint another arbitrator	If the arbitrator ceases to act

Table 3.07:   Employer's Powers under IFC 84

Clause	Power	Comment
2.1	Defer giving possession of the site to the contractor for a limited period	Where clause 2.2 is stated in the appendix to apply Deferment is for a period not to exceed the stated period and the usual maximum period is six weeks
	Use or occupy the site or the works before issue of practical completion certificate	With contractor's written consent
2.7	Deduct liquidated damages for late completion	The architect must have issued a certificate of non-completion and the employer must have required liquidated damages by writing to the contractor not later than the date of the final certificate
2.10	Consent to the contractor being paid to remedy defects	
3.1	Assign the contract	Only if the contractor consents in writing
3.3.1 and 3.3.4	Have a named person's work carried out by his employees or direct contractors under clause 3.11	Where the contractor has been unable to sub-contract with the named person *and* the architect has instructed its omission or has so omitted it and substituted a provisional sum Such instructions are valued as a variation and give rise to a contractor's claim for both extension of time and loss and/or expense
3.3.6	Indemnify the contractor against legal costs	If the employer requires the contractor to begin legal or arbitral proceedings against a defaulting named person
3.5	Employ and pay other persons to execute work	If the contractor does not comply within seven days of the receipt of a written notice from the architect requiring compliance with an instruction
3.7	Agree with the contractor the amount of an adjustment to the contract sum	For variation or provisional sum instructions, and before the contractor complies with them
3.9	Consent to the architect instructing the contractor that	An appropriate deduction is to be made to the contract sum

Table 3.07: Employer's Powers under IFC 84 – (continued)

Clause	Power	Comment
	setting out errors are not amended	
3.10	Appoint a clerk of works to act as an inspector under the architect's directions	
3.11	Require work not forming part of the contract to be carried out by himself or by people employed or engaged by him	Where the contract documents so provide or with the contractor's consent
6.2.2	Require documentary evidence of insurance	
6.2.3	Insure and deduct premium amounts from monies due to contractor or recover them as a debt	If contractor fails to insure against personal injury or death or injury to real or personal property
6.2.4	Approve insurers Insure against damage to property other than the works	In regard to insurance against damage to property other than the works – employer's liability If the contractor fails to insure
6.3A.2	Approve insurers Insure against all risks and deduct sums from monies due or recover them as a debt	In regard to insurance against all risks to be taken out by the contractor If contractor fails to insure
6.3A.3.1	Inspect documentary evidence or the policy	If the contractor maintains a policy independently of his obligations under the contract and it is in joint names
6.3C.4.3	Determine the contractor's employment	Within 28 days of clause 6.3C.4 loss or damage It must be just and equitable to do so; and 7 days notice must be given during which time either party may request arbitration

Table 3.07: Employer's Powers under IFC 84 – (continued)

Clause	Power	Comment
6.3D.1	Require the contractor to accept the quotation in respect of liquidated damages insurance	Architect must so instruct
7.1	Serve written notice on the contractor by registered post or recorded delivery specifying a default	If the contractor, without reasonable cause, wholly suspends the works before completion; or fails to proceed regularly and diligently with the works; or refuses, or persistently neglects, to comply with a written notice from the architect requiring him to remove defective work or improper materials or goods and by such refusal or neglect the works are materially affected; or fails to comply with clause 3.2 (sub-contracting), 3.3 (named persons) or 5.7 (fair wages)
	Determine the contractor's employment by written notice served by registered post or recorded delivery	The notice must not be given unreasonably or vexatiously. It can be served only if the contractor continues his default for 14 days after receipt of the preliminary notice or if at any time thereafter he repeats that default
7.2	Reinstate the contractor's employment in agreement with the contractor and his trustee (in bankruptcy), liquidator, etc	If the contractor has become insolvent, etc, his employment is determined automatically
7.3	Determine the contractor's employment under this or any other contract	Where the employer is a local authority *and* the contractor is guilty of corrupt practices. No procedure is prescribed, but determination should be effected by written notice
7.8	Immediately determine the contractor's employment by written notice served by registered post or recorded delivery	Where all or nearly all of the uncompleted works is suspended for three months because of *force majeure*; or Loss or damage caused by clause 6.3 perils, for instance fire; or Civil commotion The notice must not be given unreasonably or vexatiously

Table 3.08: Employer's Duties under IFC 84

Clause	Duty	Comment
1.6	Be custodian of the contract documents	Contract documents must be available for contractor's inspection at all reasonable times
1.8	Not to divulge or use any of the contractor's rates and prices	Except for purposes of the contract
2.1	Give possession of the site to the contractor on the date for possession Notify insurers under clause 6.3A or 6.3B or 6.3C.2 to .4 and obtain confirmation that use or occupation will not prejudice insurance	Clause 2.2, if applicable, enables giving of possession to be deferred for up to 6 weeks
2.8	Pay or repay liquidated damages to the contractor	Where architect cancels his certificate of delay and grants a further extension of time
3.13	Pay the contractor amounts awarded by the arbitrator for compliance with architect's instructions following failure of work, etc	If the contractor has objected in writing to compliance, with reasons, and the architect has not withdrawn or modified his instruction and the matter has gone to arbitration
4.2	Pay the amount certified to the contractor within 14 days of the date of the certificate	If the architect issues an interim certificate under clause 4.2
4.3	Pay the amount certified to the contractor within 14 days of the date of the certificate	If the architect issues an interim certificate under clause 4.3. On practical completion a further interim payment is made to bring the amount to 97½% of total value of work properly executed
4.6	Pay the contractor the amount certified within 28 days after the date of the final certificate	Subject to any amounts which the employer may properly deduct
5.5	Pay the contractor any VAT properly chargeable	

Table 3.08: Employer's Duties under IFC 84 – (continued)

Clause	Duty	Comment
6.3.3	Ensure that joint names policies referred to in clause 6.3A.1 or 6.3A.3 or 6.3B.1 or 6.3C.1 and 6.3C.2: *either*	If clause 6.3B or 6.3C applies
	● provide for recognition of each named person as sub-contractor as insured *or:*	In respect of specified perils
	● include insurers' waiver of rights of subrogation	
6.3B.1	Maintain insurance against all risks	In joint names
	Produce premium receipts to the contractor on request	Unless the employer is a local authority
6.3C.1	Maintain insurance against specified perils for existing structures	In joint names
6.3C.2	Maintain insurance against all risks for the works of alteration or extension	In joint names
6.3C.3	Produce insurance receipts	If the contractor so requests unless employer is a local authority
7.4	Pay the contractor any amount due to him after completion of the works by others	
7.7	Pay to the contractor the total value of work at the date of determination, sums ascertained as direct loss and/or expense under clause 4.11, the cost of materials or goods properly ordered for the works and for which the contractor has paid or is legally bound to pay, the reasonable cost of removal from site of all temporary buildings, plant, tools, equipment, etc, and any	Where the contractor has determined his own employment for employer default or insolvency under clauses 7.5 or 7.6 Amounts previously paid are taken into account Direct loss and/or damage will include the contractor's loss of profit

Table 3.08:   Employer's Duties under IFC 84 – (continued)

Clause	Duty	Comment
	direct loss and/or damage caused to the contractor by the determination	
7.9	Pay to the contractor the total value of work at the date of determination, any sum ascertained as a direct loss and/or expense under clause 4.11, the cost of materials or goods properly ordered for the works and for which the contractor has paid or is legally bound to pay, the reasonable cost of removal from site of all temporary buildings,plant, tools, equipment, etc	Amounts previously paid are taken into account
9.1	Give written notice to the contractor	If the employer requires a dispute to be referred to arbitration
9.7	Together with the contractor, forthwith appoint another arbitrator	If the arbitrator ceases to act

Table 3.09: Clauses that may Give Rise to Claims under IFC 84

Clause	Event	Type
1.4	Inconsistencies etc	C
1.6	Architect fails to provide documents	CL
1.8	Divulging or improper use of rates	CL
2.1	Occupation of site without contractors consent	CL
2.2	Deferment of possession Deferment exceeding time stated in appendix	C CL
2.3	Financial claims	CL
2.7	Improper deduction of liquidated damages	CL
2.8	Failure to repay liquidated damages	CL
2.9	Failure to issue certificate of practical completion	CL
2.10	Including items which are not defects	CL
	Failure to issue certificate of making good defects	CL
3.1	Assignment without consent	CL
3.2	Architect unreasonably withholding consent to sub-letting	CL
3.3.1	Failure to issue instruction	CL

Table 3.09: Clauses that may Give Rise to Claims under IFC 84 – (continued)

Clause	Event	Type
3.3.3	Failure to issue instruction	CL
3.3.3(b)	Contractor instructed to make own arrangements after determination	C
3.3.7	Failure of sub-contract design selection of materials or satisfaction of performance specification	CL
3.5.1	Instructions issued orally or by employer	CL
3.6	Valuation of variations not carried out in accordance with the contract	CL
3.9	Failure to determine levels, etc	CL
3.10	Clerk of works exceeding duties	CL
3.11	Employer's work Employer's work without going through procedure	C CL
3.12	Opening up and testing	C
3.13.2	Unreasonable instructions following failure of work	C**
3.14	Wrongly phrased instructions	CL
3.15	Postponement of work	C
4.2	Certificate not issued or not issued at the proper time	CL
4.3	Failure to certify	CL

Table 3.09: Clauses that may Give Rise to Claims under IFC 84 – (continued)

Clause	Event	Type
4.4	Retention money, interest	CL
4.5	Failure to send computations to the contractor forthwith	CL
4.6	Failure to issue final certificate or in proper form	CL
4.9, 4.10	Fluctuations	C
4.11	Disturbance of regular progress	C
5.1	Statutory fees and charges	C
5.2	Divergence between statutory requirements and contract documents	C
5.4	Emergency compliance	C
5.5	Recovery of VAT	C
6.3A.4.4	Failure to pay insurance monies	CL
6.3B.2	Employer's failure to insure (unless a local authority)	C
6.3C.3	Employer's failure to insure (unless a local authority)	C
7.1	Invalid determination	CL
7.8.1	Invalid determination	CL

KEY:
C = Contractual claims
CL = Common law claims
** Dealt with by arbitrator
Contractual claims are usually dealt with by the architect. Common law claims are usually dealt with by the employer

Table 3.10: Certificates to be Issued by the Architect under IFC 84

Clause	Certificate
2.6	Certificate of non-completion
2.9	Certificate of practical completion
2.10	Certificate of making good defects
4.2	Interim certificates
4.3	Interim certificate on practical completion
4.6	Final certificate

Table 3.11: Architect's Instructions Empowered by IFC 84

Clause	Instruction
1.4	Correcting inconsistencies between contract documents and drawings Correcting errors in the contract documents Correcting errors in particulars of a named person Correcting departures from the method of preparation of the contract bills
2.10	Not to make good defects
3.3.1	In regard to named persons as sub-contractors: *either* Change particulars to remove impediment; *or* Omit work; *or* Omit work and substitute a provisional sum Naming a person other than the person in the specification/schedules of work/ contract bills
3.3.3	As necessary after determination of employment of named person; *either* Name another person; *or* Require the contractor to make his own arrangements; *or* Omit the work
3.5.1	General power to issue instructions empowered by the conditions
3.6	Requiring a variation
3.8	To expend provisional sums
3.9	That setting out errors shall not be amended and an appropriate deduction be made from the contract sum
3.12	Requiring opening up or testing
3.13.1	Requiring opening up or testing at contractor's cost if similar work or materials have failed
3.14	To remove defective work from the site
3.15	Postponing work
6.2.4	To take out insurance against employer's liabilities
6.3C.4.4	To remove and dispose of any debris
6.3D.1	To obtain quotation for insurance against loss of liquidated damages To accept or not to accept the quotation
7.4(b)	To remove temporary buildings etc after determination

Table 3.12: Adjustment of Contract Sum under IFC 84

Clause	Provision
2.10	Deduction for defects not to be made good
3.3.4(a)	Adjustment after determination of named person's employment
3.7	Additions or deductions in respect of instructions requiring a variation
3.9	Deduction for setting out errors not to be amended
3.12	Additions to cover the cost of opening up or testing if the work is in accordance with the contract
4.5	Final adjustment of the contract sum
4.9	Adjustment to take account of fluctuations
4.10	Adjustment to take account of fluctuations in respect of named person
4.11	Additions for loss and/or expense
5.1	Additions for statutory fees and charges
6.2.4	Additions for insurance for the liability etc of the employer
6.3B.2	Additions for employer's failure to insure
6.3C.3	Additions for employer's failure to insure

Table 3.13: Contract Provisions which Entitle the Employer to Deduct from any Sum Due or to Become Due to the Contractor under IFC 84

Clause	Provision
2.7	Liquidated damages
3.5.1	Costs of employing other persons to carry out instructions
6.2.3	Contractor's failure to insure
6.3A.2	Contractor's failure to insure

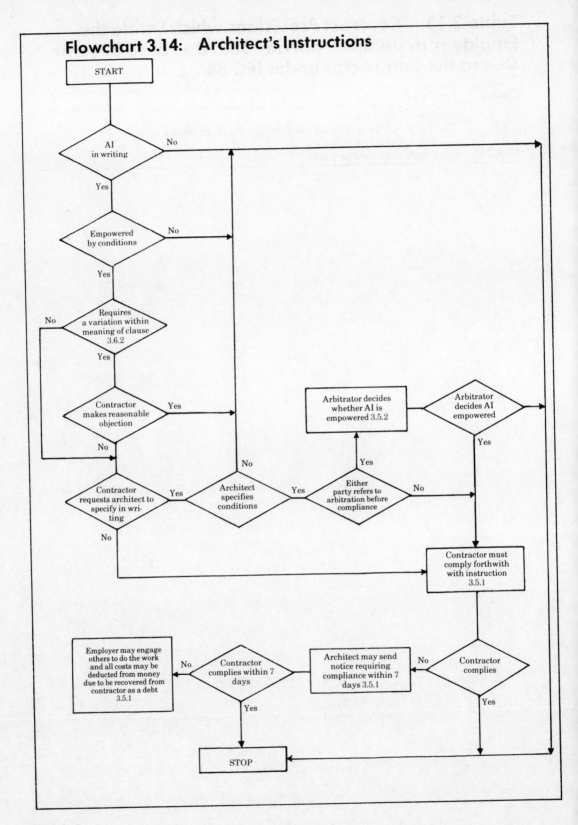

Flowchart 3.14: Architect's Instructions

START

AI in writing — No →

Yes ↓

Empowered by conditions — No →

Yes ↓

Requires a variation within meaning of clause 3.6.2 — No →

Yes ↓

Contractor makes reasonable objection — Yes →

No ↓

Contractor requests architect to specify in writing — Yes → Architect specifies conditions — Yes → Either party refers to arbitration before compliance — Yes → Arbitrator decides whether AI is empowered 3.5.2 — Yes → Arbitrator decides AI empowered — Yes →

No

No

No

Contractor must comply forthwith with instruction 3.5.1

Contractor complies — No → Architect may send notice requiring compliance within 7 days 3.5.1 — No → Contractor complies within 7 days — No → Employer may engage others to do the work and all costs may be deducted from money due to be recovered from contractor as a debt 3.5.1

Yes

Yes ↓

STOP

Flowchart 3.15: Failure of Work

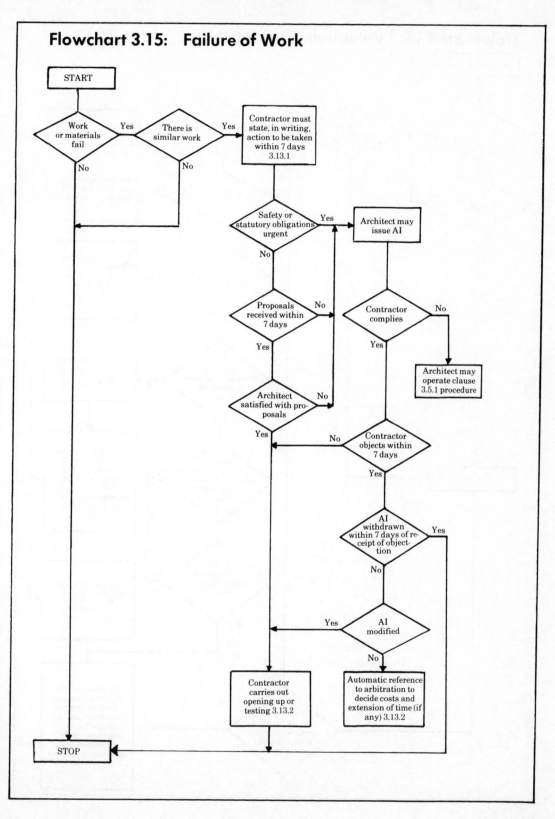

Flowchart 3.16: Valuation of Variations

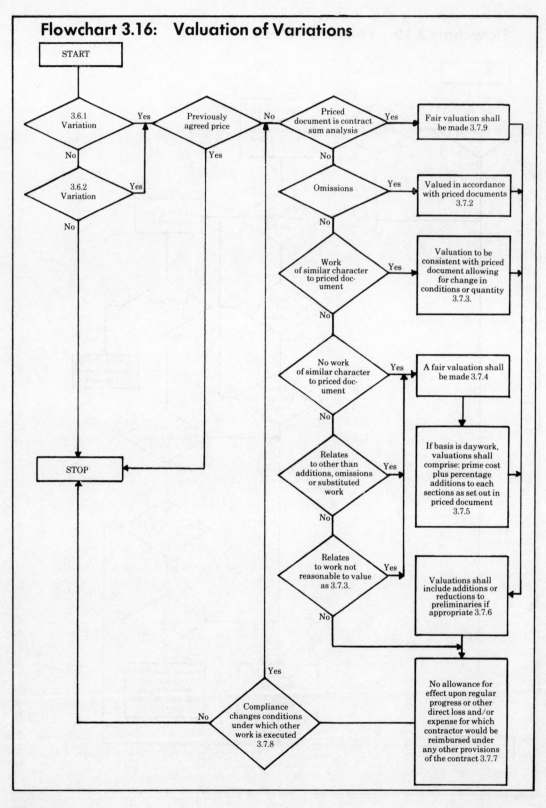

Flowchart 3.17: Named Persons as Sub-contractors

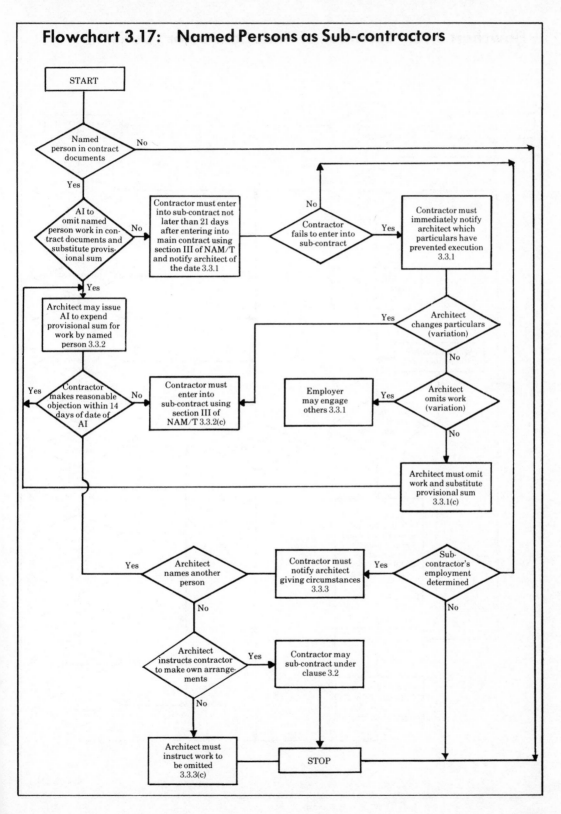

Flowchart 3.18:   Extension of Time: Contractor's Duties

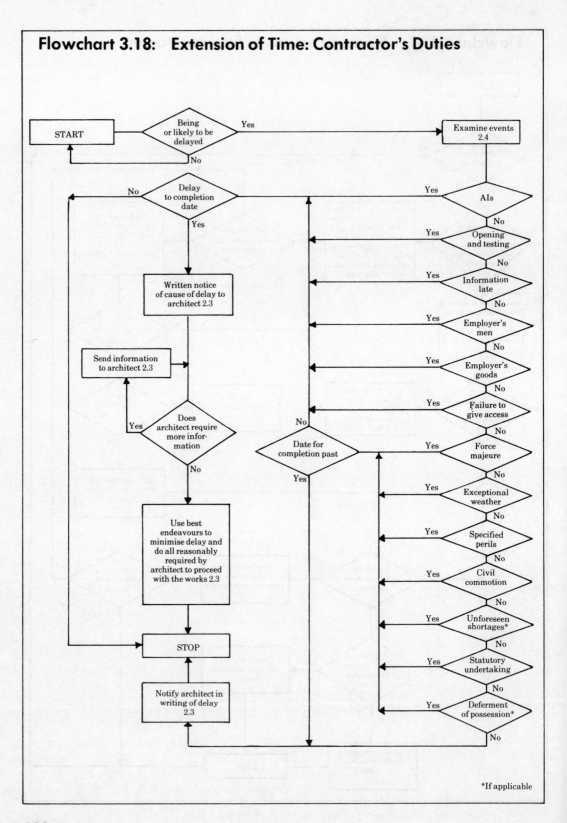

START

Being or likely to be delayed — Yes → Examine events 2.4

No

Delay to completion date — No

Yes → AIs — Yes
No

Opening and testing — Yes
No

Information late — Yes
No

Employer's men — Yes
No

Employer's goods — Yes
No

Failure to give access — Yes
No

Force majeure — Yes
No

Exceptional weather — Yes
No

Specified perils — Yes
No

Civil commotion — Yes
No

Unforeseen shortages* — Yes
No

Statutory undertaking — Yes
No

Deferment of possession* — Yes
No

Written notice of cause of delay to architect 2.3

Send information to architect 2.3

Does architect require more information — Yes
No

Date for completion past — No / Yes

Use best endeavours to minimise delay and do all reasonably required by architect to proceed with the works 2.3

STOP

Notify architect in writing of delay 2.3

*If applicable

166

Flowchart 3.19: Extension of Time: Architect's Duties

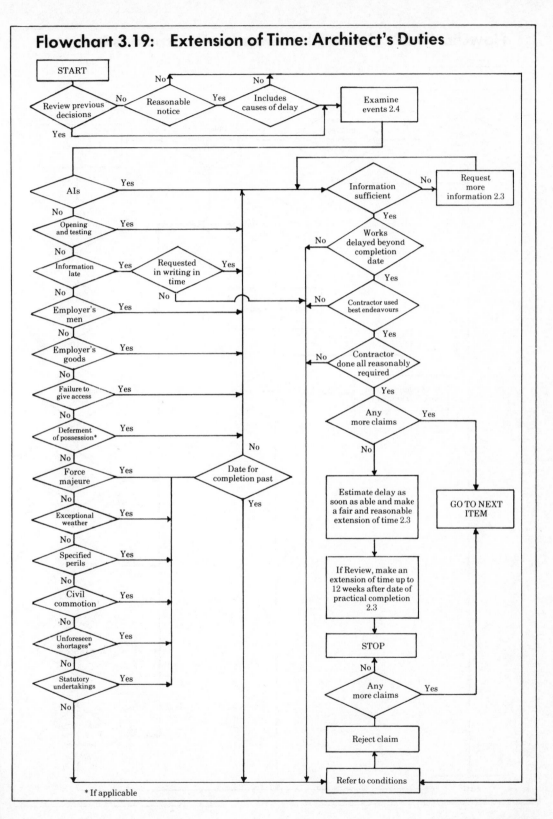

* If applicable

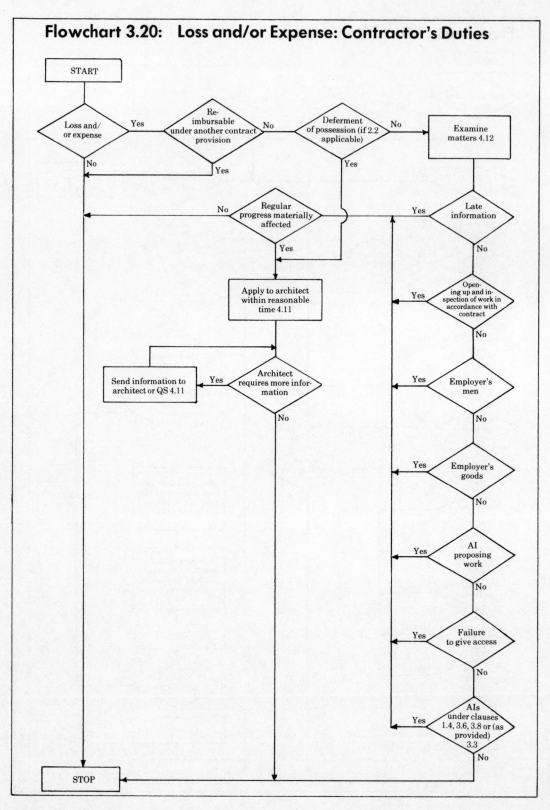

Flowchart 3.20:   Loss and/or Expense: Contractor's Duties

START

Loss and/ or expense
— Yes → Re-imbursable under another contract provision
— No → Deferment of possession (if 2.2 applicable)
— No → Examine matters 4.12

Loss and/ or expense — No

Re-imbursable under another contract provision — Yes

Deferment of possession (if 2.2 applicable) — Yes

Regular progress materially affected — No

Regular progress materially affected — Yes → Apply to architect within reasonable time 4.11

Late information — Yes

Late information — No

Opening up and inspection of work in accordance with contract — Yes

Opening up and inspection of work in accordance with contract — No

Architect requires more information — Yes → Send information to architect or QS 4.11

Architect requires more information — No

Employer's men — Yes

Employer's men — No

Employer's goods — Yes

Employer's goods — No

AI proposing work — Yes

AI proposing work — No

Failure to give access — Yes

Failure to give access — No

AIs under clauses 1.4, 3.6, 3.8 or (as provided) 3.3 — Yes

AIs under clauses 1.4, 3.6, 3.8 or (as provided) 3.3 — No

STOP

Flowchart 3.21: Loss and/or Expense: Architect's Duties

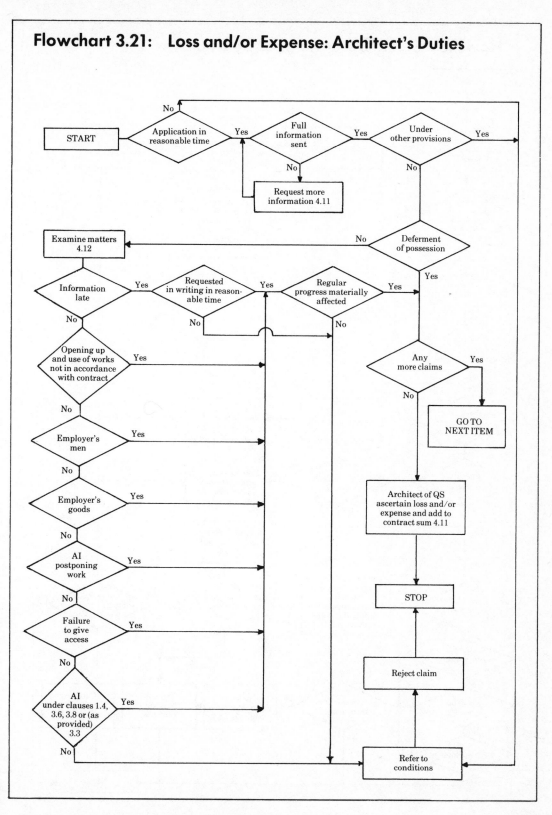

START

Application in reasonable time — No

Application in reasonable time — Yes

Full information sent — Yes

Full information sent — No → Request more information 4.11

Under other provisions — Yes

Under other provisions — No

Deferment of possession — No → Examine matters 4.12

Deferment of possession — Yes

Examine matters 4.12

Information late — Yes → Requested in writing in reasonable time

Information late — No

Requested in writing in reasonable time — Yes → Regular progress materially affected

Requested in writing in reasonable time — No

Regular progress materially affected — Yes

Regular progress materially affected — No

Opening up and use of works not in accordance with contract — Yes

Opening up and use of works not in accordance with contract — No

Employer's men — Yes

Employer's men — No

Employer's goods — Yes

Employer's goods — No

AI postponing work — Yes

AI postponing work — No

Failure to give access — Yes

Failure to give access — No

AI under clauses 1.4, 3.6, 3.8 or (as provided) 3.3 — Yes

AI under clauses 1.4, 3.6, 3.8 or (as provided) 3.3 — No

Any more claims — Yes → GO TO NEXT ITEM

Any more claims — No

Architect of QS ascertain loss and/or expense and add to contract sum 4.11

STOP

Reject claim

Refer to conditions

169

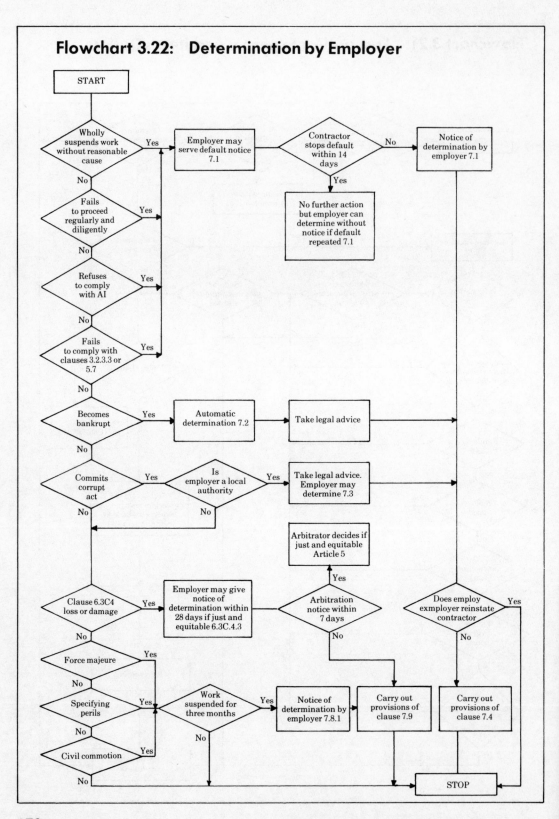

Flowchart 3.22: Determination by Employer

START

- **Wholly suspends work without reasonable cause** — No ↓ / Yes →
  - Yes → **Employer may serve default notice 7.1** → **Contractor stops default within 14 days**
    - No → **Notice of determination by employer 7.1**
    - Yes → **No further action but employer can determine without notice if default repeated 7.1**
- **Fails to proceed regularly and diligently** — No ↓ / Yes →
- **Refuses to comply with AI** — No ↓ / Yes →
- **Fails to comply with clauses 3.2.3.3 or 5.7** — No ↓ / Yes →
- **Becomes bankrupt** — No ↓ / Yes →
  - Yes → **Automatic determination 7.2** → **Take legal advice**
- **Commits corrupt act** — No ↓ / Yes →
  - Yes → **Is employer a local authority** — No / Yes →
    - Yes → **Take legal advice. Employer may determine 7.3**
- **Clause 6.3C4 loss or damage** — No ↓ / Yes →
  - Yes → **Employer may give notice of determination within 28 days if just and equitable 6.3C.4.3** → **Arbitration notice within 7 days**
    - Yes → **Arbitrator decides if just and equitable Article 5**
    - No → **Carry out provisions of clause 7.9**
- **Force majeure** — No ↓ / Yes →
- **Specifying perils** — No ↓ / Yes →
  - Yes → **Work suspended for three months**
    - Yes → **Notice of determination by employer 7.8.1** → **Carry out provisions of clause 7.9**
    - No → **STOP**
- **Civil commotion** — No ↓ / Yes →

Does employ exmployer reinstate contractor
- Yes → **Carry out provisions of clause 7.4**
- No → **STOP**

STOP

170

Flowchart 3.23: Determination by Contractor

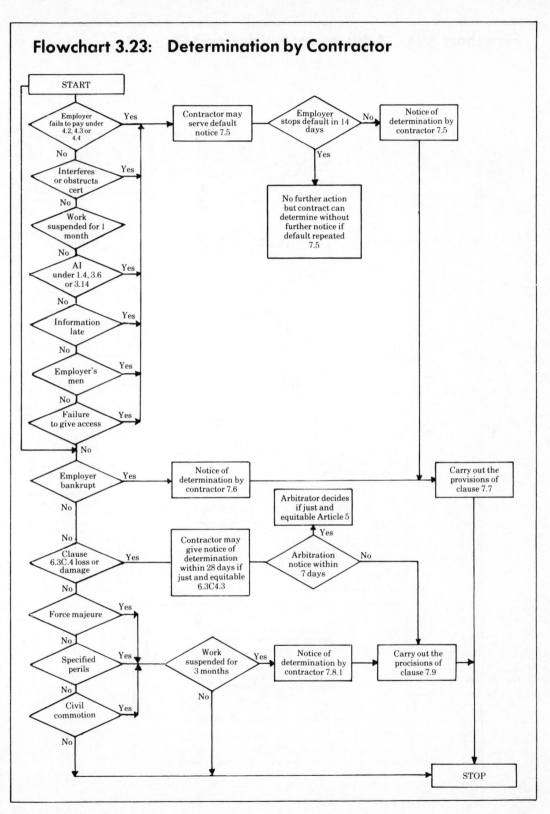

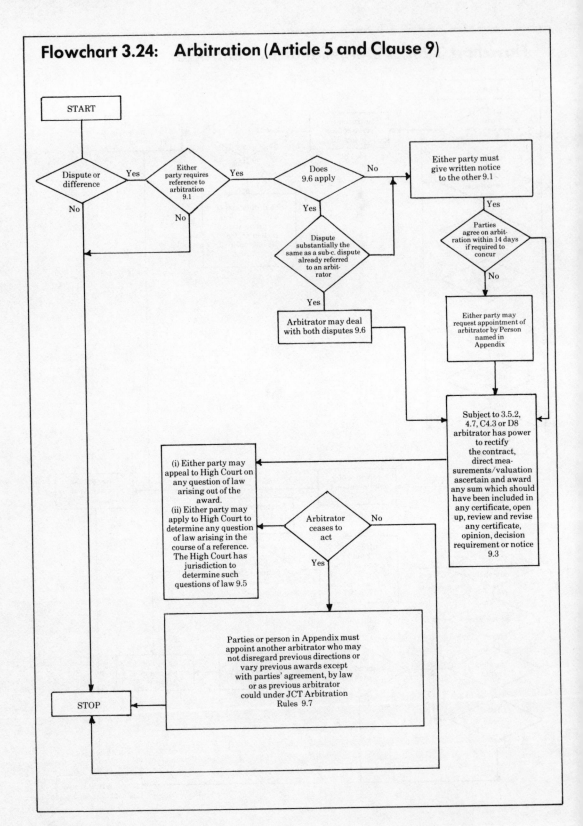

Flowchart 3.24:   Arbitration (Article 5 and Clause 9)

START

Dispute or difference — Yes → Either party requires reference to arbitration 9.1 — Yes → Does 9.6 apply — No → Either party must give written notice to the other 9.1

No

No

Yes

Dispute substantially the same as a sub-c. dispute already referred to an arbit-rator

Yes

Arbitrator may deal with both disputes 9.6

Parties agree on arbit-ration within 14 days if required to concur

Yes

No

Either party may request appointment of arbitrator by Person named in Appendix

Subject to 3.5.2, 4.7, C4.3 or D8 arbitrator has power to rectify the contract, direct mea-surements/valuation ascertain and award any sum which should have been included in any certificate, open up, review and revise any certificate, opinion, decision requirement or notice 9.3

(i) Either party may appeal to High Court on any question of law arising out of the award.
(ii) Either party may apply to High Court to determine any question of law arising in the course of a reference. The High Court has jurisdiction to determine such questions of law 9.5

Arbitrator ceases to act — No

Yes

Parties or person in Appendix must appoint another arbitrator who may not disregard previous directions or vary previous awards except with parties' agreement, by law or as previous arbitrator could under JCT Arbitration Rules 9.7

STOP

4: The JCT Agreement for Minor Building Works (MW 80)

4.01   Introduction

The JCT Agreement for Minor Building Works is one of the most popular of the standard forms published by the Joint Contracts Tribunal. It was first published in 1968 and was revised in 1977. The current edition was issued n 1980. It has been amended six times, the last revision being April 1989.

It is a lump sum contract and the endorsement on its back states that Practice Note M2 has been issued which sets out five criteria for its use. These are:

- Where minor building works are to be carried out for an agreed lump sum and the employer has appointed an architect
- The contractor's lump sum offer is based on drawings and/or specifications and/or schedules without detailed measurements. This *prima facie* excludes the use of bills of quantities

173

- The period required for the execution of the works must be such that full labour and materials fluctuation provisions are not required
- Subject to the above, the form is generally suitable for contracts up to the value of £70,000 at 1987 prices
- There is no provision in the form for those situations where the employer wishes to control the selection of specialist sub-contractors, and accordingly the Joint Contracts Tribunal suggest that this is best achieved by the employer entering into a direct contract with the specialist. Moreover, since there is no provision for employer's licensees (see section 3.9) a suitably-worded clause must be included. Although the employer could name a specialist in the tender documents or in a PS instruction, there are no provisions in MW 80 to deal with the consequences nor is there any appropriate form of sub-contract.

In fact, the Minor Works Form can be used, regardless of contract value, for simple works; what precludes its use is the wish to impose design liability on the contractor or the need to employ nominated sub-contractors, or very complex works. Simplicity is the keynote.

A very useful amendment (5th Recital and Supplementary Memorandum Part E) provides for a guarantee/warranty scheme to apply (BEC Guarantee Scheme) if the employer so wishes. Part E makes amendment to certain insurance clauses and incorporates the "Scheme documents" as part of the contract. There are dangers for the employer in using MW 80 unamended, and notably the fact that, with one exception (see 4.06), the contract contains no provision for the contractor to be reimbursed any direct loss and/or expense which he may suffer or incur as a result of acts or defaults of the employer or of the architect on his behalf: late instructions, drawings or details, for example. The result of this is that the contractor has no right to reimbursement under the contract terms, but must pursue his claim by way of arbitration or an action at common law; unless, of course, the employer is prepared to accept and settle the claim without recourse to legal action. Probably the most effective method of dealing with this problem is to amend the contract by means of a suitably-worded clause.

There comes a point, of course, when rather than inset a multitude of amendments (which may turn the form into the "employer's standard terms of business") it makes sense to use the Intermediate Form (IFC 84) instead.

Table 4.01 summarises the contents of the form.

4.02   Contractor's Obligations

The contractor's basic obligation is stated in clause 1.1. It is, "with due diligence and in a good and workmanlike manner" to "cary out and complete the Works in accordance with the Contract Documents using materials and workmanship of the quality and standards specified" in those documents. The contract documents are:
- Drawings
- *and/or* a specification
- *and/or* schedules
- *and/or* schedules of rates.

The proviso to clause 1.1 is very important. Where quality or standards of materials or workmanship are made matters for the architect's opinion, they are to be to his reasonable satisfaction. From the architect's point of view, while it is desirable to specify quality and standards in the contract documents, it is most unwise to use a blanket phrase such as "all work shall be to the reasonable satisfaction of the architect" as this would most certainly act to reduce the contractor's obligation.

That obligation, as defined in clause 1.1, is a lesser obligation than would be imposed by the general law, since the express contractual terms override those which would otherwise be implied. Moreover, the architect's expression of satisfaction with an interm would prevent the employer from bringing any action to recover from the contractor in respect of such item if, in the event, it was not in accordance with the contract.

4.03   Contract Documentation and Information

Clause 1.2 makes the architect responsible for providing the contractor with "any further information necessary for the proper carrying out of the Works" and what further information is necessary is sometimes a matter of dispute. Inevitably, some further clarification of the drawings and specifications will be required and the architect's obligation to provide it is not conditioned on the contractor's application.

"Further information" must be issued in the form of an architect's instruction and, unless it merely clarifies the contract documents, it will rank as a variation and must then be valued and paid for under clause 3.6. Failure by the architect to supply the information at the right time and so impeding the contractor's progress will be a breach of contract for which the employer is responsible (*Neodox Ltd* v *Swinton & Pendlebury UDC* (1958) 5 BLR 34) giving rise to a claim for damages by the contractor. At the very best, the late provision of further information which causes delay to contract progress will rank for an extension of time under clause 2.2 as being a reason beyond the control of the contractor.

There is no obligation on the contractor to provide the architect with a copy of his programme, but this can be remedied by means of an appropriate clause in the specification. Such a clause should specify the type of programme which the architect requires.

The contract documentation is vitally important and MW 80 is very flexible. Provision is made for different types of documents:

- Drawings which are to be identified in the first recital
- A specification which should be precisely drafted and must cover not only workmanship and materials but also all other necessary information
- Schedules and schedules of rates – schedules can in practice include priced bills.

Discrepancies in and between the contract documents are dealt with by clause 4.1 which merely states that "any inconsistency in or between the contract drawings and the contract specification and the schedules shall be corrected" and that if the correction results in an addition, omission or other change it is to be treated and valued as a variation. There is no express requirement that the contractor is to notify the architect if he finds any inconsistency in or between the contract documents, but obviously he would be wise to do so. There is no variation unless the correction is a change and the position is made clear in Practice Note 1:

"It may be necessary to determine which of two inconsistent documents is the ruling document or which of two inconsistent statements prevails. For example, if written descriptions appear on a drawing and it is stated in the Contract Documents that any figure in a description shall prevail over any figures otherwise shown on a drawing there would only be a change if it were necessary to correct a figure in a description where the inconsistent figure on the drawing was actually required".

The final sentence of clause 4.1 is similar to the provision in clause 2.2.1. of JCT 80 (see chapter 2, section 2.2) and emphasises that, contrary to normal rules of legal interpretation, the printed contract conditions are to take precedence in case of conflict.

4.04   Commencement and Completion

Clause 2.1 gives a date on which the works *may* be commenced by the contractor and provides for them to be completed by another specified date. Unlike JCT 80, clause 23.1 (see chapter 2, section 2.4) it does not stipulate expressly that the employer shall give possession of the site on the stated date. However, it is an implied term in every building contract that the employer must give possession of the site to the contractor in sufficient time to enable the contractor to complete his obligations by the contractual date: *Freeman & Son* v *Hensler* (1900) 64 JP 260. "Sufficient time" will be taken as the contract period, however long or short that may appear to be. If the employer cannot give possession on the date written into clause 2.1 he will be in breach of contract.

The use of the word "may" could be significant since, taken at its face value, the contractor is under no obligation to start work on the specified date; he must, of course, complete by the completion date, and if a generous contract period has been allowed, the contractor may well take advantage of this: *Greater London Council* v *Cleveland Bridge and Engineering Co Ltd* (1986) 8 Con LR 30.

If the works are not completed by the completion date inserted in clause 2.1, or any extended date fixed under clause 2.2, the contractor is liable to pay liquidated damages at the weekly rate specified in clause 2.3. The employer may now deduct liquidated damages from amounts certified as due to the contractor. Alternatively, but less attractively, the employer may sue to recover the liquidated damages as a debt.

There is no express power given to the architect to postpone the execution of any work to be executed under the contract, but it is thought that his general power to issue instructions (clause 3.5) is sufficiently wide to enable him to do so, giving the contractor a claim for extension of time under clause 2.2. If for some reason the employer cannot in fact provide the contractor with possession of the site on the due date, this is a matter for negotiation with the contractor.

Clause 2.4 – headed "Completion Date" – is straightforward. It places an obligation on the architect to certify when, in his opinion, the works have reached "practical completion". The works do not have to be completed in every detail before practical completion is achieved. The issue of this certificate is important because its issue starts the running of the defects liability period.

The length of the defects liability period is to be three months, unless a different period is required. During this time "defects, excessive shrinkages or other faults which appear" are to be made good by the contractor. Note that the shrinkages are to be "excessive", unlike the position under JCT 80, clause 17.2. It is a sensible provision but it could give rise to dispute. There is no requirement for the architect to issue a schedule of defects, but it makes good sense for him to do so on the last day of the defects liability period. The architect is to certify when making good is complete.

4.05 Extensions of Time

Clause 2.2 deals with extensions of time and gives the architect power to extend the contract period in specified circumstances. Those circumstances are "reasons beyond the control of the Contractor including compliance with any instruction of the Architect ... under this contract whose issue is not due to a default of the Contractor", and there are several points to note:

- *Any* reason beyond the contractor's control gives rise to an entitlement to an extension of time
- Although the clause states that the contractor must notify the architect if it becomes apparent to him that the works are not likely to be completed by the currently-fixed completion date this should not be relied upon as a precondition ("condition precedent") to the operation of the clause in those cases where the cause of the delay is the fault of the employer or the architect, eg late instructions or information (see *London Borough of Merton* v *Stanley Hugh Leach Ltd* (1985) 32 BLR 51). Where the cause of delay is within the control of the employer (or of the architect on his behalf) failure properly to grant an extension of time may result in the completion date being set "at large" and the employer would then forfeit his right to liquidated damages: *Peak Construction (Liverpool) Ltd* v *McKinney Foundation Ltd* (1970) 1 BLR 111
- *Any* cause of delay which is beyond the contractor's control qualifies for an extension of the contract period – bad weather, strikes, failure of suppliers and the like, and it is probable that this extends to acts of prevention or hindrance or other breaches of contract by the employer or those for whom he is responsible – including the architect. Sensibly it should do so, and in practice the clause should be so read. There is no requirement that the events must be *wholly* outside the contract's control and due weight must be given to the contributory factors in each case
- The critical factor is that the delay must affect the date for completion and it is suggested, in light of *Amalgamated Building Contractors Ltd* v *Waltham Holy Cross UDC* [1952] 2 All ER 452 that if the event causing delay is one *outside* the control of the architect or the employer, eg bad weather, the architect need not decide on whether or not to make an extension of time until – or even after – the works are actually completed, even though the current completion date has passed, provided he does so before the issue of the final certificate. Where the event causing delay is *within* the control of the employer or the architect, it is suggested that the extension should be granted *before* the current completion date is passed so as to preserve the employer's right to liquidated damages.

Provided the conditions set out in the clause are met, the architect must certify in writing "such extension of time as may be reasonable". Although the grounds for extension are apparently very broad, the architect cannot grant an extension of time for delays which are within the contractor's control, in contrast to the situation under JCT 80. Moreover, the clause is not thought broad enough to cover extension of time for failure to give possession of the site, unlike other JCT contracts which make special provision for that eventuality.

4.06 Architect's Instructions

Clause 3.5 empowers the architect to issue "written instructions" which the contractor must carry "forthwith", ie as soon as reasonably can be: *London Borough of Hillingdon* v *Cutler* [1968] 1 QB 124. Oral instructions are, in fact, permissible, because provision is made for the architect to confirm oral instructions in writing within two days of their issue. There is no provision enabling the contractor to challenge the validity of an architect's instruction by requiring the architect to state in writing the clause authorising its issue. It must, however, be emphasised that the architect's power to issue instructions is limited: he must act within the scope of his authority and has no general dispensing power.

Should the contractor fail to comply with a valid architect's instruction, the architect is empowered to issue a written notice requiring compliance. That notice should be in specified terms. If the contractor fails to comply with the instruction within 7 days of the written notice, the employer may employ others to carry out the work involved and may recover the costs from the contractor either by deduction from amounts due or to become due to him or by means of legal action.

Apart from the general power to issue written instructions, the architect is expressly authorised to issue certain specific instructions. These are as follows:

- Clause 2.5   Excluding from the works any person employed thereon
- Clause 3.6   Variations by way of additions, omissions or other changes in the works or the order or period in which they are to be carried out
- Clause 3.7   Expenditure of provisional sums
- Clause 6.3B   Reinstatement and making good of any work damaged by risks insured by the employer.

As regards variations under clause 3.6 it should be noted that the contractor has no right to object to compliance with a variation instruction which changes the sequence or period in which the works are to be carried out. However, all variations are to be valued by the architect "on a fair and reasonable basis" using the priced documents as appropriate. There is no provision in clause 3.6 or elsewhere for valuing and including in payment certificates such things as the architect's failure to provide information to the contractor at the right time, but the "fair and reasonable" valuation will, in other cases, include an element for profit, overheads and so on and there is now (amendment MW 5) provision for the architect to include direct loss and/or expense incurred by the contractor due to regular progress being *affected* by the instruction.

4.07 Contractor's Claims

With the exception of the very limited provision in clause 3.6 (see 4.06), this form of contract unusually contains no express provision for the contractor to recover direct loss and/or expense, but there are many occasions on which a claim of this sort will arise. In theory, the contractor's remedy is to seek to recover damages by way of arbitration or an action at common law, but in practice such claims will be referred to the architect in one form or another. The architect must refer any claim of this nature to the employer because the fact that the contract contains no provision for the regulated payment of damages does not mean that the contractor has no entitlement to pursue it. In some cases the employer may extend the architect's authority so as to enable him to deal with such claims; in the absense of that authority, only the employer can deal with them. A sensible amendment to MW 80 would be to include a money claims clause.

4.08 Certificates and Payment

Clause 4.2 deals with progress payments and retention. Progress payments are conditioned on a request from the contractor. If such a request is made, the architect must certify progress payments at not less than four weekly intervals, calculated from the date of commencement. Such progress payments must include:

- The value of work properly executed
- Any amounts ascertained or agreed in respect of variations or provisional sum expenditure
- The value of any materials or goods reasonably and properly brought to site for the purposes of the works provided that they are adequately stored and properly protected against weather and other risks.

There is no provision for the value of off-site goods and materials and in fact the greatest care is needed when dealing with unfixed materials because of the prevalence of "retention of title" clauses in the supply contracts of builders merchants. The validity of these clauses has been upheld time and again (eg in *Clough Mills Ltd* v *Martin* [1984] 3 All ER 982), but the terms of clause 4.2 contain no restriction requiring the contractor to provide proof of ownership. Thus, if unfixed materials are included in an interim certificate and in fact the contractor does not own them, the employer is at serious risk: *Dawber Williamson Roofing Ltd* v *Humberside County Council* (1979) 14 BLR 70. In this respect, clause 4.2 needs urgent amendments, for example by deleting the provision "and the value of any materials or goods ... protected against the weather and other casualties..."

The gross amount so certified by the architect is subject to a retention of 5% so that the contractor is paid 95% of the gross value, less any previous payments made by the employer. The employer must pay the net amount to the contractor within 14 days of the date of the certificate.

Unlike the corresponding provision in JCT 80, the retention is not expressly stated to be trust money, and it is doubtful whether the retention under MW 80 would be so regarded under the general law. From this two consequences follow:

- The contractor is not entitled to any interest on the percentage retained
- Should the employer become insolvent, the retention would form part of his assets in the hands of his trustee in bankruptcy or liquidator, and the unpaid contractor would merely rank as an unsecured creditor.

Once practical completion has been achieved, the architect has 14 days in which to issue a *penultimate certificate* (clause 4.3), the effect of which is to release to the contractor the balance of monies due on the full value of the works executed to date, plus half of the retention previously held, leaving a retention of only 2½% in the employer's hands. This is the last certificate which is issued before the final certificate and the "total amount to be paid to the contractor under this contract" which is to be included is only mandatory "so far as that amount is ascertainable at the date of practical completion", ie on the information available. In practice the architect should issue the penultimate certificate contemporaneously with the certificate of practical completion under clause 2.4.

Within 3 months from the date of practical completion the contractor must submit to the architect all documents reasonably required for the computation of the amount to be included in the final certificate. The architect should ask the contractor for any information which he needs.

The architect then has 28 days in which to issue the final certificate, and this period runs from the date of receipt of the contractor's information. There is a precondition, namely that the architect must have certified that the contractor has discharged his defects liability (clause 2.5). The final certificate will show a sum as due to the contractor or employer as appropriate and must be honoured within 14 days.

4.09   Sub-Contractors and Employer's Licensees

Neither the employer nor the contractor may assign the contract without the consent of the other party (clause 3.1). This assignment – or transfer of rights and obligations under the contract – is not the same thing as sub-letting, which is dealt with by clause 3.2, which prevents the contractor from sub-letting without the architect's consent, though consent must not be unreasonably withheld. The only effect of sub-letting is that the contractor is enabled to perform some of his obligations through a third person – the sub-contractor – and sub-letting in no way affects the contractor's liability to the employer. The contractor is responsible for the acts and defaults of any of his sub-contractors and, of course, all instructions to a sub-contractor must pass through him.

The contract contains no provision for nominated sub-contractors or for named sub-contractors, as does IFC 84, but there is no reason why such a provision should not be made by an appropriately-worded clause, if a nominated or "named" specialist sub-contractor is thought to be absolutely necessary.

Similarly, there is no provision enabling the employer to have work carried out by his direct employees or contractors, and once again the contract would need to be amended to provide for that eventuality or, alternatively, the consent of the contractor would be required. The only power to employ others direct is that found in clause 3.5 where the contractor has failed to comply with an architect's instructon, after 7 days' written notice requiring him to do so. In that event the employer may bring in other contractors to execute the work covered by the instruction, recovering the cost from the contractor.

Clause 3.3 requires the contractor to have a representative on site "at all reasonable times", which is beautifully vague. What appears reasonable to the architect may seem unreasonable to the contractor and *vice versa*. The phrase reflects the fact that very small works may be carried out under this contract form and possibly the representative will have responsibility for more than one job. He should, at least, be on site if the architect gives prenotification of a visit, and also to ensure that the works are being carried out in accordance with the contract. In fact, the contract uses the time-honoured phrase "a competent person-in-charge" and any instructions given to him by the architect are deemed to have been given to the contractor.

The architect has power, under clause 3.4, to order the exclusion from the works of any person employed on them, subject to the proviso that an instruction of this nature must not be given unreasonably or vexatiously. Incompetence would be a good ground for the exercise of the power conferred by this clause.

Curiously, MW 80 confers no express right of access to the works upon the architect or his representatives, but it is generally accepted that this is an implied term of the contract.

4.10   Statutory Obligations

Clause 5.1 obliges the contractor to comply with all statutory obligations relating to the works, eg Building Regulations, give the necessary notices and pay all necessary fees and charges. Should he find any divergence between the statutory requirements and the contract documents or an architect's instruction, he must notify the architect. Provided he complies with the provisions of this sub-clause, contractually he is freed from liability to the employer if the works do not in fact comply with statutory requirements if that non-compliance results from his carrying out the works in accordance with the contract documents and any architect's instructions. This does not, of course, free the contractor from his duty of complying with the Building Regulations as far as the local authority is concerned.

If the contractor has to carry out any additional work in order to make the work comply with statutory requirements, eg in consequence of an architect's instruction under clause 5.2, then of course he is entitled to be paid for it.

4.11   Injury, Damage and Insurance

The insurance provisions are broadly similar to those in JCT 80, although stated more briefly, but there is no provision for insurance to be taken out against employer's liability or loss of liquidated damages. This merely reflects the anticipated small scale of the works. There is no contractual power for the employer himself to ensure in the event of the contractor's failure to do so, nor to deduct premiums from the monies due to the contractor, but the party with the obligation to insure is required to produce evidence to the other party on request.

4.12 Determination

Clause 7 provides for the determination of the contractor's employment and separate sub-clauses deal with determination by the employer and by the contractor respectively.

Determination by Employer

Clause 7.1 specifies three grounds which entitle the employer to bring the contractor's employment to an end. They are if the contractor:

- Fails to proceed diligently with the works *without reasonable cause*. It would certainly be a reasonable cause if the employer failed to pay a certificate on time, for example: *J M Hill & Son Ltd* v *London Borough of Camden* (1981) 18 BLR 31. This ground is very difficult to establish in practice
- *Wholly* suspends the carrying out of the works before completion. A partial suspension is not sufficient
- Becomes bankrupt or otherwise insolvent as specified in the sub-clause.

Determination of the contractor's employment is effected by means of a written notice, served on the contractor by registered post or recorded delivery, and there is no requirement for a preliminary notice or warning. However, because of the serious consequences of a wrongful determination of the contractor's employment, it may be thought prudent to issue a warning notice giving the contractor a specific date by which the default must be ended.

Assuming that a valid notice of determination is served, the contractor must immediately surrender possession of the site and the employer need make no further payment to him until after completion of the works by others, but the clause is remarkably silent on various vital matters. It contains no provision for dealing with the contractor's plant and materials, for example. However, the employer's common law rights are preserved and this would enable him to recover "direct loss and/or expense" by way of an action for damages in an appropriate case.

Determination by Contractor

Clause 7.2 provides for the contractor to determine his own employment on four grounds. They are:

- If the employer fails to make progress payments within 14 days of the due date
- If the employer or any person for whom he is responsible interferes with or obstructs the carrying out of the works or fails to make the premises available for the contractor on the commencement date
- If the employer suspends the carrying out of the works for a continuous period of at least one month
- If the employer becomes bankrupt or otherwise insolvent as specified in the sub-clause.

With the exception of the last ground, when no preliminary notice is required, the employer must continue his default for 7 days after receipt of a default notice from the contractor. This must be served by registered post or recorded delivery.

Should the contractor validly determine his employment he is entitled to be paid:

- A fair and reasonable sum for the value of the work begun and executed, the value of materials on site, and for removing his temporary buildings, plant, tools and equipment.

Since the contractor's common law rights are preserved by the clause, he can presumably bring an action to recover any direct loss and/or damage which he suffers or incurs as a consequence of the determination.

4.13 Disputes

The procedure for the settlement of disputes is contained in article 4 referring to clause 9. All disputes must be referred to arbitration. The arbitrator is to be appointed by agreement between the parties or, failing agreement by the President or Vice-President of the Royal Institute of British Architects or of the Royal Institution of Chartered Surveyors as appropriate.

The arbitration agreement is not as widely worded as is the corresponding provision in JCT 80 (see chapter 2, section 2.11) but it should be noted that arbitration can take place before practical completion. The effect of the previous arbitration clause in its original form was considered by the High Court in *Oram Builders Ltd* v *Pemberton & Pemberton* (1985) 2 ConLR 94 where it was held that, despite the difference in wording between the then Minor Works provision and the corresponding provision in JCT 80, the court had no power to go behind the architect's certificates and decisions. "Where there is an arbitration clause in general terms referring any dispute or difference between the parties concerning the contract to the arbitrator . . . then even on a narrow interpretation of the reasoning of the Court of Appeal in *Northern Regional Health Authority* v *Derek Crouch Construction Co Ltd* [1984] 2 All ER 175, the High Court has no jurisdiction to go behind" an architect's certificate: Judge David Smout QC. This is certainly true of the current clause as well.

The following points should be noted:

- The arbitrator now has extensive express powers to rectify the contract, open up, revise and review architect's certificates, decisions and opinions
- The award is stated to be final and binding. This, of course, is subject to the Arbitration Act 1979 which makes limited provision for an appeal on a point of law arising out of the award
- There is provision for another arbitrator to be appointed if the original arbitrator dies or, for another reason, ceases to act
- The arbitration is to be conducted in accordance with the JCT Arbitration Rules, introduced in July 1988, unless the clause is deleted.

Table 4.01: Contents of MW 80 Summarised

Clause	Comment
1.0	Intention of the parties
1.1	Contractor's obligations
1.2	Architect's duties
2.0	Commencement and completion
2.1	Commencement and completion
2.2	Extension of contract period
2.3	Damages for non-completion
2.4	Completion date
2.5	Defects liability
3.0	Control of the works
3.1	Assignment
3.2	Sub-contracting
3.3	Contractor's representative
3.4	Exclusion from the works
3.5	Architect's instructions
3.6	Variations
3.7	Provisional sums
4.0	Payment
4.1	Correction of inconsistencies
4.2	Progress payments and retention
4.3	Penultimate certificate
4.4	Final certificate
4.5	Contribution, levy and tax changes
4.6	Fixed price
5.0	Statutory obligations
5.1	Statutory obligations, notices, fees, charges
5.2	Value added tax
5.3	Statutory tax deduction scheme
5.4	[Number not used]
5.5	Prevention of corruption
6.0	Injury, damage and insurance
6.1	Injury to or death of persons
6.2	Damage to property
6.3A	Works insurance: new works
6.3B	Works insurance: existing structures
6.4	Evidence of insurance
7.0	Determination
7.1	Determination by employer
7.2	Determination by contractor
8.0	Supplementary memorandum
9.0	Settlement of disputes – Arbitration

Table 4.02: MW 80 – Time Chart

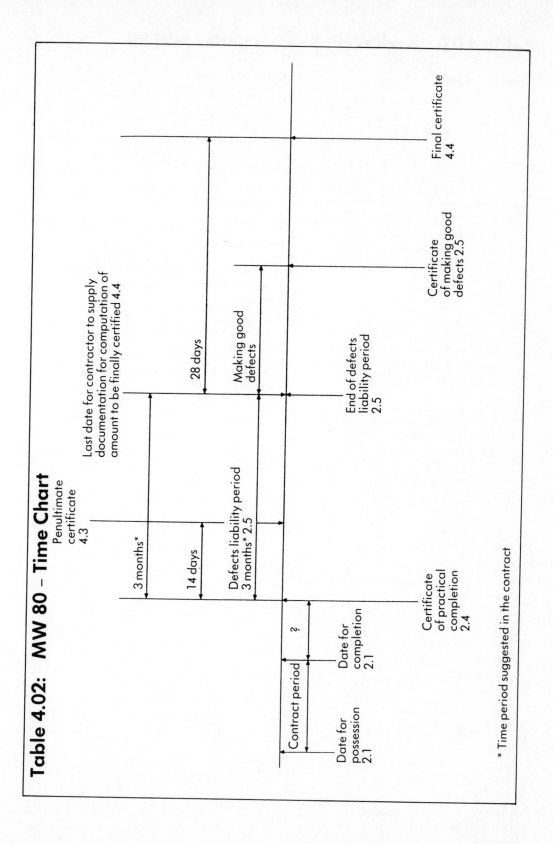

* Time period suggested in the contract

185

Table 4.03:   Architect's Powers under MW 80

Clause	Power	Comment
3.2	Consent in writing to sub-contracting	Consent must not be unreasonably withheld
3.4	Issue instructions requiring the exclsuion from the works of any person employed thereon	The power must not be exercised unreasonably or vexatiously
3.5	Issue written instructions	
3.5	Required the contractor to comply with an instruction by serving written notice on him	The contractor has 7 days from receipt of the written notice in which to comply. If he fails to do so the employer may employ and pay others to carry out the work and may recover the costs involved from the contractor
3.6	Order in addition to or omission from or other change in the works or the order or period in which they are to be carried out	The variation is to be valued by the architect on a fair and reasonable basis unless its value is agreed with the contractor before the instruction is carried out. Direct loss and/or expense due to compliance must be included
3.6	Agree the price of variation with the contractor prior to the contractor carrying out the instruction	

Table 4.04: Architect's Duties under MW 80

Clause	Duty	Comment
1.2	Issue any further information necessary for the proper carrying out of the works Issue all certificates Confirm all instructions in writing	See table 4.10 Clause 3.5 specifies the procedures
2.2	Make in writing such extension of time as may be reasonable	If it becomes apparent that the works will not be completed by the stated completion date and the causes of delay are beyond the control of the contractor and the contractor has so notified the architect
2.4	Certify the date when in his opinion the works have reached practical completion	
2.5	Certify the date when the contractor has discharged his obligations in respect of defects liability	The contractor's obligation is limited to remedying defects, excessive shrinkages or other faults appearing within the defects liability period *and* Which are due to materials or workmanship not in accordance with the contract *or* Frost occurring before practical completion
3.5	Confirm oral instructions in writing	This must be done within 2 days of *issue*
3.6	Value variation instructions	The valuation is to be on a fair and reasonable basis and where relevant the prices in the priced documents must be used. Direct loss and/or expense must be included if regular progress is affected by compliance
3.7	Issue instructions as to expenditure of provisional sums	The instruction is to be valued as a variation under clause 3.6
4.1	Correct inconsistences in or between the contract drawings, specification and schedules	If the correction results in a change it is to be valued as a variation under clause 3.6
4.2	Certifying progress payments to the contractor	If the contractor so requests Such payments are to be certified at intervals of not less than 4 weeks calculated from commencement
4.3	Certify payment to the contractor of 97.5 per cent of the total amount to be paid to him	This must be done within 14 days of the date of practical completion certified under clause 2.4
4.4	Issue a final certificate	Provided the contractor has supplied all documentation reasonably required for the computation of the final sum; *and* The architect has issued his clause 2.5 certificate (defects liability). The final

Table 4.04: Architects's Duties under MW 80 – (continued)

Clause	Duty	Comment
		certificate must be issued within 28 days of receipt of the contractor's documentation
6.3B	Issue instructions for the reinstatement and making good of loss or damage	Should loss or damage be caused by clause 6.3B events

Table 4.05: Contractor's Powers under MW 80

Clause	Power	Comment
2.1	Commence the works on the specified date	
3.1	Assign the contract	If the employer gives written consent
3.2	Sub-let the works or part thereof	Only if the architect consents in writing Consent must not be unreasonably withheld
3.6	Agree the price of variations	If the architect consents; and Before executing the variation instruction
7.2	Forthwith determine the employment of the contractor by notice	The notice must not be given unreasonably or vexatiously and must be served on the employer by registered post or recorded delivery Notice can be served: ● If the employer fails to make any progress payment due within 14 days of payment being due; and ● If the default has continued for 7 days after receipt of a notice from the contractor specifying the default, served by registered or recorded delivery post; or ● If the employer or any person for whom he is responsible interferes with or obstructs the carrying out of the works; and ● The default has continued likewise; or ● If the employer fails to make the premises available to the contractor on the specified date; and ● If the default has continued likewise; or ● If the employer suspends the carrying out of the works for a continuous period of at least one month; and ● If the default has continued likewise; or ● If the employer becomes insolvent

Table 4.06:   Contractor's Duties under MW 80

Clause	Duty	Comment
1.1	Carry out and complete the works in accordance with the contract documents in a good and workmanlike manner and with due diligence	
2.1	Complete the works by the specified date	The architect must insert the date
2.2	Notify the architect of delay	If: It becomes apparent that the works will not be completed by the specified date; and This is because of reasons beyond the control of the contractor including compliance with architect's instruction
2.3	Pay liquidated damages to the employer	If the works are not completed by the specified date or by any later date fixed under clause 2.2
2.5	Make good at his own cost any defects, excessive shrinkages or other faults	The defects, shrinkages or other faults must have appeared within 3 months of the date of practical completion and Must be due to materials or workmanship not in accordance with the contract or to frost occurring before practical completion and Unless the architect has instructed otherwise
3.3	Keep a competent person in charge upon the works at all reasonable times	Under clause 3.4 the architect may instruct this person's exclusion
3.5	Carry out all architect's instructions forthwith	The instructions must be in writing
4.4	Supply the architect with all documentation reasonably necessary to enable the final sum to be computed	Within three months of the date of practical completion It is not conditioned upon a request from the architect
5.1	Comply with and give all notices required by any statute, etc Pay all fees and charges in respect of the works Give immediate written notice to the architect specifying any divergence	Provided they are legally recoverable from him If the contractor finds any divergence between the statutory requirements and the contract documents or between such requirements and an architect's instruction
6.1	Indemnify the employer against any expense, liability, loss, claim	If the expense, etc arises out of or in the course of or is caused by reason of the carrying out of

Table 4.06:   Contractor's Duties under MW 80 – (continued)

Clause	Duty	Comment
	or proceedings in respect of personal injury or death Maintain and cause his sub-contractors to maintain the insurances necessary to meet his liability under clause 6.1	the works except to the extent due to any act or neglect of the employer or those for whom he is legally responsible
6.2	Indemnify the employer against and insure and cause his sub-contractors to insure against any expense, liability, loss, claim or proceedings for damage to property	This is subject to clause 6.3A or 6.3B. The indemnity operates if the expense, etc: Arises out of or in the couse of or is caused by reason of the carrying out of the works *and* To the extent due to any negligence, omission or default of the contractor or any sub-contractor or any person for whom they are legally responsible
6.3A	Insure against the specified risks in joint names Restore or replace work or materials, etc dispose of debris, and proceed with and complete the works	New works only After any inspection by the insurers
6.4	Produce evidence of insurances and cause sub-contractors so to do	If the employer so requires
7.1	Immediately give up possession of the site	Where the employer determines the contractor's employment

Table 4.07: Employer's Powers under MW 80

Clause	Power	Comment
2.3	Deduct liquidated damages	
3.1	Assign the contract	If the contractor consents
3.5	Employ and pay others to carry out the works	If the contractor fails to comply with a written notice from the architect requiring compliance with an instruction and within 7 days from its receipt
5.5	Cancel the contract and recover resulting loss from the contractor	If the contractor is guilty of corrupt practices as specified in the clause
7.1	Determine the employment of the contractor by written notice	If the contractor ● Fails to proceed diligently with the works without reasonable cause; or ● Wholly suspends the carrying out of the works before completion; or ● Becomes insolvent, etc The determination notice must not be served unreasonably or vexatiously

Table 4.08: Employer's Duties under MW 80

Clause	Duty	Comment
4.2	Pay to the contractor amounts certified by the architect	Payment must be made within 14 days of the date of the certificate issued under clause 4.2
4.3	Pay similarly	If the architect issues a certificate under clause 4.3
5.2	Pay to the contractor any VAT properly chargeable	
6.3A	Pay insurance monies to the contractor	On certification under clause 4.0
6.3B	Maintain adequate insurances against the specified risks in joint names	Existing structures and contents and the works
7.2	Pay to the contractor such sum as is fair and reasonable for the value of work begun and executed, materials on site, and removal costs as specified	If the contractor determines his employment under clause 7.2

Table 4.09: Clauses that may Give Rise to Claims under MW 80

Clause	Event	Type
1.2	Failure to issue further necessary information	CL
2.1	Failure to allow commencement on the due date by lack of possession or otherwise	CL
2.2	Failure to give extension adequately or in good time	CL
2.3	Wrongful deduction of damages	CL
2.4	Failure to certify practical completion at the proper time or at all	CL
2.5	Wrongful inclusion of work not being defects, etc	CL
	Failure to issue certificate that the contractor has discharged his obligations	CL
3.1	Assignment without consent	CL
3.2	Unreasonably withholding consent to sub-letting	CL
3.4	Unreasonably or vexatiously instructing removal of employees from works	CL
3.5	Failure to confirm oral instructions	CL
	Instructions altering the whole character or scope of the work	CL
	Wrongful employment of others to do work	CL
3.6	Variations	C
4.1	Errors or inconsistencies in the contract documents	C
4.2	Failure to certify payment if requested	CL
4.3	Failure to certify payment at practical completion	CL
4.4	Failure to issue final certificate	CL
4.5	Contribution, levy and tax changes	C

Table 4.09: Clauses that may Give Rise to Claims under MW 80 – (continued)

Clause	Event	Type
5.1	Divergence between statutory requirements and contract documents or architect's instruction	C
7.1	Invalid determination	CL
	Payment after determination	C
7.2	Payment after determination	C

KEY
C = Contractual claims
CL = Common law claims

Contractual claims are usually dealt with by the architect
Common law claims are usually dealt with by the employer

Note. There is no full loss and/or expense clause in this contract. Such claims have to be made at common law.

Table 4.10: Certificates to be Issued by the Architect under MW 80

Clause	Certificate
2.4	Practical completion
2.5	Making good of defects
4.2	Progress payments
4.3	Penultimate certificate
4.4	Final certificate

Table 4.11: Adjustment of Contract Sum under MW 80

Clause	Adjustment
2.5	Defects etc during the defects liability perod
3.6	Variations
3.7	Provisional sums
4.1	Inconsistencies in the contract documents
4.4	Computation of the final amount
4.5	Contribution, levy and tax changes
6.3A	Insurance money
6.3B	Making good of loss or damage

Flowchart 4.12: Architect's Instructions

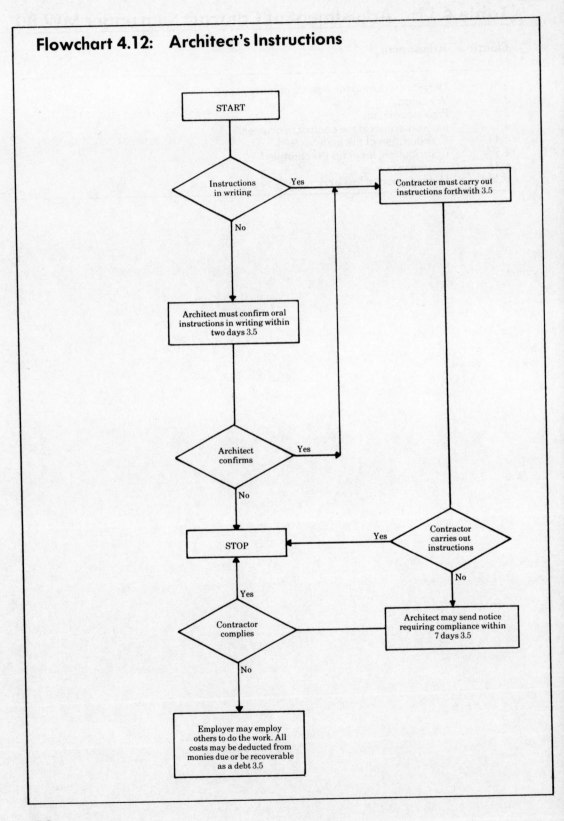

START

Instructions in writing

Yes → Contractor must carry out instructions forthwith 3.5

No

Architect must confirm oral instructions in writing within two days 3.5

Architect confirms

Yes

No

STOP

Contractor carries out instructions

Yes

No

Contractor complies

Yes

No

Architect may send notice requiring compliance within 7 days 3.5

Employer may employ others to do the work. All costs may be deducted from monies due or be recoverable as a debt 3.5

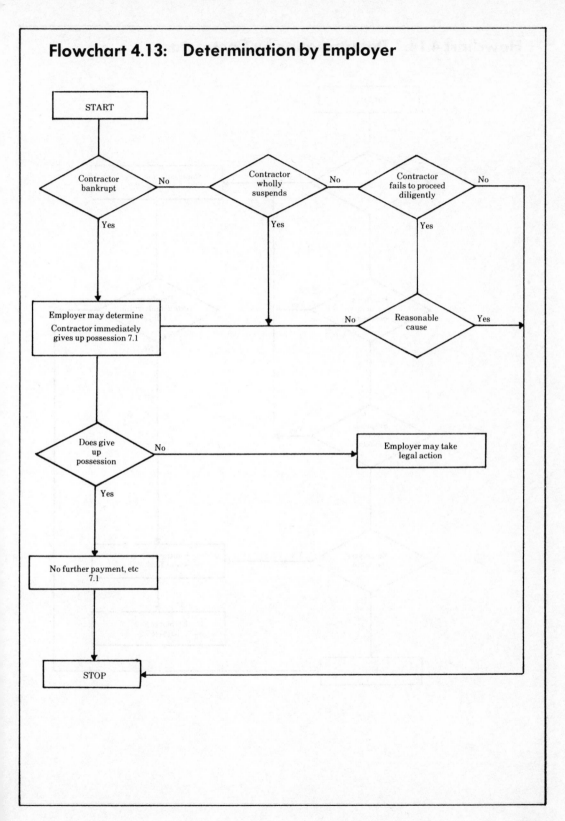

Flowchart 4.13: Determination by Employer

Flowchart 4.14: Determination by Contractor

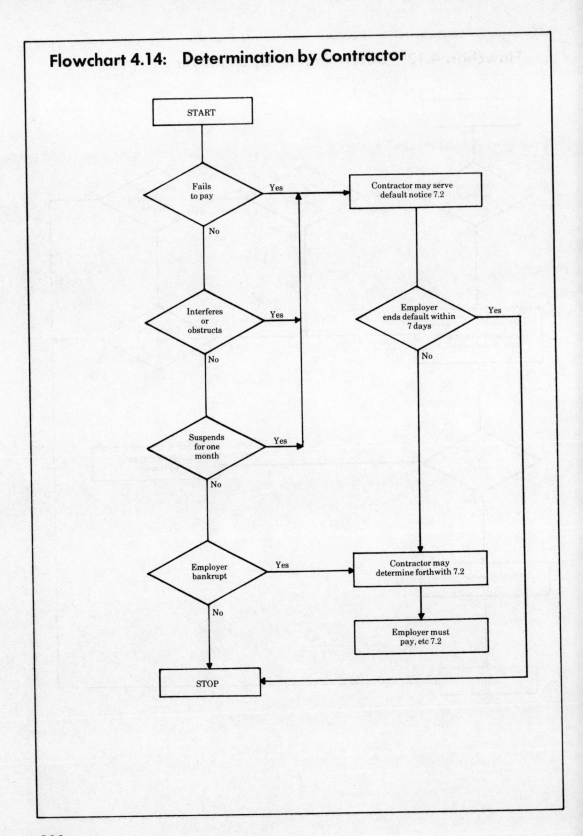

START

Fails to pay — Yes → Contractor may serve default notice 7.2

No

Interferes or obstructs — Yes

No

Suspends for one month — Yes

No

Employer bankrupt — Yes → Contractor may determine forthwith 7.2

No

Employer ends default within 7 days — Yes

No

Employer must pay, etc 7.2

STOP

Flowchart 4.15: Arbitration (Article 4 and Clause 9)

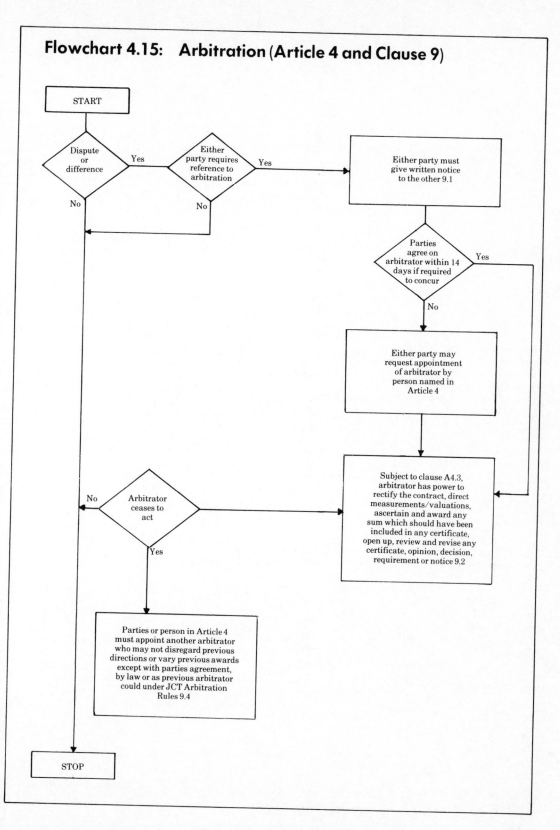

START

Dispute or difference — Yes → Either party requires reference to arbitration — Yes → Either party must give written notice to the other 9.1

No

No

Parties agree on arbitrator within 14 days if required to concur — Yes

No

Either party may request appointment of arbitrator by person named in Article 4

Arbitrator ceases to act — No

Yes

Subject to clause A4.3, arbitrator has power to rectify the contract, direct measurements/valuations, ascertain and award any sum which should have been included in any certificate, open up, review and revise any certificate, opinion, decision, requirement or notice 9.2

Parties or person in Article 4 must appoint another arbitrator who may not disregard previous directions or vary previous awards except with parties agreement, by law or as previous arbitrator could under JCT Arbitration Rules 9.4

STOP

5: The JCT Standard Form of Management Contract (JCT 87)

5.01   Introduction

The JCT Management Contract package was issued in response to the demand for standardised documentation to cover this popular form of building procurement. Management contracting essentially involves the early appointment of a contractor whose function is to manage the execution of the works in return for a fee. The management contractor takes no part in carrying out the works. This is undertaken by works contractors employed by the management contractor. The employer simply pays the prime cost of the works contracts and management contractor's on site expenses together with a management fee. The employer takes a greater share of the risk than is usual in traditional contracts; management contracting is low risk from the point of view of the contractor.

The idea is to use the contractor's management skills for the benefit of the employer. In theory, the management contractor is more closely identified with the employer's interest, but in practice, this contract (JCT 87) does not always promote this approach.

The contract has two phases:
- Pre-construction period
- Construction period.

The management contractor is intended to be involved in both phases. However, there is a "break clause" allowing the employer to stop the process at the end of the pre-construction period.

The total package consists of:
- Standard Form of Management Contract 1987
- Standard Form of Works Contract 1987:
  - Works Contract 1 – Invitation, Tender, Articles of Agreement
  - Works Contract 2 – Conditions
- Standard Form of Employer/Works Contractor Agreement:
  - Works Contract 3
- JCT Sub-Contract/Works Contract Formula Rules
- Phased Completion Supplements for Management Contract and Works Contract
- Practice Notes MC/1 and MC/2.

Practice Note MC/1 lays down the recommended criteria for using the form:
- The employer wishes the design to be carried out by an independent architect and design team
- There is a need for early completion
- The project is fairly large
- The project requirements are complex
- The project entails, or might entail, changing the employer's requirements during the construction period
- The employer while requiring early completion wants the maximum possible competition in respect of the price for the building works.

Both management contract and works contract follow the structure of IFC 84 in that they are divided into nine logically grouped sections. The wording, however, particularly as regards Works Contract 2 is closely related to JCT 80 and NSC/4. The management contract introduces a number of new concepts which will be discussed below.

5.02 Contractor's Obligations

The contractor's basic obligations are stated in clause 1.4 to 1.8 inclusive. Briefly, they are to:
- Co-operate with the professional team during the design stages and in planning, programming and cost estimating for an securing the carrying out and composition of the project including the services set out in the third schedule

- Set out, manage, organise, supervise and secure the carrying out and completion of the project on or before the date for completion
- Prepare all necessary programmes
- Enter into works contracts in sufficient time to enable the project to be completed on or before completion date
- Ensure that work by works contractors is in accordance with project specification and works contracts. There is a proviso similar to JCT 80 and other JCT contracts that if quality or standards of materials or workmanship are matters for the architect's opinion, they are to be to his reasonable satisfaction
- Provide site facilities listed in the fifth schedule
- Provide continual supervision and everything necessary for the organisation of the work
- Ensure the contract is carried out economically and expeditiously
- Keep all records to enable the quantity surveyor to verify work
- Be fully liable to the employer for any breach of contract including breaches of works contractors, subject to same limitations
- Forthwith comply or secure compliance with all instructions unless within the definition of "works contract variation".

The apparent severity of some of these obligations is very much reduced by the effect of clause 3.21: Breach of works contract by works contractor. In effect it grants absolute relief to the management contractor when he cannot obtain satisfactory recompense from a defaulting works contractor, and effectively the employer's protection is non-existent in these circumstances.

Clause 3.21 provides for the situation where a works contractor is in breach of any of the terms of the works contract or if his employment has been brought to an end under clauses 7.1 to 7.5 of the works contract or if another person has been engaged under clause 7.4.1 to carry out part of the works.

In such cases, after consulting with the employer and architect, the management contractor must take the necessary steps to enforce the works contract terms to ensure that the breach is remedied. If the works contractor contests the breach, the management contractor must go to arbitration or litigation after consulting the employer and the architect. If the works contractor refuses to remedy the breach, the management contractor must exercise all the powers of the works contract, determining the defaulter's employment if necessary, and getting the breach remedied and the work completed by another works contractor, and seeking to recover the losses etc from the defaulting works contractor, if necessary by arbitration or litigation.

If, as a result of the breach by a works contractor, other works contractors properly make resultant claims, the management contractor must meet those claims.

The employer also has duties. He must pay the management contractor all amounts properly incurred in operating the appropriate terms, including the legal costs associated with arbitration or litigation and employing another works contractor. In addition, he must keep account of liquidated damages due as a result of delays, but which he is not entitled to recover under clauses 2.10 and 2.11. The employer may recover from the management contractor all the amounts paid to him in respect of the operation of appropriate terms of the sub-contract and employment of another sub-contractor, together with the liquidated damages of which he has kept account. His right of recovery is however conditioned. He is only entitled to recover to the extent that the management contractor has recouped himself from the works contractor who is in breach. If the management contractor has been unable to recover in respect of other works contractors' claims, the employer must pay the shortfall to him.

This is a valuable safeguard for the management contractor. The idea is that he should not suffer if he is unable to recover. Under normal circumstances, the management contractor would be unable to recover the amount of liquidated damages payable to the employer from the works contractor in breach, because the management contractor would be unable to show that he had suffered any loss. Clause 1.6.2 has been inserted into the works contract in an attempt to overcome the problem by preventing the works contractor from contending that his liability should be reduced because the management contractor has suffered no loss. It is unlikely that the problem can be dealt with so easily.

If other works contractors make claims as a result of the breach of a works contractor, the management contractor may deduct the amount of the claims from monies due to the works contractor in breach. If there is a shortfall, the management contractor must attempt to recover the amount from the defaulting works contractor, but if he is not successful, the employer is liable to make up the difference, as already explained. The employer's protection is largely illusory in practice.

If the works contractor alleges breaches of the works contract against the management contractor, the management contractor must immediately inform the architect and, unless instructed otherwise, take any necessary action including settling the claim, taking legal advice or defending the claim. Once again the employer is required to stand foursquare behind the management contractor and reimburse him any amounts expended, but only in so far as the management contractor's obligation to pay is not the result of any breach of the management contract.

5.03   Contract Documentation and Information

The contract documents are defined in clause 1.3 as "the Project Drawings, the Project Specification, the Articles of Agreement, the Conditions, the Appendix, the Contract Cost Plan annexed hereto and the Schedules".

The actual process of forming the contract is very much less clear than in traditional contracts. Article 6 stipulates that the employer must cause the project drawings and specification, describing the general scope of the project, to be prepared as soon as practicable *after* the date of the contract unless previously prepared. At the time of entering into the contract, the management contractor may have only the merest outline of what the project involves. The contract cost plan is prepared by the quantity surveyor in collaboration with the rest of the professional team and the management contractor. The management contractor is required formally to consent to the cost plan and also to the entries to be inserted in part two of the appendix, alterations to be made to the third schedule (setting out the services he is to provide) and the entries to the fifth schedule (site facilities and services he is to provide). Clearly, by the time everything is ready for the second phase to begin, the contractor will not only be fully aware of what the project involves, he will have played his part in shaping it.

The employer undertakes, by article 7, that all necessary drawings, specifications and bills of quantities for works contracts will be prepared and issued so that the management contractor can properly discharge his functions under the contract. The architect must supply copies of such information to the management contractor together with any other information reasonably necessary to enable the project to be carried out and completed in accordance with the contract.

Unlike most other JCT standard forms, there is no stipulation regarding the priority of documents. In view of the character of this contract, such a stipulation would be superfluous.

5.04   Commencement and Completion

The second stage of the contract, the construction period, is activated by the employer. The procedure is that the management contractor initials alterations to the third schedule, initials the fifth schedule and signs part 2 of the appendix indicating that all outstanding matters have been agreed. The architect then notifies the employer, with a copy to the management contractor, of a date it will be practicable to commence on site. This date, of course, will be the same date as the date for possession in part 2 of the appendix. The employer has 14 days from the date of the written notification in which to notify the management contractor whether or not he is to proceed.

If the employer notifies the management contractor that he is not to proceed, or if he fails to notify him within the prescribed period, the management contractor's employment is deemed to have been determined. The management contractor is entitled to the balance of the pre-construction management fee, but the employer is entitled to reduce the fee to take account of any default of the management contractor which contributed to the employer's decision not to proceed.

If the employer gives notice to proceed, he must give the management contractor possession of the site on the date stated in the appendix. In common with other JCT forms of contract, the employer is entitled to defer possession for a period of up to 6 weeks, but only where clause 2.3.2 is stated in the appendix to apply. If the employer does so defer possession, the management and works contractors may be entitled to an extension of time and, in addition, the works contractors may be entitled to payment for loss and/or expense.

On taking possession of the site, the management contractor must secure the commencement of the project and its diligent progress to completion on or before the completion date. The contract makes clear what was always the position under the general law, that the contractor is entitled to retain possession until the date of issue of the certificate of practical completion. The employer is not entitled to take possession until that date – except of course by agreement. There is a valuable saving provision for the employer. Provided the management contractor consents and the insurers confirm that insurance cover will not be prejudiced, the employer may use or occupy any part of the site before practical completion for storage of goods or otherwise.

Clause 2.8 entitles the employer to take possession of part of the project on terms similar to those in JCT 80. The provisions dealing with practical completion and defects liability echo JCT 80. The architect must issue a certificate when he is satisfied that practical completion has been achieved. The management contractor must secure the making good of defects, shrinkages or other faults which appear during the defects liability period and which are due to materials and workmanship not in accordance with the contract or due to frost occurring before practical completion. The list of defects must be given to the management contractor not later than 14 days after the end of the defects liability period, although, by clause 3.12, it appears that the architect can require defects to be corrected at any time. When the defects listed have been made good, the architect must issue a certificate of completion of making good defects.

If the management contractor fails to secure completion of the project by the due date, the architect must issue a non-completion certificate (clause 2.9). If an extension of time is granted subsequently, the certificate must be cancelled and a new certificate issued: If:

- The architect issues a certificate of non-completion; *and*
- The employer so notifies the management contractor, the employer may deduct or recover liquidated damages at the rate in the appendix, but such recovery is to be subject to the provisions of clause 3.21 which effectively prevents the employer from recovering such damages from the management contractor, who need account for them only if he can recover them from the appropriate works contractors.

5.05   Extensions of Time

Clause 2.12 deals with extensions of time.
For the clause to operate:
- It must be reasonably apparent to the management contractor that the completion date has not or is not likely to be achieved
- The management contractor must forthwith advise the architect of the cause of the delay.

If the architect is of the opinion that completion has been or is likely to be delayed by any of the project extension items, he must give in writing a fair and reasonable extension of time "as soon as he is able to *assess* the length of delay". The architect must be sure to give an extension whenever the cause of delay is some default of the employer, otherwise the completion date may become unenforceable and the employer may be unable to recover liquidated damages.

The project extension items are:
- Default by the employer or any person for whom he is responsible
- Late issue of specifications or bills for works contracts or instructions, drawings, details and levels for which specific application has been made in writing
- Deferment of possession (if clause 2.3.2 is stated to apply)
- Any relevant event in the works contract which entitles a works contractor to an extension of time except delay caused by another works contractor.

The relevant events in the works contract are similar to the relevant events in JCT 80. A badly drafted clause 2.14 requires the management contractor to notify the architect of any decision to grant a works contractor an extension of time. Unlike the provisions in respect of nominated sub-contractors in JCT 80, the architect's consent is not required. Instead, the management contractor must notify the architect in sufficient time for the architect to express any dissent in writing before the management contractor must give his decision to the works contractor. Under the terms of the works contact (clause 2.3.1) the management contractor must pass on the architect's dissent to the works contractor. The management contractor's obligation is to notify the architect, but *not* to withhold the extension if the architect dissents. The architect's dissent is clearly not a condition precedent to the management contractor granting an extension to the works contractor. Therefore, a grant by the management contractor of an extension, in the face of the architect's dissent, will still fall within the last project extension item and entitle the management contractor to an extension of time himself. Clearly, the management contractor will not wish to act against the wishes of the architect, but pressure from a works contractor may leave him little option.

In other respects, the project extension items are very comprehensive and include the sensible provision that no project extension item must be considered in so far as it is caused by the management contractor's or his servant's default. Although there is no positive obligation on the management contractor to use his best endeavours, a strict reading of clause 2.12.1 prohibits the granting of an extension altogether in the case of a delay which the management contractor has not used his best endeavours to avoid or reduce.

Unique among JCT contract forms, this form includes provision for acceleration of the project. The procedure is briefly that if the employer desires an earlier completion date or to retain the completion date despite the management contractor's entitlement to an extension of time, the architect may issue a preliminary instruction to that effect. The management contractor passes the instruction to the works contractor. If the management contractor or the works contractor makes reasonable objection, the instruction must be withdrawn or varied to meet the objection and re-issued.

Thereafter, or if there is no objection, the management contractor must inform the architect of either:

- The lump sum required to comply with the instruction; *or*
- That the cost must be ascertained in accordance with the relevant works contract conditions.

In addition:

- The date which can become the completion date; *or*
- The extent to which any proposed extension can be avoided.

If the details are acceptable to the employer, the architect must then issue an instruction confirming all the details. The procedure is applicable only if so stated in the appendix. Whether it is worth including the provision, as it stands, is debatable. It is complex and the possibility of objection infinite. The same result can be achieved in any contract provided only that the parties agree on time and cost.

5.06 Architect's Instructions

The architect must issue all instructions in writing (clause 3.3.1). Oral instructions may be confirmed by either architect or management contractor within seven days, otherwise, they are of no effect. It should be noted that, unlike JCT 80, there is no provision for the architect to dissent from the management contractor's confirmation, but there seems to be no good reason why the architect should not do so if he disagrees.

The architect is empowered to issue "such instructions as are reasonably necessary to enable the management contractor properly to discharge his obligations". This is a usefully broad statement and a vast improvement on the strangely convoluted mode of expression in clause 4.1.1 of JCT 80. Nevertheless, it is to be regretted that the opportunity was not taken to provide a definitive statement of the whole of the architect's powers to issue instructions (**see Table 5.11**). There are other situations, for example variations, which do not fall under the heading of instructions necessary to enable the management contractor to discharge his obligations. Clause 3.4 deals with this point and also with instructions in regard to the expenditure of provisional sums, but expressed to be without prejudice to the generality of clause 3.3.1. Clause 3.5 empowers the architect to issue instructions postponing the work.

The management contractor must forthwith comply or ensure compliance with any instruction unless it is an instruction requiring a works contract variation, ie:

- Change in design, quality or quantity of work in the works contract including additions or omissions, removal of work, materials or goods from site
- Imposition by employer or management contractor of obligations or restrictions or amendment of such in regard to access, limitation of working space or hours, or sequence of working.

In such a case, the management contractor must submit to the architect any written objection or consent by the works contractor before compliance. The management contractor is excused compliance or ensuring compliance insofar as the objection or withholding of consent is reasonable. It is, of course, in the first instance for the architect to decide if the objection is reasonable. If the management or works contractors disagree, it becomes a dispute and a matter for arbitration under clause 9.1 of the management contract and/or clause 9.1 of the works contract.

Under clause 3.7 of the works contract, the works contractor may require the management contractor to request the architect to specify in writing the provision of the management contract empowering the issue of the instruction. If the works contractor accepts the reply, the provision becomes the authority for the instruction for all the purposes of the contract. If not, the works contractor may through the management contractor, refer the point to immediate arbitration under the management contract.

Two very useful powers are contained in clauses 3.11 and 3.12. The architect may issue instructions to remove from site, work, materials or goods which are not in accordance with the contract. In addition, he may "whenever he considers it necessary to do so" issue instructions requiring the making good of any defects, shrinkages, etc due to workmanship or materials not in accordance with the contract, or frost before practical completion. The latter is to be at no cost to the employer, but subject to clause 3.21 which, as noted in section 7.02, effectively prevents financial recovery by the employer unless the management contractor has similarly recovered from the works contractor in breach.

5.07 Contractor's Claims

In a contract of this kind there is no room for a clause enabling the management contractor to claim loss and/or expense. By clause 8.5, however, there is provision for the management contractor to pass on to the architect claims by a works contractor. The application must be made by the works contractor under clause 4.45 of the works contract. This provides for the payment of direct loss and/or expense in much the same terms as clause 26 of JCT 80. On receipt of the application, the management contractor must pass it to the architect together with any comments. It is for the architect to decide whether the application is valid. If it is, the architect or the quantity surveyor must ascertain the amount of loss and/or expense in collaboration with the management contractor.

5.08 Certificates and Payment

The scheme of payment is divided into two parts: the pre-construction period and the construction period. During the pre-construction period, the architect must certify, at intervals as stated in the appendix, appropriate instalments of the pre-construction period management fee.
During the construction period, the architect must certify:

- Amounts payable under the various works contracts in accordance with Part 2 of the Second Schedule
- Amounts for site staff and facilities provided by the management contractor
- An instalment of the construction period management fee released in accordance with amount of work certified up to a maximum of 97%
- Any costs incurred by the management contractor for which he is entitled to reimbursement under the contract.

From the above sums must be deducted the amount of payments or credits received by the management contractor in respect of materials or to which the employer is entitled under clause 3.21. The quantity surveyor must have made interim valuations no more than seven days before the certificates are issued. The employer has fourteen days from the date of issue in which to pay.
The retention to be deducted from prime cost due to the management contractor and works contractors is to amount to 3%. 1.5% is to be released at practical completion of the project and the remaining 1.5% after the issue of the certificate of making good defects. The employer holds the retention as trustee for the management contractor and any works contractor. Unless the employer is a local authority, the management contractor, or through him any works contractor, may request, and the employer must comply, that the retention is placed in a separate banking account.
The construction period management fee may be adjusted in accordance with the formula in clause 4.10.4 if prior to the issue of the final certificate, the prime cost exceeds or is less than the contract cost plan by more than 5% or such percentage as is stated in the appendix.
Within 6 months of practical completion of the project the management contractor must provide the quantity surveyor with all documents necessary to ascertain the prime cost. Within 3 months of receipt of all the relevant documents, the quantity surveyor must give the architect a statement of the

prime cost and management fee (adjusted if necessary). The architect must send a copy to the management contractor including, if applicable, the reasons for disallowing any part of the prime cost where this is stated to have been done. A general clause in Part 1 of the Second Schedule has the effect of excluding any part of the prime cost which is incurred as a result of negligence by the management contractor in discharging his obligations under the contract.

Clause 4.11 obliges the architect to issue an interim certificate not less than 28 days before the issue of the final certificate. The interim certificate must include the final amounts due to the works contractors. The earliest time at which this certificate can be issued is after the issue of the certificate of making good defects.

The architect must issue the final certificate not more than 2 months after the latest of the following:

- The end of the defects liability period
- The issue of the certificate of making good defects
- The delivery to the architect of the quantity surveyor's statement of prime cost and management fee.

The conclusivity of the certificate is precisely the same as the final certificate under JCT 80. There is, however, an express term (clause 1.14.4) to emphasise that the final certificate is in no circumstances conclusive in respect of the sufficiency of design of a works contractor where the works contractor is responsible for such design to the employer under Works Contract/3 or the management contractor under Works Contract clause 1.7.4.

5.09   Sub-Contractors and Employer's Licensees

Clause 3.19 is the usual prohibition against either party assigning the contract without written consent. This modifies the position under the general law whereby rights, but not duties, may be assigned without consent. However, where clause 3.20 is stated in the appendix to apply, the clause allows the employer to assign the right to bring proceedings. The clause would operate if, after practical completion, the employer transferred his interest in the project to another.

The third party might need to enforce the terms originally made for the employer's benefit. It is unclear why it was thought necessary in JCT 80, but not in this contract, that the third party's right of action should be in the employer's name. The clause attempts to prevent, with what success remains to be seen, the third party from disputing agreements made between the employer and the management contractor before the date of the assignment.

The works contractors are an essential ingredient of the management contracting system. Under this form, the management contractor is precluded from carrying out any of the physical work. The works contractors are to be chosen by agreement between the architect (note, not the employer) and the management contractor. The agreement must be in writing and the architect must confirm by issuing an architect's instruction. The procedure will be that the project will be divided into works contract packages with the advice of the management contractor (Second Schedule, item 6), the architect will provide the necessary documentation (article 7) and the contractor will complete and send out invitations to tender on Works Contract/1. The management contractor will thus be very heavily involved in the choice of works contractors. The contract further stipulates that a person employed as a works contractor must enter into a contract with the management contractor on the basis of Works Contract/1 and 2. He must also enter into the Employer/Works Contractor Agreement (Works Contract/3) if so required. Where the management contract is under seal, these contracts should be under seal also.

Clause 8.2.2 makes provision for the architect to approve in writing any restrictions or exclusions which a nominated supplier may impose in a contract of sale with a works contractor. Where such a restriction is sufficient to restrict the liability of the nominated supplier, the works contractor's liability to the management contractor will be similarly restricted under works contract clause 8.4.1 and the management contractor's liability to the employer will be similarly restricted.

Clause 8.3 sets out some of the management contractor's duties under the management contract in respect of the works contractors. It first puts an obligation on the management contractor to carry out his duties as laid down in the individual works contracts. This overcomes the principle of privity of contract and enables the employer to take action against the management contractor if he fails to carry out his duties under the works contracts. The clause then goes on to stipulate that the architect must direct the management contractor the amounts payable to works contractors in each interim certificate, the management contractor must inform the architect if the works contractor wishes to be informed of the amounts directly and the management contractor must operate the appropriate procedure in respect of all practical completion notifications from works contractors. It should be noted, however, that there is no provision for the employer to make any direct payments to works contractors.

Clause 8.4 provides that the architect may include for final payment to any works contractor in an interim certificate before the time stipulated in clause 4.11 if:

- The works contractor so requests; *and*
- The employer wishes to pay; *and*
- The works contractor satisfactorily indemnifies the management contractor against latent defects.

Employer's licensees are covered by clauses 3.23 to 3.25 in terms similar to those in JCT 80. The consequences are indicated in works contract clauses 2.10.8 and 4.46.5 which entitle the works contractor to extension of time and loss and/or expense in such circumstances.

Clause 3.13 obliges the management contractor to "constantly keep upon the site a competent manager". The architect must have approved the appointment during the pre-construction period, but the approval must not be unreasonably withheld. The architect's approval is also needed if the manager is to be changed and the architect may order his removal provided the order is not issued unreasonably or vexatiously. It is absolutely vital in a contract of this kind that the manager has the confidence of the architect, because the manager's is the pivotal role. All management personnel must be named in an attachment to the Second Schedule prior to the construction period. Any replacement, addition or deletion is subject to the reasonable consent of the architect (clause 3.1).

5.10   Statutory Obligations

Clause 5.1 requires the management contractor to secure compliance with and give all statutory notices. Unlike JCT 80, there is no express term requiring the management contractor to pay all necessary fees and charges, but reimbursement of such charges is covered in the Second Schedule, section 3B.

If the management contractor finds any divergence between statutory requirements and any contract document or architect's instruction, he must specify the divergence immediately in writing to the architect. Any instructions issued by the architect in consequence of discovery of such divergence are to be treated as variations. The management contractor may act without instruction in an emergency provided he does only such work and provides only such materials as are necessary (clause 5.4).

Provided the management contractor carries out his duty to report discovered divergences, clause 5.5 states that the employer cannot hold him liable if the project does not comply with statutory requirements. The provision, of course, cannot protect the management contractor against any action which may be taken against him by a third party such as the local authority.

The remainder of section 5 deals with VAT and the statutory tax deduction scheme, in terms similar to JCT 80.

5.11   Injury, Damage and Insurance

The insurance and indemnity provisions relating to injury or death of persons and damage to property other than the project follow JCT 80 provisions very closely. Where it is stated in the appendix that the employer may require insurance against the loss of liquidated damages and/or insurance against matters which are the liability of the employer, the provisions (of clauses 6.6 and 6.11) are also similar to JCT 80.

In keeping with the overall philosophy of this contract, there is no provision for a choice so far as the insurance of new work is concerned; the management contractor must take out All Risks insurance in joint names (clause 6.4). The full reinstatement value must be included and the cover must last until the earliest of:

- The date of issue of the practical completion certificate; *or*
- The date of determination.

If the management contractor maintains his own insurance policy which satisfies the criteria laid down, he is excused from taking out another policy.

Where the project comprises alterations or extensions to existing structures, it is the employer's responsibility to take out and maintain insurance in joint names against specified perils to cover the existing structure and contents. If the employer defaults, the management contractor has power to take out the requisite insurance himself and to enter the property for the purpose of survey and inventory. The employer has no similar right if the management contractor defaults on his insurance. It is no doubt felt that the management contractor can have no motivation to default since he is entitled to reimbursement of all his expenses under the Second Schedule, Part 3B, item 11.

In accordance with the provisions of clause 6.3, all joint names policies must provide for the recognition of each works contractor as an insured, or include a waiver of subrogation in respect of loss or damage by specified perils – a somewhat limited protection.

5.12 Determination

The provisions are similar, but not identical to those in JCT 80. The employer may determine the management contractor's employment if the management contractor defaults in any of the following ways:

- He wholly suspends his obligations under article 1 (his general obligations to co-operate and secure the carrying out of the project) or fails to proceed with them regularly and diligently. The precise meaning of "diligence" as applied to an engineering form was discussed at length by the Court of Appeal in *Greater London Council* v *Cleveland Bridge & Engineering Co Ltd* (1986) 8 Con LR 30. An employer attempting determination on this ground would be brave indeed, unless the management contractor had entirely left the site
- He refuses or neglects to comply with the architect's written notice requiring him to secure removal of defective work, etc. The project must be *materially* affected by such refusal for this ground to be applicable
- He attempts to assign the contract without consent.

The architect must serve a notice on the management contractor by registered post or recorded delivery. If the management contractor continues the default for a further 14 days, or if he ever repeats the default, the employer may determine the management contractor's employment. This must be done within 10 days of the end of the 14 day period or any period of repetition by registered post or recorded delivery.

Clauses 7.2 and 7.3 deal with determination in the case of the management contractor's insolvency or corruption. Insolvency within the meaning of the clause results in automatic determination, but reinstatement can take place if the parties agree. In the case of corruption, the employer is entitled to determine the management contractor's employment, but no particular form is prescribed. At the very least, service by recorded delivery is advisable. The consequences of such determination are set out in terms which follow JCT 80.

Clause 7.5 sets out the grounds upon which the management contractor may determine his own employment:

- If the employer fails to pay the amount on any certificate within the stipulated period
- If the employer interferes with the issue of any certificate
- If substantially the whole of the uncompleted project is suspended for a continuous period named in the appendix due to:
  - variation or postponement instructions unless caused by the negligence of the management contractor, his servants or agents. The equivalent term was considered by the Court of Appeal in *John Jarvis Ltd* v *Rockdale Housing Association Ltd* (1986) 10 Con LR 51 in JCT 80. As a result, the term was amended to read somewhat like this one except that the JCT 80 term expressly excluded nominated sub-contractors. In this contract, works contractors have not been excluded. It appears, therefore, that a negligent act of a works contractor would be sufficient to prevent the management contractor from determining his own employment, if the act caused the issue of the instruction
  - late issue of information specifically applied for in due time
  - delay by employer's men
  - opening up of work unless the work was found not to be in accordance with the contract
  - the employer's failure to provide access
- If the employer becomes insolvent.

The mode of determination in each case is by notice by registered post or recorded delivery. Only in the first instance (non-payment) must the management contractor first send a warning, by registered post or recorded delivery, giving the employer 7 days' notice from receipt thereof.

The consequences of the management contractor's determination are covered by clause 7.6. The management contractor is entitled to be paid the prime cost of the work done or materials delivered and the appropriate proportion of the management fee. Moreover, he is entitled to recover any direct loss and/or damage caused by the determination. The major item will undoubtedly be loss of profit.

Clause 7.7 follows JCT 80 and IFC 84 in setting out three grounds which entitle either party to determine the employment of the management contractor. They are:

- *Force majeure*
- Loss or damage to the project caused by any of the specified perils
- Civil commotion.

Either party may determine without preamble if any of the grounds result in suspension of substantially the whole of the project for a period named in the appendix. The consequences are the same as if the management contractor determines under clause 7.5 except that he is not entitled to any loss and/or damage.

Clause 7.10 entitles the employer to determine the management contractor's employment at will. The employer simply has to give notice in writing for the determination to become effective. The respective rights and duties of the parties are set out in clause 7.11. They are said to be without prejudice to the accrued rights and remedies of either party or to any liabilities under clauses 6.7 and 6.8. The employer indemnifies the management contractor against any valid claims made by works contractors in relation to the project. If the employer or the architect so requires within 14 days, the management contractor must assign the benefits of all contracts made in connection with the management contract without payment, but the appropriate works contractors or suppliers have the right to object to any further assignment. If the determination takes place during the pre-construction period, the management contractor is due to be paid an appropriate proportion of the management fee. If determination takes place during the construction period, the management contractor is entitled to be paid as if he had determined under clause 7.5.

5.13 Disputes

The arbitration agreement is contained in Article 8 and the details are set out in Section 9. It is similar to JCT 80 provisions. The principal points are:

- If either party requires a dispute referring to arbitration that party must give the other a notice to that effect
- The appendix provides for the appointor to be noted as the President or Vice President of the Royal Institute of British Architects, the Royal Institution of Chartered Surveyors, or the Chartered Institute of Arbitrators
- There is provision for joinder of related disputes involving a works contractor
- Except for certain specified items, arbitration may not be commenced until after practical completion, abandonment or termination of the project

216

- The arbitrator's powers are expressly stated
- The parties agree that either may appeal to the High Court on questions of law arising out of an award or may apply to the High Court for a determination of a question of law arising in the course of a reference
- If the arbitrator ceases to act, the parties must forthwith appoint a successor. The new arbitrator may not disregard a direction of the former arbitrator, neither must he vary an award other than the former arbitrator had power to do so, or the parties so agree or the law so allows or requires
- The arbitration must be conducted in accordance with the JCT Arbitration Rules current at the date the management contract was entered into.

Table 5.01:   Contents of JCT Management Contract Summarised

Clause

Section 1:   Intentions of the Parties

1.1	Method of reference to clauses
1.2	Articles etc to be read as a whole
1.3	Definitions
1.4	Co-operation with Professional Team
1.5	Specific obligations of Management Contractor
1.6	Obligations in Third Schedule
1.7	Management Contractor's liability to Employer
1.8	Compliance with Instructions
1.9	Custody and copies of Contract Documents
1.10	Further drawings and details
1.11	Limits to use of documents
1.12	Copies of Works Contracts
1.13	Issue of certificates
1.14	Effect of Final Certificate
1.15	Effect of certificates other than the Final Certificate

Section 2:   Possession and Completion

2.1	Employer's notice requiring Management Contractor to proceed
2.2	Management Contractor not to proceed – deemed determination of Management Contractor's employment
2.3.1	Possession of the site
2.3.2	Deferment of possession
2.3.3	Possession by Management Contractor
2.3.4	Use or occupation by Employer
2.3.5	Insurers – additional premium
2.4	Certificate of Practical Completion
2.5	Schedule of defects – securing the making good of defects
2.6	Certificate of Completion of Making Good Defects
2.7	Frost
2.8	Employer's wish – Management Contractor's consent
2.8.1	Practical Completion – relevant part
2.8.2	Defects etc – relevant part
2.8.3	Insurance – relevant part
2.8.4	Liquidated damages – relevant part
2.9	Failure to secure Project completion – Architect's/Contract Administrator's certificate
2.10	Liquidated and ascertained damages
2.11	Clause 2.9 certificate – cancellation
2.12	Extension of Project Completion Date
2.13	Project Extension Items
2.14	Extension of period or periods for completion of Works Contracts

Section 3:   Control of the Project

3.1	Management personnel of Management Contractor – consent of Architect/Contract Administrator
3.2	Access to Management Contractor's documentation
3.3	Architect's/Contract Administrator's Instructions
3.4	Project Changes – Works Contract Variations – provisional sums in Works Contracts

Table 5.01:   Contents of JCT Management Contract Summarised – (continued)

Table 5.01:   Contents of JCT Management Contract Summarised – (continued)

Clause	
	Value Added Tax – supplemental provisions
5.6	Definitions – VAT Agreement
5.7	Prime Cost – Management Fee – exclusive of VAT
5.8	Possible exemption from VAT
	Finance Act (No.2) Act 1975 – statutory tax deduction scheme
5.9	Definitions
5.10	Whether Employer a "contractor"
5.11	Provision of evidence – tax certificate
5.12.1	Uncertified Management Contractor obtains tax certificate
5.12.2	Expiry of tax certificate
5.12.3	Cancellation of tax certificate
5.13	Vouchers
5.14	Statutory deduction – direct cost of materials
5.15	Correction of errors
5.16	Relation to other clauses
5.17	Application of arbitration agreement

Section 6:   Injury, Damage and Insurance

6.1	Insurance of the Project – insurance of existing structures
6.2	Definitions
6.3	Benefit of Joint Names Policies – Specified Perils – Works Contractors
6.4.1	Joint Names Policy for All Risks Insurance – excesses
6.4.2	Premium receipts and Policy endorsements
6.4.3	Use of annual policy maintained by the Management Contractor – alternative to use of clause 6.4.1 – excesses
6.4.4 to 6.4.9	Loss or damage – insurance claims – Management Contractor's obligations – payment by Employer
6.7	Liability of Management Contractor – personal injury or death – indemnity to Employer
6.8	Liability of Management Contractor – injury or damage to property – indemnity to Employer
6.9	Injury or damage to property – exclusion of the Project and Site Materials
6.10	Management Contractor's and Works Contractor's insurance – personal injury or damage to property
6.11	Insurance – liability etc of Employer
6.12	Excepted Risks
6.13	Effect of war damage
6.14	Compensation for war damage
6.15	Definition of war damage

Section 7:   Determination

7.1	Default by Management Contractor
7.2	Management Contractor becoming insolvent
7.3	Corruption
7.4	Determination of employment of Management Contractor – rights and duties of Employer and Management Contractor
7.5	Acts etc, giving ground for determination of employment by Management Contractor
7.6	Determination of employment by Management Contractor under clause 7.5 – rights and duties of Employer and Management Contractor

Table 5.01: Contents of JCT Management Contract Summarised – (continued)

Clause	
7.7	Grounds for determination of employment of Management Contractor by Employer or Management Contractor
7.8	Specified Perils – negligence etc by Management Contractor
7.9	Rights and duties of Employer and Management Contractor
7.10	Employer's option
7.11	Determination under clause 7.10 – rights and duties of Employer and Management Contractor
7.12	Determination before Construction Period
7.13	Determination after Construction Period

Section 8:   Works Contracts

8.1	Items of work – Works Contractors
8.2.1	Selection of Works Contractors – terms of Works Contracts
8.2.2	Nominated suppliers to Works Contractors
8.3	Duties required from Management Contractor under Works Contracts
8.4	Final payment to Works Contractor
	Loss and expense caused by matters materially affecting regular progress – Works Contracts (8.5)

Section 9:   Settlement of Disputes – Arbitration

9.1	Dispute or difference – appointment of Arbitrator
9.2	Arbitration – joinder
9.3	Time of opening of arbitration
9.4	Powers of Arbitrator
9.5	Award final and binding
9.6	Appeals – questions of law
9.7	Proper law of the Contract

APPENDIX: PART 1
APPENDIX: PART 2

SUPPLEMENTAL PROVISIONS (the VAT Agreement)

SCHEDULES

First	**Description of the Project**
Second	**Definition of Prime Cost payable to the Management Contractor** – see Article 2 and clause 4.1
Third	**The services provided or to be provided by the Management Contractor pursuant to Article 1 (paras 1 to 53)**
Fourth	**List of Project Drawings**
Fifth	**Site facilities and services to be provided by the Management Contractor: Second Recital and clause 1.5.4**

Table 5.02: JCT Form of Management Contract – Time Chart

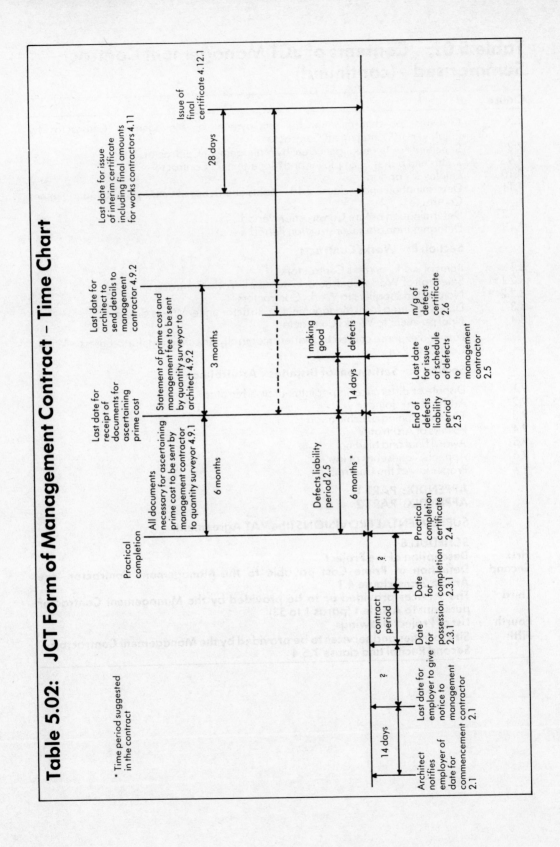

* Time period suggested in the contract

Architect notifies employer of date for commencement contractor 2.1

14 days

Last date for employer to give notice to management contractor 2.1

?

Date for possession completion 2.3.1

contract period

Date for completion 2.3.1

?

Practical completion certificate 2.4

Practical completion

All documents necessary for ascertaining prime cost to be sent by management contractor to quantity surveyor 4.9.1

Last date for receipt of documents for ascertaining prime cost

6 months

Statement of prime cost and management fee to be sent by quantity surveyor to architect 4.9.2

Last date for architect to send details to management contractor 4.9.2

3 months

Last date for issue of interim certificate including final amounts for works contractors 4.11

28 days

Issue of final certificate 4.12.1

Defects liability period 2.5

6 months *

End of defects liability period 2.5

14 days

Last date for issue of schedule of defects to management contractor 2.5

defects

making good

m/g of defects certificate 2.6

Table 5.03: Architect's Powers under JCT Form of Management Contract

Clause	Power	Comment
1.5.4	Instruct the management contractor to secure site facilities and services	
2.7	Certify that frost damage appearing after practical completion is due to injury that took place before practical completion	Otherwise the management contractor is not liable for the cost of making good such frost damage
2.12.2	Fix a completion date earlier than previously fixed	If fair and reasonable having regard to omission of work or obligations. Must be done in writing
2.14	Express dissent from the management contractor's decision in respect of extensions of a works contract period	Must be in writing before management contractor is required to notify the works contractor of his decision in accordance with the works contract
3.1	Consent to the number and names of salaried staff and operatives to be employed by the management contractor	On site or in connection with the project as listed by the management contractor
	Consent to the replacement, addition or deletion of such staff	Not to be unreasonably withheld
3.2	Have access to all documentation of the management contractor related to the project	To the extent necessary for proper execution of the project or ascertainment of any payment due
3.3.2	Confirm an oral instruction	Within 7 days or of no effect
3.4	Issue instructions requiring project changes or works contract variations	Without prejudice to the generality of clause 3.3.1

Table 5.03:   Architect's Powers under JCT Form of Management Contract – (continued)

Clause	Power	Comment
3.5	Issue postponement instructions in regard to any work to be executed under the contract provisions	
3.9	Request the management contractor to provide vouchers	To prove that the materials and goods comply with clause 3.8.1
3.10	Instruct the management contractor to open up for inspection or carry out tests	Shall be at no cost to the employer if work is not in accordance with the contract
3.11	Instruct the management contractor to remove from site work or goods not in accordance with the provisions of clause 3.8	Removal shall, subject to clauses 3.21 and 3.22, be at no cost to the employer
3.12	Issuing instructions requiring any defect, shrinkage or other fault appearing or discovered at any time to be made good	Whenever the architect considers it necessary and if due to material, goods or workmanship not being in accordance with the contract or to frost occurring before practical completion
3.13	Approve manager on site or approve his change	Not to be unreasonably withheld
3.14	Issue instructions ordering removal of project manager and replacement by suitable person	Not unreasonably or vexatiously
	Approve person proposed by the management contractor as replacement manager	Not to be unreasonably withheld
3.15	Consent to removal of goods and materials unfixed from site	Must be in writing and must not be unreasonably withheld

Table 5.03: Architect's Powers under JCT Form of Management Contract – (continued)

Clause	Power	Comment
3.17	Access to the site of the project, to workshops or other places where work is being prepared for the project	At all reasonable times subject to reasonable restrictions of management contractor necessary to protect any proprietary right in such work
3.18	Direct the clerk of works	Clerk of work duty to act solely as an inspector on behalf of the employer
6.11.1	Instruct the management contractor to take out and maintain a joint names policy for the amount of indemnity in the appendix	If the appendix states that clause 6.11 insurance may be required by the employer
6.13.2	Issue instructions requiring the management contractor to remove and/or dispose of any debris and so on and execute specified protective work	If the project sustains war damage
7.1	Serve a default notice on the management contractor	If the management contractor suspends the work without reasonable cause or fails to proceed regularly and diligently or refuses or persistently neglects to remove defective work and so on and thereby the project is materially affected or if he fails to comply with the provisions of clauses 3.19 or 3.28 to 3.35 inclusive
7.13	In writing require the management contractor to remove from the site temporary buildings and so on belonging to or hired by him	In the event of determination taking place after issue by employer of clause 2.1 notice to proceed
7.4.2.1	Require the management contractor to assign to employer benefit of any agreement for the supply of materials or goods	Only to the extent that they are assignable *and* the supplier or works contractor may make reasonable objections to further assignment
7.4.3	In writing require the management contractor to remove from the site temporary	If the management contractor does not comply within a reasonable time, the employer may remove and sell them. The management

Table 5.03: Architect's Powers under JCT Form of Management Contract – (continued)

Clause	Power	Comment
	buildings and so on belonging to or hired by him	contractor must not remove them before the receipt of architect's instruction
8.2.1	Agree in writing with the management contractor the works contractors to carry out items of work identified in the contract cost plan or in architect's instructions	To be confirmed by architect's instruction
8.4	Issue an interim certificate including an amount to cover the final payment to the works contractor	If the works contractor so requests *and* the employer wishes such final payment to be made before final payment to the management contractor *and* the works contractor against any latent defects

Table 5.04: Architect's Duties under JCT Form of Management Contract

Clause	Duty	Comment
1.9	Provide the management contractor with one copy certified on behalf of the employer of the contract documents	Immediately after the execution of the contract (unless previously provided) without charge to the management contractor
1.10	Provide the management contractor with copies of such further drawings and so on	Without the charge to the management contractor. The reproduction methods to be agreed in writing with the management contractor
1.11	Preserve the confidentiality of rates or prices	
1.13	Issue certificates to the employer and duplicates to the management contractor	Except where specifically provided otherwise
2.4	Certify practical completion	When of the opinion that it has been achieved
2.5	Deliver a schedule of defects to the management contractor specifying defects and so on that appear during the defects liability period	Not later than 14 days after the end of the defects liability period
2.6	Certify making good of defects	When the architects is of the opinion that the defects and so on he required to be made good have been so
2.8	Issue on behalf of the employer a written statement identifying the part or parts taken into possession giving the date	If before practical completion, the employer with management contractor's consent takes possession of part of the project
2.9	Issue a certificate Issue a written cancellation of the clause 2.9 certificate and issue a further certificate	If the management contractor fails to secure completion of the project by the completion date If extension of time is made after issue of clause 2.9 certificate

Table 5.04: Architect's Duties under JCT Form of Management Contract – (continued)

Clause	Duty	Comment
2.12.1	Give the management contractor in writing a fair and reasonable extension of time as soon as he is able to estimate the length of delay beyond completion date	If the architect is of the opinion that the completion of the project is likely to be delayed beyond the completion date *and* if the delaying items are project extension items *and* if the contractor has used his best endeavours to avoid or remedy the delay
3.3.1	Issue in writing such instructions as are reasonably necessary to enable the management contractor properly to discharge his obligations	
3.3.3	Specify in writing the provision within the contract which empowers the issue of instruction by the management contractor to the works contractor	If so requested by the management contractor
3.4	Shall issue instructions in regard to the expenditure of provisional sums in Works Contracts	Without prejudice to the generality of clause 3.3.1
3.6.3	Set out the exact nature of the desire of the employer in regard to the completion date as referred to in clause 3.6.2	If the employer causes the architect to issue a preliminary instruction to accelerate or alter sequence or timing of work
3.6.4	Re-issue the preliminary instruction	If the management contractor or any works contractor makes reasonable objection to compliance and after variation if not withdrawn
3.7	Determine levels that may be required and provide accurately dimensioned drawings	The management contractor is responsible for setting out the project
3.27	Issue instructions regarding antiquities	On receipt of the management contractor's notice under clause 3.26.3

Table 5.04: Architect's Duties under JCT Form of Management Contract – (continued)

Clause	Duty	Comment
4.2	Issue interim certificates stating the amount due to the management contractor from the employer according to the rules contained in clauses 4.5 to 4.8	During the period stated
4.8.2	Prepare a statement total retention in respect of management contractor and total retention in respect of each works contractor	At the date of each interim certificate. Statement to be issued to the management contractor. Architect may instruct the quantity surveyor to issue this
4.9.2	Send a copy of the statement of prime cost and management fee of the project to the management contractor	After receipt from quantity surveyor. If the statement refers to any disallowance of costs there shall be included the reasons for such disallowance
4.11	Issue an interim certificate to include finally adjusted works contract sums	Not less than 28 days before the issue of the final certificate
4.12.1	Issue the final certificate	Not later than 2 months from the latest of the end of the defects liability period or the certificate of making good defects under clause 2.6 or receipt from the clause 4.9.2 statement
5.3	Issue instructions regarding divergence between statutory requirements and contract documents or variations instructions	If the management submits written notice or if the architect otherwise discovers. Instructions must be issued within 7 days and management contractor is entitled to payment as for a variation
6.4.1.2	Notify the employer of the amount of any excess in respect of each insurance risk in the policy	On receipt of notification from the management contractor
6.6.1	*Either* inform the management contractor that no liquidated damages insurances is required *or* instruct the management contractor to obtain a quotation for such insurance	If it is stated in the appendix that liquidated damages insurance may be required

Table 5.04: Architect's Duties under JCT Form of Management Contract – (continued)

Clause	Duty	Comment
	Obtain from the employer any further information that the management contractor reasonably requires to obtain the quotation	
	Instruct the management contractor whether or not the employer wishes the management contractor to accept the quotation	After receipt of quotation from the management contractor. The instruction is not to be unreasonably withheld or delayed
6.13.3	Fix such later completion date as in his opinion is fair and reasonable	If the project sustains war damage
7.4.4	Certify the amount of expenses properly incurred by the employer and the amount of direct loss and/or damage caused to the employer by the determination	If the employer determines certification must take place upon completion and verification within a reasonable time of the accounts for the completion of the project
8.2.1	Issue an instruction in writing to the management contractor confirming the identities of the works contractors	After agreement in writing between the architect and management contractor
8.3.2	Direct the management contractor as to the amounts in respect of each works contractor	On the issue of each interim certificate
8.3.3	Inform a works contractor directly of the amount included in each relevant interim certificate	If the works contractor so requests at the commencement of work
8.3.4	Consent to the management contractor issuing a practical completion certificate to the works contractor	When in the opinion of the architect practical completion of the works contractor's work is achieved. Management contractor must pass on all notification from works contractor under clause 2.13 of the works contract

Table 5.04: Architect's Duties under JCT Form of Management Contract – (continued)

Clause	Duty	Comment
8.5	Ascertain or instruct the quantity surveyor to ascertain the amount of loss and/or expense incurred by the works contractor	In collaboration with the management contractor. If the management contractor passes a copy of the works contractor's written application together with the management contractor's comments and if the architect considers regular progress of the works contract or part thereof has been or is likely to be affected as referred to in works contract clause 4.45

Table 5.05: Management Contractor's Powers under JCT Standard Form of Management Contract

Clause	Power	Comment
1.8	Not to comply or secure compliance with an architect's instruction	If the instruction requires a Works Contract variation as defined in clause 1.3 paragraph 2 *and* the management contractor has submitted to the architect a reasonable written objection to compliance received from the works contractor
2.3.4	Consent in writing to the employer's use or occupation of the site or part thereof before issue of practical completion certificate	Before consent is given, insurers must be notified under clauses 6.4.1.1 or 6.4.3.1 for confirmation that such use will not prejudice the insurance. Subject to such assurance the consent must not be withheld unreasonably
2.8	Consent to the employer taking possession of any part or parts of the project before practical completion	Not to be unreasonably withheld
3.3.2	Confirm an oral instruction	Within seven days or of no effect unless architect confirms
3.6.4	Make a reasonable objection to instruction to alter sequence of timing	Preliminary instruction may be withdrawn or varied to meet such objections
3.17	Impose reasonable restrictions on access of the professional team to the site and workshops or other places where work is being prepared	As are necessary to protect any proprietary right of the management contractor or any works contractor in such work
3.19	Assign the contract	With the employer's consent
3.21.3	Deduct from amounts payable to a works contractor under interim certificates amounts equal to the claims made by other works contractors referred to in clause 3.21.1.3 which the management contractor has paid or is liable to pay	If the works contractor is in breach

Table 5.05: Management Contractor's Powers under JCT Standard Form of Management Contract – (continued)

Clause	Power	Comment
3.24	Consent to the execution of work not forming part of the contract by employer's men	If the information is not in the contract documents. Consent must not be unreasonably withheld
4.8.3	Request the employer to place retention held on an interim certificate in a separate bank account so designated as to identify the amount of retention held by the employer on trust and to certify to the architect with a copy to the management contractor that the amount has been so placed	At the date of payment of each interim certificate. This clause does not apply if the employer is a local authority
6.4.8.1	Determine his employment	Within 28 days of occurrence of clause 6.4.4 loss or damage. It must be just and equitable to do so, and 7 days' notice must be given during which time either party may request arbitration
6.5.3	Reasonably require the employer to produce documentary evidence and receipts	To show that clause 6.5 insurance has been taken out
	Take out and maintain joint names policy. Right of entry and inspection	If employer defaults in respect of any risk. To make inventory of existing structure and contents
6.6.1	Reasonably require further information to obtain a quotation	If the architect instructs the management contractor to obtain liquidated damages insurance
6.10.1.2	Chose a greater sum than that stated in the appendix	In respect of personal injury or death, or injury or damage to property insurance
7.5.1	Serve default notice on the employer	If he does not pay the management contractor the amounts properly due on any certificate within 14 days of the issue of the certificate

Table 5.05: Management Contractor's Powers under JCT Standard Form of Management Contract – (continued)

Clause	Power	Comment
7.5.3	Forthwith determine his employment under the contract	If: The employer does not comply with a default notice under clause 7.5.1 within 7 days; or The employer interferes with or obstructs any certificate; or The carrying out of substantially the whole of the project is suspended for a period stated in the appendix by reason of: Architect's instructions under clause 3.4 or 3.5; or late instructions; or employer's men; or opening up or testing; or access; or employer becomes bankrupt
7.7	Forthwith determine his employment under the contract	If: The carrying out of substantially the whole of the project is suspended for a period stated in the appendix by reason of *force majeure*; or loss by a specified peril; or civil commotion
8.2	Agree in writing with the architect the works contractors to carry out items of work identified in the contract cost plan or in architect's instructions	To be confirmed by architect's instruction
8.3.4	Issue a certificate of practical completion to the works contractor	With the architect's consent
9.1	Agree to a person to act as arbitrator	If the employer requests the management contractor to concur in the appointment
	Request the employer to concur in the appointment of an arbitrator	If a dispute or difference arises
	Request the appointment of an arbitrator by the person named in the appendix	If the employer will not concur
9.2	Require the dispute or difference under this contract to be referred to a different arbitrator	If there is a related dispute under: works contract 3; or any works contract; or nominated supplier contract; and the management contractor reasonably considers that the arbitrator appointed is not qualified to determine the dispute

Table 5.06: Management Contractor's Duties under JCT Standard Form of Management Contract

Clause	Duty	Comment
1.4	Collaborate with the professional team as stated in article 1	Subject to the conditions
1.5.1	Prepare programmes for the project	
1.5.2	Enter into works contracts so that they can be completed in good time	
1.5.3	Ensure that works contractor items are in accordance with the contract, to the reasonable satisfaction of the architect where so stated	
1.5.4	Provide site facilities	As listed in the fifth schedule or agreed with or instructed by the architect
1.5.5	Provide continual supervision and do everything necessary for the organisation and management of the project	
1.5.6	Ensure project is carried out in an economical and quick way in accordance with the contract	
1.5.7	Keep such records as will enable the quantity surveyor to verify the prime cost of the project	Must be kept in the form prescribed by or agreed with the quantity surveyor
1.6	Carry out the specific obligations listed in the third schedule	Without prejudice to the generality of clause 1.5
1.8	Forthwith comply or secure compliance with instructions issued by the architect	Unless the management contractor has submitted an objection from a works contractor to an instruction requiring a

Table 5.06: Management Contractor's Duties under JCT Standard Form of Management Contract – (continued)

Clause	Duty	Comment
		clause 1.3 paragraph 2 Works Contract variation
	Submit to the architect any written objections of a works contractor to compliance with a variation instruction under Works Contract clause 3.4.1	Management contractor need not comply or secure compliance to the extent that the objection is reasonable
1.11	Use all contract and contractual documents only for the purposes of the contract	
1.12	Provide the architect with one certified copy of the Works Contract	Immediately after the execution of each Works Contract
2.3.1	Secure the commencement, the regular and diligent progress and the completion of the project before completion date	On receiving possession of the site from the employer after notice to proceed
2.3.3	Retain possession of the site up to the date of practical completion	For insurance purposes subject to clause 2.8 and the remainder of clause 2.3
2.3.4	Notify insurers for confirmation that employer's use or occupation of the site will prejudice insurance under clause 6.4.1.1 or 6.4.3.1	Before giving consent to such use or occupation if the employer does not so notify
2.3.5	Notify the employer of the amount of additional premium	If the insurers require such premium as a condition of the confirmation requested in clause 2.3.4. If the employer continues to require use or occupation, the management contractor is entitled to reimbursement for the premium as prime cost under schedule 2
	Pay any additional premium required	If the employer continues to require use or occupation under clause 2.3.4

Table 5.06: Management Contractor's Duties under JCT Standard Form of Management Contract – (continued)

Clause	Duty	Comment
2.5	Make good defects in the schedule of defects within a reasonable time	Defects must have appeared within the defects liability period, *and* be due to materials or workmanship not in accordance with the contract or frost occurring before practical completion, *and* be notified not later than 14 days after the end of the defects liability period
2.7	Make good damage by frost appearing after practical completion	If the architect certifies that it is due to injury taking place before practical completion
2.10	Pay liquidated damages to the employer	If the employer requires in writing not later than the final certificate *and* provided that the architect has issued his certificate in accordance with clause 2.9
2.12.1	Forthwith advise the architect of the cause of the delay	Upon it becoming reasonably apparent that the completion date is not likely to be or has not been achieved Note that the management contractor must do this even if he does not intend to claim any extension of time
2.14	Notify the architect of any proposed decision on extensions of works contract periods	Must be done in sufficient time for the architect to express written dissent, if he wishes, before the management contractor must notify the works contractor in accordance with Works Contract clauses 2.3 and 2.4
3.1	Obtain the consent of the architect to the number and names of the salaried staff and number of operatives to be employed on site	Unless previously agreed
	Obtain the consent of the architect to the replacement, addition or deletion of such staff	The consent is not to be unreasonably withheld

Table 5.06: Management Contractor's Duties under JCT Standard Form of Management Contract – (continued)

Clause	Duty	Comment
3.3.3	Request the architect to specify in writing the provision empowering an instruction Deliver to the works contractor a copy of the architect's answer	If so required by a works contractor
3.6.5	Inform the architect in writing in respect of each works contractor affected by the instruction: *Either* the lump sum required by the works contractor, or it is not reasonably practicable so to state and the cost must be ascertained in accordance with the relevant works contract conditions *And either* the earlier (than current) completion date which can become the contract completion date, or the extent to which an extension of time otherwise due can be cancelled or reduced and the resulting completion date become the contract completion date	As soon as reasonably practicable after receipt of a preliminary or reissued (under clause 3.6.4) instruction accelerating or altering the sequence or timing of any work
3.7	Set out the project	Architect must provide levels and accurately dimensioned drawings. Management contractor must correct errors at his own cost
3.8.1	Provide or secure materials and goods of kinds and standards in project specification or any bills of quantities or specification in any Works Contract	Only so far as procurable. Must be to reasonable satisfaction of the architect to the extent required in the project specification or clause 1.5.3
3.8.2	Provide or secure workmanship of standards in project specification or any bills of quantities or specification in any works contract or, if no standards described, to a standard appropriate to the project	Must be to reasonable satisfaction of the architect to the extent required in the project specification or clause 1.5.3

Table 5.06: Management Contractor's Duties under JCT Standard Form of Management Contract – (continued)

Clause	Duty	Comment
3.9	Secure the provision of vouchers to prove the goods and so on comply with clause 3.8.1	If the architect so requests
3.12	Comply or secure compliance with architect's instruction requiring defects to be made good	Within a reasonable time after receipt of such instructions
3.13	Constantly keep a competent manager on site	Must be approved by the architect and must not be changed without the architect's prior approval. Instructions given to the manager are deemed to have been given to the management contractor
3.14	Propose the name of a replacement manager	If the architect orders removal of the manager
3.15	Not to allow unfixed goods and so on intended for the project to be removed therefrom	Unless the architect gives his written consent. If goods and so on have become the property of the employer, the management contractor remains responsible for loss or damage
3.16	Not to allow off-site goods and so on to be removed except for use on the project	If the works contractor has been paid for them and the management contractor has been paid and the property has passed to the employer
3.18	Give every reasonable facility to enable the clerk of works to carry out his duties	
3.21.1.1	Take all necessary steps to operate the terms of the works contract for dealing with a breach of the works contract by the works contractor including arbitration or litigation to obtain damages due to the management contractor and the employer	If there is any breach of the works contract by a works contractor or a determination under works contract clause 7.1 to 7.5. In consultation with the architect and the employer

Table 5.06: Management Contractor's Duties under JCT Standard Form of Management Contract – (continued)

Clause	Duty	Comment
3.21.1.2	Secure the satisfactory completion of the Works Contract works	After a works contractor's breach. A further works contractor may be engaged for the purpose if the Works Contract so provides or a Works Contract of employment has been determined
3.21.1.3	Meet any claim under Works Contracts by works contractors in respect of delays or disturbance caused to them by the breach	Applies to works contractors other than the one in breach
3.21.3	Seek to recover any shortfall in reimbursement from a works contractor in breach through arbitration or litigation if necessary	To the extent that the management contractor is not reimbursed by deductions under clause 8.3.2. If the management contractor is not successful in recovering, the employer must pay him the shortfall
3.22.1	Immediately inform the architect	If the works contractor alleges a breach of the Works Contract by the management contractor and makes a claim therefor
3.22.2	Take all such action as may be necessary including, on legal advice, settlement or defence of the claim Pay the works contractor the amount of any settlement, award or judgment including any costs	Subject to any instructions from the architect
3.23	Permit the execution of work by the employer or his employees and so on	Provided that: the work does not form part of the contract *and* the contract documents provide sufficient information to enable the management contractor to secure the carrying out and completion of the project
3.26	Forthwith: Leave antiquities undisturbed, take all necessary steps to preserve and inform the architect or clerk of works	On discovery

Table 5.06: Management Contractor's Duties under JCT Standard Form of Management Contract – (continued)

Clause	Duty	Comment
4.8.2	Issue a statement setting out the total amount of retention held in respect of each works contractor	At the date of each interim certificate
4.8.3	Inform each works contractor that retention money has been placed by the employer in a separate bank account properly designated	Applies to works contractors in respect of whom the employer is holding retention The employer must certify to the architect with a copy to the management contractor
4.9.1	Provide the quantity surveyor with all documents necessary to ascertain the prime cost of the project	Not later than six months after practical completion
5.1	Secure compliance with and give all notices required by statutory requirements	
5.2	Inform the architect immediately of any divergence between the statutory requirements and any documents referred to in clause 1.9 and 1.10	
5.4.1	Secure the supply of such limited materials and workmanship as reasonably necessary	If the management contractor has to comply with statutory requirements as an emergency measure
5.4.2	Forthwith inform the architect	Of the emergency and the steps being taken
5.11	*Either* Provide evidence to the employer of entitlement to payment without statutory deduction *or* inform employer in writing, copy to architect, that he is not entitled to be paid without deduction	Not later than 21 days: Before first contractual payment, or after the employer has become a contractor

Table 5.06: Management Contractor's Duties under JCT Standard Form of Management Contract – (continued)

Clause	Duty	Comment
5.12.1	Inform employer if he gets tax certificate	If previously not entitled to payment without deduction. Deduction not made thereafter
5.12.2	Provide evidence to employer of entitlement to payment without statutory deduction	If tax certificate expires before final payment due, management contractor must take action at least 28 days before expiry. if not satisfied, employer will make deduction
	Inform the employer in writing of the cessation of entitlement after expiry of certificate	
5.12.3	Immediately write to employer	If tax certificate is cancelled
6.3	Ensure that the joint names policy in clauses 6.4.1.1 or 6.4.3.1 *either:* provide for recognition of each works contractor as insured; or includes a waiver of subrogation against the works contractor	If clause 6.5 applies, policy in clause 6.5.3 also affected in respect of loss or damage by specified perils to his works and site materials or existing structures as applicable
6.4.1.1	Insure in joint names against loss or damage to the project and site materials for all risks	Excludes temporary buildings and so on owned or hired by the management contractor or any works contractor
6.4.1.2	Notify the architect of the amount of any excess in respect of each insurance risk in the policy	Before taking out the joint names policy
6.4.2	Send to the architect for deposit with the employer the policy and premium receipts	
6.4.4	Forthwith give written notice to architect and employer stating extent, nature and location of damage	On discovering loss or damage under clause 6.4.1.1 or 6.4.3.1

Table 5.06: Management Contractor's Duties under JCT Standard Form of Management Contract – (continued)

Clause	Duty	Comment
6.4.6	With due diligence secure restoration of damaged works and so on dispose of debris and carry out and complete the project	After damage under clause 6.4.1.1 or 6.4.3.1 and the insurers have completed any required inspection
6.4.7	Authorise the insurers to pay insurance monies in respect of clause 6.4.1.1 or 6.4.3.1 damage to the employer	
6.4.9.2	Secure the restoration, replacement or repair of loss or damage by a works contractor appointed in accordance with a clause 8.1 instruction	Where clause 6.4.9.1 is not applicable
6.6.1	Take out and maintain liquidated damages insurance until practical completion. Send policy, premium receipts and any relevant endorsements to the architect for deposit with the employer	If: the appendix states that such insurance may be required by the employer; and the architect instructs the management contractor to obtain a quotation for such insurance, and the architect instructs the management contractor to accept the quotation
6.7	Indemnify the employer against any claim in respect of personal injury or death	Arising out of the carrying out of the contract unless due to employer's act or neglect
6.8	Indemnify the employer against any claim and so on in respect of injury or damage to real or personal property	Arising out of the carrying out of the contract and to the extent due to contractor's negligence and so on
6.10.1.1	Maintain and cause all works contractors to maintain insurance against personal injury or death and damage to real or personal property	
6.10.2	Send and cause any works contractor to send to the architect for inspection by the	If so required by the employer but not unreasonably or vexatiously

Table 5.06: Management Contractor's Duties under JCT Standard Form of Management Contract – (continued)

Clause	Duty	Comment
	employer evidence of insurance and premium receipts	
6.11.1	Take out and maintain a joint names policy against claims against employer due to collapse and so on of property other than the project	If the appendix states that the employer may require the insurance *and* the architect so instructs
6.11.2	Send to the architect for deposit with the employer the policy and premium receipts	
6.13.3	Secure the reinstatement of the war damage and carry out/ complete the project	If war damage sustained
7.1	Comply with a default notice from the architect	
7.4.2.1	Assign to the employer without payment the benefit of any agreement for work or materials	If so required by the employer within 14 days of the date of determination; *and* provided that the determination is not due to winding up. To the extent that the agreements are assignable. A supplier or works contractor is entitled to object to any further assignment by the employer
7.4.3	Remove from the site any temporary buildings and so on	After the employer has determined and as and when required to do so by the architect
7.4.4	Allow or pay to the employer direct loss and/or expense after determination	To be taken into account when the architect makes a final certification of monies after determination
7.6.1	Remove from site all temporary buildings, etc and give facilities to works contractors to do the same	With reasonable dispatch and with due precautions to prevent injury, death or damage
7.11.2	Assign to the employer the benefit of any agreement for work or materials	If so required by the employer within 14 days of the date of determination. To the extent that the agreements are assignable. A supplier or

Table 5.06: Management Contractor's Duties under JCT Standard Form of Management Contract – (continued)

Clause	Duty	Comment
		works contractor is entitled to make reasonable objection to any further assignment by the employer
7.13	Remove from site all temporary buildings and so on and when required by the architect in writing	If determination under clause 7.10 taking place after the employer has issued a notice to proceed
8.2.1	Only to employ works contractors who will: ● enter into JCT works contract and execute such contract under seal if the management contract is under seal; *and* ● enter into JCT employer/ works contractors agreement and execute such agreement under seal if the works contract is under seal	If so required
8.2.2	Send the architect any submissions by a works contractor	In respect of restrictions and so on in a proposed contract of sale between works contractor and nominated supplier
	Confirm architect's approval of restrictions and so on to works contractor	Immediately it is received by the management contractor
8.3.1	Fulfil all duties required of the management contractor by the works contract	
8.3.4	Immediately inform the architect of works contract clause 2.13 notification from works contractors of practical completion of their work Include observations on the notification	Management contractor may issue the practical completion certificate with the consent of the architect
8.5	Pass any written application of the works contractor under works contract clause 4.45 to the architect together with the management contractor's comments	On receipt from a works contractor

Table 5.07: Employer's Powers under JCT Standard Form of Management Contract

Clause	Power	Comment
2.3.2	Defer the giving of possession	Where clause 2.3.2 is stated in the appendix to apply. Deferment period must not exceed six weeks
2.3.4	Use or occupy the site of the project or part thereof before the date of practical completion	With the management contractor's consent in writing
2.3.5	Continue to require use or occupation under clause 2.3.4. Request the management contractor to provide premium receipt	After being notified of additional premium payable to insurers
2.8	Take possession of part of the project	With the management contractor's consent
2.10	In writing require the management contractor to pay or allow liquidated damages for the period between completion date and practical completion or recover the liquidated damages as a debt	If the architect has issued a certificate under clause 2.9 *and* the employer acts before the date of the final certificate
3.6.2	Cause the architect to issue a preliminary instruction under clause 3.6.3	If the employer desires *either* an earlier completion date than current *or* the cancellation or reduction of length of an extension of time
3.18	Appoint a clerk of works	His duties are purely that of inspector on behalf of the employer under the direction of the architect
3.19	Assign the contract	With the management contractor's consent
3.20	Assign the right to bring proceedings to enforce any term of the contract made for the benefit of the employer	To any transferee or lessee to whom the employer may transfer his freehold or grant a leasehold interest in the project. At any time after practical completion. If the appendix states that clause 3.20 applies

Table 5.07: Employer's Powers under JCT Standard Form of Management Contract – (continued)

Clause	Power	Comment
3.23	Carry out or employ others to carry out work	If the work does not form part of the contract *and* the contract documents contain enough information to enable the management contractor to complete the project in accordance with the contract
3.24	Carry out or employ others to carry out work	If the work does not form part of the contract *and* the contract documents do not provide sufficient information *but* the management contractor agrees
3.28.7	Require proof of rates of wages and hours observed by the management contractor and works contractors	If he has grounds for believing that the requirements of clause 3.28 are not being observed. This clause only applies where stated in the appendix and the employer is a local authority
4.3.2	Make deductions from money due under any interim certificate	If the right exists under the provisions of the contract and even though retention money is held
4.7	Deduct and retain as retention: 3 per cent of amount subject to retention before practical completion; 1.5 per cent of amount subject to retention between practical completion and making good defects	Half the retention must be released in the interim certificate following practical completion, the other half must be released in the interim certificate following the issue of the making good of defects certificate
6.4.1.2	Require alteration to the amounts of excess in respect of insurance risks	Insurers must agree
6.4.3.2	Inspect documentary evidence or the policy	If the management contractor maintains a policy independently of his obligations under the contract and it is in joint names in respect of the project
6.4.8	Determine his employment	Within 28 days of occurrence of clause 6.4.4 loss or damage. It must be just and equitable to do so *and* seven days' notice must be given during which time either party may request arbitration

Table 5.07: Employer's Powers under JCT Standard Form of Management Contract – (continued)

Clause	Power	Comment
6.6.4	Insure against liquidated damages loss	If the management contractor fails to insure
6.10.2	Reasonably require the management contractor to send and cause any works contractor to send to the architect for inspection by the employer documentary evidence and premium receipts	
6.10.3	Insure and deduct premium amounts from monies due to the management contractor or recover them as a debt	If the management contractor fails to insure against personal injury or death or injury to real or personal property
6.11.2	Approve insurers	In regard to clause 6.11.1 insurance
6.11.3	Take out insurance against employer's liability for damage to property other than the project	If the management contractor fails to insure
7.1	Forthwith determine the management contractor's employment under the contract	If the management contractor continues his default for 14 days after receipt of a default notice from the architect under this clause or if the management contractor repeats the default at any time thereafter. Notice of determination must be given within 10 days after continuance or repetition
7.2	Reinstate the management contractors' employment	If the management contractor, his liquidator and so on agree after automatic determination
7.3	Forthwith determine the management contractor's employment under the contract	If the management contractor has committed a corrupt act
7.4.1	Employ and pay other persons to carry out and complete the project	After the employer has determined the management contractor's employment. The other persons or the employer have the right to enter the site and use all temporary plant and so on belonging to the management contractor

Table 5.07: Employer's Powers under JCT Standard Form of Management Contract – (continued)

Clause	Power	Comment
7.4.2.1	Require the management contractor to assign to him without payment the benefit of any agreement for goods or work	Must be done within 14 days of the date of determination and the works contractors or suppliers have the right of reasonable objection to further assignment by the employer
7.4.2.2	Pay any supplier or works contractor for goods or work	If not already paid by the management contractor. Does not apply in the case of bankruptcy and so on
7.4.3	Remove and sell the management contractor's temporary buildings and so on holding the proceeds less all the costs to his credit	If the management contractor does not remove within a reasonable time. The employer is not responsible for loss or damage
7.7	Forthwith determine the management contractor's employment under the contract	If the carrying out of substantially the whole of the project is suspended for a period stated in the appendix by reason of *force majeure* or loss by a specified peril or civil commotion
7.10	Forthwith by notice in writing determine the management contractor's employment under the contract	At any time
7.11.2	Require the management contractor to assign him the benefits of any agreements for goods or work	Must be done within 14 days of the date of determination and the works contractors and suppliers have the right of reasonable objection to any further assignment by the employer
8.2	Agree with the management contractor/works contractors who are not required to observe the provisions of clause 8.2	
8.4	Secure final payment to works contractors	If requested by the works contractor and he indemnifies the management contractor for latent defects
9.1	Agree to a person to act as arbitrator	If the management contractor requests the employer to concur in the appointment

Table 5.07: Employer's Powers under JCT Standard Form of Management Contract – (continued)

Clause	Power	Comment
	Request the management contractor to concur in the appointment of an arbitrator	If a dispute or difference arises
	Request the appointment of an arbitrator by the person named in the appendix	If the management contractor will not concur
9.2	Require the dispute or difference under this contract to be referred to a different arbitrator	If there is a related dispute under Works Contract/3 or any works contract or nominated supplier contract *and* the employer reasonably considers that the arbitrator appointed is not appropriately qualified to determine the dispute under the management contract

Table 5.08: Employer's Duties under JCT Standard Form of Management Contract

Clause	Duty	Comment
1.11	Preserve the confidentiality of the rates or prices in the contract cost plan or any works contract and the management fee in the appendix	
2.1	Give written notice to the management contractor stating whether or not he is to continue collaboration with the professional team and to proceed to set out and secure the carrying out and completion of the project	Not later than 14 days from the date of the architect's written notice to the management contractor of the date it will be practicable to commence construction
	Initial any alterations made to the third schedule, initial the fifth schedule, sign and date the appendix part 2	If the employer's written notice requires the management contractor to proceed
2.2	Pay the management contractor the amounts due computed in accordance with clause 7.6	Within the period stated in the appendix from the latest date when the employer's notice to proceed might have been given. This payment is made if *either* the employer's notice states that the management contractor is not to proceed *or* the employer fails to notify the management contractor in accordance with clause 2.1. The employment of the management contractor will be deemed to be determined
2.3.1	Give possession of the site to the management contractor	If the employer gives the notice to proceed under clause 2.1
2.11	Pay or repay the management contractor any amounts recovered, allowed or paid in respect of liquidated damages	If the architect's certificate of non-completion is cancelled. The effect of any further certificate of non-completion must be taken into account
3.6.6	Cause the architect to issue an instruction: confirming acceleration, alteration of sequence or timing including any required changes in works contract periods *and* fixing the completion date	If the employer has received the information given to the architect under clause 3.6.5 *and* he wishes to pay the amounts in clauses 3.6.5.1 *and* he accepts the completion date stated by the management contractor under clause 3.6.5.2

Table 5.08:   Employer's Duties under JCT Standard Form of Management Contract – (continued)

Clause	Duty	Comment
3.21.2.1	Pay the management contractor amounts incurred in carrying out obligations following breach of the works contract by a works contractor	In accordance with the payments clauses and second schedule but subject to the employer's right of recovery to the extent that the management contractor is able to recover from the works contractor
3.21.2.2	Keep an account of loss of liquidated damages due to the completion date being exceeded by a works contractor's breach	Such damages are not to be recovered from the management contractor except to the extent that he is able to recover from the works contractor
3.21.3	Pay the amount of shortfall to the management contractor	In respect of claims by other works contractors following a breach by a works contractor and to the extent that the management contractor is unable to recover from the works contractor in breach by deduction from monies due or litigation or arbitration
3.22.3	Reimburse the management contractor amounts incurred in settling or defending a claim under clause 3.22.2	Only to the extent that the amounts are not payable as a result of the management contractor's negligent discharge of the contract
4.1	Pay the management contractor in accordance with the provisions of the payments clauses: prime cost ascertained in accordance with the second schedule; and the management fee	
4.3.3	Give written reasons for deduction to the management contractor	If the employer deducts from monies due or to become due to the management contractor
4.8.3	Pay retention money into separate bank account identified as retention held on trust. Certify the fact to the architect with a copy to the management contractor	If the employer deducts retention and the management contractor or any works contractor so requests. The employer is said to be entitled to full beneficial interest on any interest accruing, but the matter is thought to be debatable. This clause does not apply if the employer is a local authority

Table 5.08: Employer's Duties under JCT Standard Form of Management Contract – (continued)

Clause	Duty	Comment
4.8.4	Include in the written information to the management contractor under clause 4.3.3 details of deduction from retention held for management contractor or works contractors	If the employer deducts from monies due or to become due to the management contractor
5.10.2	Notify the management contractor	If the employer becomes a "contractor" for the purposes of the Finance (No 2) Act 1975 *and* the words "if a contractor" have been deleted from the appendix
5.11.2	Give written notification to the management contractor that he intends to make the statutory deduction from payments due under the conditions of the contract	If he is not satisfied with the evidence submitted by the management contractor that he is entitled to be paid without statutory deduction
5.13	Promptly pass all vouchers submitted by the management contractor to the Inland Revenue	If the employer is a "contractor"
5.14.1	Notify the management contractor in writing	If he considers that the Act requires him to make statutory deduction from payment due to be made
	Require the management contractor's statement of the amount to be included representing direct cost of materials used in carrying out the works	Not later than seven days before each future payment becomes due (or within 10 days of the notification above if that would be later)
5.15	Repay to or deduct from payments to the management contractor to correct errors	If an error has occurred, unless there is a contrary statutory obligation
6.3	Ensure that the joint names policy in clause 6.5.2 *either* provides for recognition of each works contractor as insured *or* includes a waiver of subrogation against the works contractor	If clause 6.5 applies. In respect of loss or damage by specified perils to existing structures

Table 5.08: Employer's Duties under JCT Standard Form of Management Contract – (continued)

Clause	Duty	Comment
6.5.2	Take out and maintain joint names policy for specified perils	In respect of existing structures and contents
6.5.3	Produce documentary evidence and receipts	When reasonably required by management contractor
7.5	Comply with default notice from management contractor	
7.6.2	Pay the management contractor:	After the management contractor had determined his employment under the contract
	Prime cost	
	Prime cost as part 4B of second schedule of materials not delivered but with legal obligation to pay by the management contractor	Goods become the property of the employer
	Management fee in accordance with formula	
	Reasonable cost of removal of temporary plant	
	Direct loss and/or damage caused to the management contractor by the determination	This may include the management contractor's loss of expected profit
7.11.1	Indemnify the management contractor against claims by works contractors and others in relation to the project	If the employer determines the employment of the contractor under clause 7.10. Indemnity is limited to sums properly due that have not already been paid to the management contractor
7.12	Pay the management contractor the pre-construction period management fee or appropriate proportion less any amount paid under interim certificate	If clause 7.10 determination takes place before issue of a written notice under clause 2.1 or the employer states in the notice that the management contractor is not to proceed or the employer fails to notify the management contractor under clause 2.1
7.13	Pay the management contractor:	After the management contractor has determined his employment under the contract

Table 5.08: Employer's Duties under JCT Standard Form of Management Contract – (continued)

Clause	Duty	Comment
	Prime Cost	
	Prime cost as part 4B of second schedule of materials not delivered but with legal obligation to pay by the management contractor	Goods become the property of the employer
	Management fee in accordance with formula	
	Reasonable cost of removal of temporary plant	
	Direct loss and/or damage caused to the management contractor by the determination	This may include the management contractor's loss of expected profit

Table 5.09: Clauses that may Give Rise to Claims under JCT Form of Management Contract

Clause	Event	Type
1.9	Failure to provide copy of the contract documents	CL
1.10	Failure to supply necessary information at all or in such a way as to enable the management contractor properly to discharge his obligations	CL
1.11	Use or divulging of rates, prices or management fee	CL
1.13	Failure to send duplicate copies of certificates to the management contractor	CL
2.2	Unjust reduction in pre-construction management fee	CL
2.3.1	Failure to give possession of the site on the due date if there is no provision for deferment stated in the appendix	CL
2.3.2	Failure to give possession of the site after deferment of the period stated in the appendix	CL
2.3.4	Employer's use of site without consent	CL
2.4	Failure to issue certificate of practical completion	CL
2.5	Failure to deliver a schedule of defects in due time	CL

Table 5.09: Clauses that may Give Rise to Claims under JCT Form of Management Contract – (continued)

Clause	Event	Type
2.6	Failure to issue certificate of making good defects	CL
2.7	Wrongful instructions to make good frost damage	CL
2.8	Possession without consent Failure to issue written statement identifying parts and dates taken into possession	CL CL
2.8.2	Failure to issue certificate of making good defects	CL
2.8.4	Failure to reduce the amount of liquidated damages correctly or at all	CL
2.9	Failure to issue non-completion certificate correctly Failure to issue cancellation of certificate	CL CL
2.10	Deduction of damages without written notification Wrongful deduction	CL CL
2.11	Failure to repay damages	
2.12	Architect failing to carry out duties	CL
3.1	Unreasonable withholding of consent to replacement personnel	CL
3.3.1	Failure to issue necessary instructions	CL

Table 5.09: Clauses that may Give Rise to Claims under JCT Form of Management Contract – (continued)

Clause	Event	Type
3.3.3	Failure to respond to request for empowering clause	CL
3.5	Postponement	CL
3.7	Failure to supply levels or accurately dimensioned drawings for setting out	CL
3.8.1	Materials, etc not procurable	CL
3.10	Opening up and testing found to be in accordance with the contract	CL
3.11	Unreasonable instructions	CL
3.12	Unreasonable instructions	CL
3.13	Unreasonable withholding of approval to change of manager	CL
3.14	Unreasonable instruction requiring removal of manager	CL
	Unreasonable withholding of approval to new manager	CL
3.15	Unreasonable withholding of consent to removal of materials	CL
3.18	Clerk of works exceeding his contractual duties	CL
3.19	Assignment by the employer without consent	CL
3.21.2.1	Failure to pay amounts properly incurred	CL

Table 5.09: Clauses that may Give Rise to Claims under JCT Form of Management Contract – (continued)

Clause	Event	Type
3.21.2.2	Wrongful deduction of damages	CL
3.21.2.3	Recovery of sums in excess of amounts recovered from works contractors in breach	CL
3.22.3	Failure to reimburse the management contractor amounts properly incurred	CL
3.23	Work by employer	CL
3.24	Work by employer	CL
3.27	Delay in the issue of instructions regarding antiquities	CL
4.1	Failure to pay on certificates	C
4.2	Failure to issue certificates	CL
4.3.3	Failure to inform management contractor of reasons for deduction	CL
4.4	Lack of interim valuations by quantity surveyor	CL
4.5	Inappropriate instalment	CL
4.6	Wrong calculation of certificate	CL
4.7	Wrong retention	CL
4.8	Interest on retention Failure to provide statement Failure to hold retention in separate bank account after	CL CL CL

Table 5.09: Clauses that may Give Rise to Claims under JCT Form of Management Contract – (continued)

Clause	Event	Type
	request and failure to furnish details	
	Failure to provide statement of deduction	CL
4.9.2	Failure to provide statement of prime cost and management fee	CL
	Failure to give reasons for disallowances	CL
4.10	Adjustment of construction period management fee	CL
4.11	Failure to issue certificate	CL
4.12	Failure to issue final certificate	CL
5.3	Divergence between statutory requirements and contract documents or instructions	C
6.4.4	Damaged work	C
6.5.3	Employer's failure to take out insurance	C
6.6.3	Liquidated damages insurance	C
6.11.1	Employer's liability insurance	C
6.13	Making good and protection of works after war damage	C
7.1	Invalid determination	CL
7.6	Payment after determination	C
7.9	Payment after determination	C

Table 5.09: Clauses that may Give Rise to Claims under JCT Form of Management Contract – (continued)

Clause	Event	Type
7.12	Payment after determination	C
7.13	Payment after determination	C
8.2.1	Failure of architect to issue confirming instruction in due time	CL
8.3.2	Failure to direct amounts payable to works contractors	CL
8.3.4	Failure to consent to practical completion certificate for works contractors	CL
8.5	Failure timeously to deal with loss and/or expense application	CL

KEY

C = Contractual claim   Contractual claims are usually dealt with by the architect

CL = Common Law claim   Common law claims are usually dealt with by the employer

Table 5.10: Certificates to be Issued by the Architect under JCT Form of Management Contract

Clause	Certificate
2.4	Certificate of practical completion
2.6	Certificate of making good defects
2.8.2	Certificate of making good defects where partial possession has taken place
2.9	Certificate of non-completion
4.2	Interim certificates
4.11	Interim certificate includings final payments to works contractors
4.12.1	Final certificate
7.4.4	Expenses incurred and loss and/or damage suffered by the employer after employer's determination due to management contractor's default

Table 5.11: Architect's Instructions Empowered by JCT Form of Management Contract

Clause	Instruction
1.5.4	Requiring site facilities or services
2.5	Not to make good defects
3.3.1	As reasonably necessary to enable the management contractor properly to discharge his obligations
3.4	Requiring project changes or works contract variations
	To expend provisional sums
3.5	Postponing work
3.6.2	Preliminary acceleration
3.6.4	Preliminary acceleration (re-issue)
3.6.6	Acceleration
3.10	Requiring opening up or testing
3.11	To remove defective work from site
3.12	Requiring making good of defects
3.14	Requiring removal of the manager from site
3.27	Regarding antiquities
5.3	In relation to divergence between statutory requirements and all or any of the contract documents or any variation instruction
6.6.1	That no liquidated damages insurance is required
	To obtain quotation for such insurance
	To accept quotation for such insurance
6.11.1	To take out and maintain joint names policy for indemnity in connection with employer's liability
6.13.2	Requiring removal and disposal of debris and execution of protective work after war damage
8.2.1	Confirming the selection of a works contractor
8.5	That the quantity surveyor shall ascertain loss and/or expense

Flowchart 5.12:   M. Contract Clause 2 – Commencement

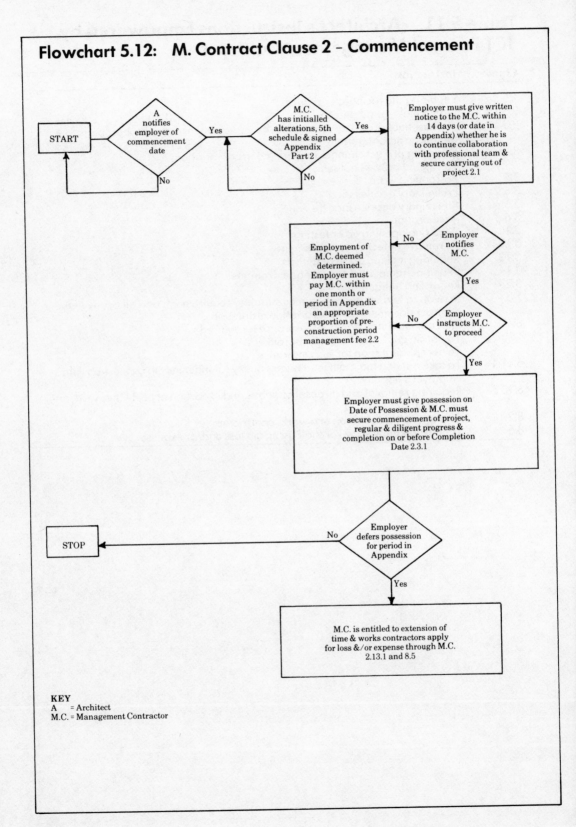

START

A notifies employer of commencement date — No (loops back to START)

Yes →

M.C. has initialled alterations, 5th schedule & signed Appendix Part 2 — No (loops back)

Yes →

Employer must give written notice to the M.C. within 14 days (or date in Appendix) whether he is to continue collaboration with professional team & secure carrying out of project 2.1

Employer notifies M.C. — No → Employment of M.C. deemed determined. Employer must pay M.C. within one month or period in Appendix an appropriate proportion of pre-construction period management fee 2.2

Yes ↓

Employer instructs M.C. to proceed — No → (to Employment of M.C. deemed determined box)

Yes ↓

Employer must give possession on Date of Possession & M.C. must secure commencement of project, regular & diligent progress & completion on or before Completion Date 2.3.1

Employer defers possession for period in Appendix — No → **STOP**

Yes ↓

M.C. is entitled to extension of time & works contractors apply for loss &/or expense through M.C. 2.13.1 and 8.5

KEY
A   = Architect
M.C. = Management Contractor

264

Flowchart 5.13: M. Contract Clause 3 – Architect's Instructions

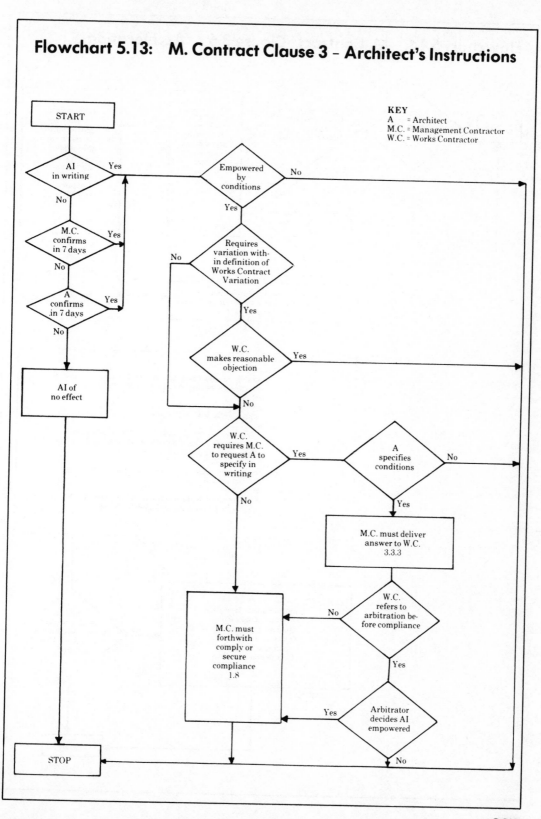

KEY
A = Architect
M.C. = Management Contractor
W.C. = Works Contractor

START

AI in writing — Yes

M.C. confirms in 7 days — Yes

A confirms in 7 days — Yes

No → AI of no effect

Empowered by conditions — No

Yes

Requires variation within definition of Works Contract Variation — No

Yes

W.C. makes reasonable objection — Yes

No

W.C. requires M.C. to request A to specify in writing — Yes

A specifies conditions — No

Yes

M.C. must deliver answer to W.C. 3.3.3

W.C. refers to arbitration before compliance — No

Yes

Arbitrator decides AI empowered — Yes

No

M.C. must forthwith comply or secure compliance 1.8

STOP

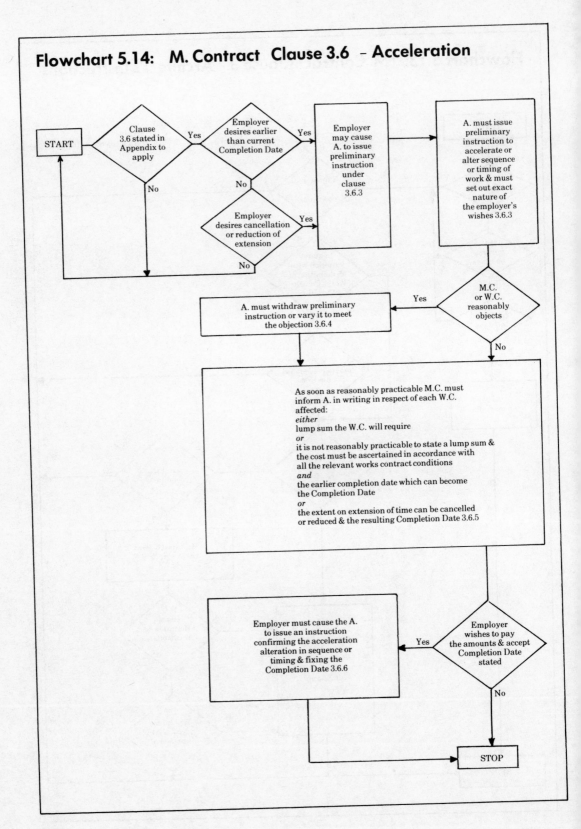

Flowchart 5.14: M. Contract Clause 3.6 – Acceleration

START

Clause 3.6 stated in Appendix to apply

Yes → Employer desires earlier than current Completion Date

No ↓

Employer desires cancellation or reduction of extension

No

Yes → Employer may cause A. to issue preliminary instruction under clause 3.6.3

A. must issue preliminary instruction to accelerate or alter sequence or timing of work & must set out exact nature of the employer's wishes 3.6.3

M.C. or W.C. reasonably objects

Yes → A. must withdraw preliminary instruction or vary it to meet the objection 3.6.4

No ↓

As soon as reasonably practicable M.C. must inform A. in writing in respect of each W.C. affected:
either
lump sum the W.C. will require
or
it is not reasonably practicable to state a lump sum & the cost must be ascertained in accordance with all the relevant works contract conditions
and
the earlier completion date which can become the Completion Date
or
the extent on extension of time can be cancelled or reduced & the resulting Completion Date 3.6.5

Employer must cause the A. to issue an instruction confirming the acceleration alteration in sequence or timing & fixing the Completion Date 3.6.6

← Yes — Employer wishes to pay the amounts & accept Completion Date stated

No ↓

STOP

266

Flowchart 5.15: M. Contract Clause 6.6 – Insurance for Liquidated Damages

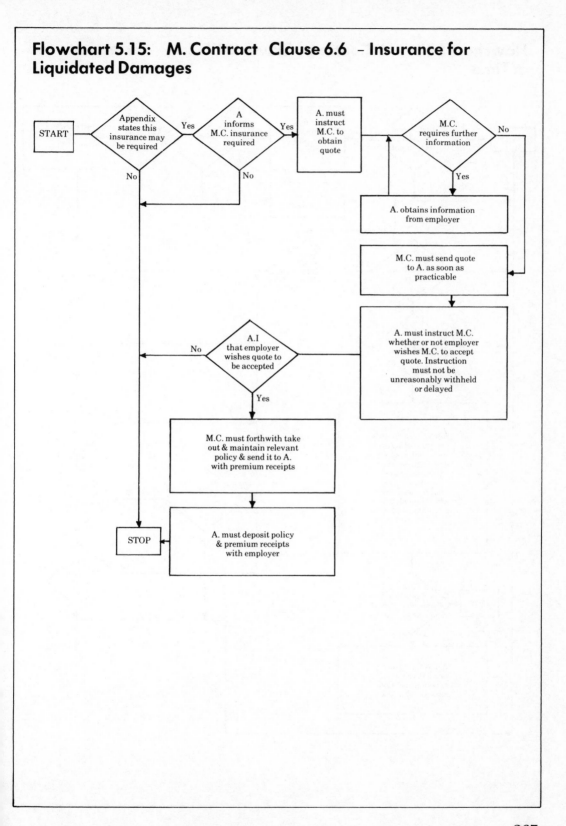

Flowchart 5.16:   M. Contract Clause 2.12–2.14 – Extension of Time

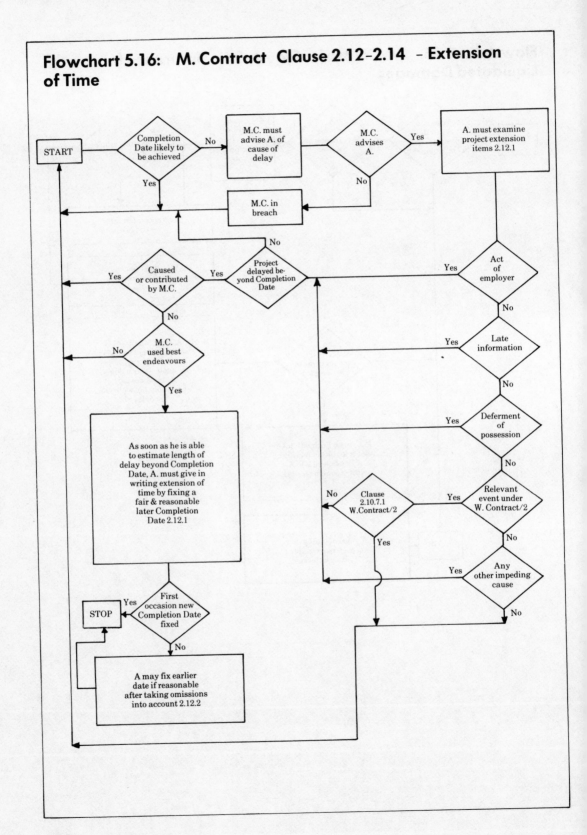

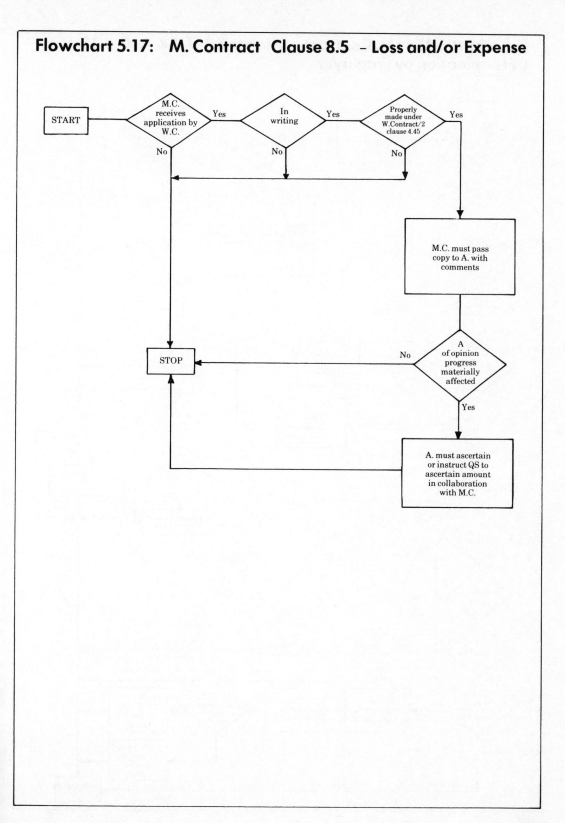

Flowchart 5.17: M. Contract Clause 8.5 – Loss and/or Expense

START

M.C. receives application by W.C.
— Yes →
In writing
— Yes →
Properly made under W.Contract/2 clause 4.45
— Yes →

No / No / No

M.C. must pass copy to A. with comments

A of opinion progress materially affected
— No → STOP

Yes

A. must ascertain or instruct QS to ascertain amount in collaboration with M.C.

STOP

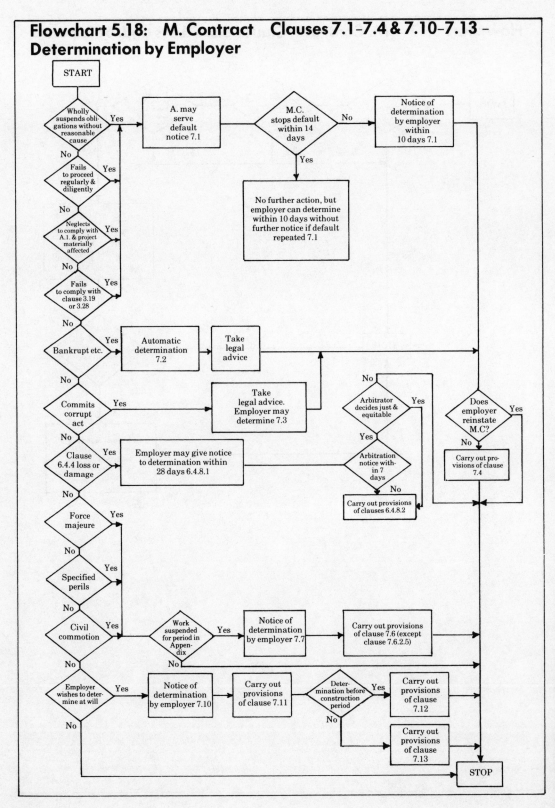

Flowchart 5.18: M. Contract Clauses 7.1–7.4 & 7.10–7.13 – Determination by Employer

START

Wholly suspends obligations without reasonable cause — Yes → A. may serve default notice 7.1 → M.C. stops default within 14 days — No → Notice of determination by employer within 10 days 7.1

M.C. stops default within 14 days — Yes → No further action, but employer can determine within 10 days without further notice if default repeated 7.1

No → Fails to proceed regularly & diligently — Yes →

No → Neglects to comply with A.1. & project materially affected — Yes →

No → Fails to comply with clause 3.19 or 3.28 — Yes →

No → Bankrupt etc. — Yes → Automatic determination 7.2 → Take legal advice →

No → Commits corrupt act — Yes → Take legal advice. Employer may determine 7.3 →

No → Clause 6.4.4 loss or damage — Yes → Employer may give notice to determination within 28 days 6.4.8.1 →

Arbitrator decides just & equitable — No → ; Yes ↓

Arbitration notice within 7 days — Yes ; No → Carry out provisions of clauses 6.4.8.2

Does employer reinstate M.C? — Yes ; No → Carry out provisions of clause 7.4

No → Force majeure — Yes →

No → Specified perils — Yes →

No → Civil commotion — Yes → Work suspended for period in Appendix — Yes → Notice of determination by employer 7.7 → Carry out provisions of clause 7.6 (except clause 7.6.2.5) →

Work suspended for period in Appendix — No →

No → Employer wishes to determine at will — Yes → Notice of determination by employer 7.10 → Carry out provisions of clause 7.11 → Determination before construction period — Yes → Carry out provisions of clause 7.12

Determination before construction period — No → Carry out provisions of clause 7.13

No → STOP

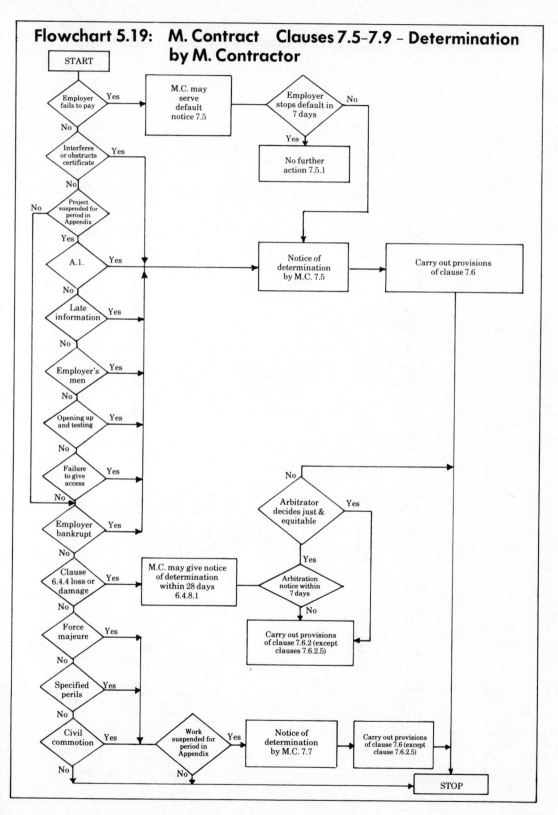

Flowchart 5.19: M. Contract   Clauses 7.5–7.9 – Determination by M. Contractor

START

Employer fails to pay — Yes → M.C. may serve default notice 7.5 → Employer stops default in 7 days — No →

Employer stops default in 7 days — Yes → No further action 7.5.1

Interferes or obstructs certificate — Yes →

Project suspended for period in Appendix — Yes / No

A.1. — Yes → Notice of determination by M.C. 7.5 → Carry out provisions of clause 7.6

Late information — Yes

Employer's men — Yes

Opening up and testing — Yes

Failure to give access — Yes

Employer bankrupt — Yes

Clause 6.4.4 loss or damage — Yes → M.C. may give notice of determination within 28 days 6.4.8.1

Arbitrator decides just & equitable — No / Yes

Arbitration notice within 7 days — Yes / No

Carry out provisions of clause 7.6.2 (except clauses 7.6.2.5)

Force majeure — Yes

Specified perils — Yes

Civil commotion — Yes → Work suspended for period in Appendix — Yes → Notice of determination by M.C. 7.7 → Carry out provisions of clause 7.6 (except clause 7.6.2.5)

No → STOP

271

Flowchart 5.20:   M. Contract Clauses 9.1–9.6 – Arbitration

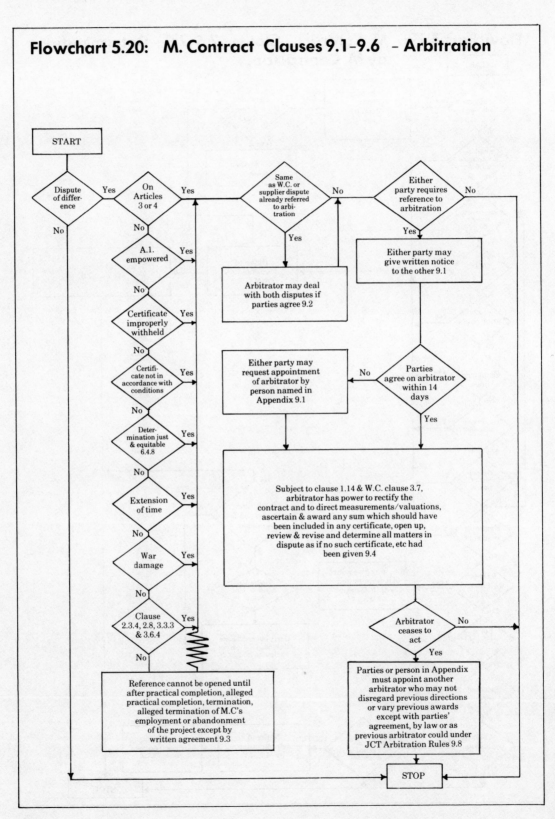

START

Dispute of difference — Yes → On Articles 3 or 4 — Yes → Same as W.C. or supplier dispute already referred to arbitration

Dispute of difference — No

On Articles 3 or 4 — No → A.1. empowered — Yes

A.1. empowered — No → Certificate improperly withheld — Yes

Certificate improperly withheld — No → Certificate not in accordance with conditions — Yes

Certificate not in accordance with conditions — No → Determination just & equitable 6.4.8 — Yes

Determination just & equitable 6.4.8 — No → Extension of time — Yes

Extension of time — No → War damage — Yes

War damage — No → Clause 2.3.4, 2.8, 3.3.3 & 3.6.4 — Yes

Clause 2.3.4, 2.8, 3.3.3 & 3.6.4 — No

Same as W.C. or supplier dispute already referred to arbitration — Yes → Arbitrator may deal with both disputes if parties agree 9.2

Same as W.C. or supplier dispute already referred to arbitration — No → Either party requires reference to arbitration

Either party requires reference to arbitration — No

Either party requires reference to arbitration — Yes → Either party may give written notice to the other 9.1

Parties agree on arbitrator within 14 days — No → Either party may request appointment of arbitrator by person named in Appendix 9.1

Parties agree on arbitrator within 14 days — Yes

Subject to clause 1.14 & W.C. clause 3.7, arbitrator has power to rectify the contract and to direct measurements/valuations, ascertain & award any sum which should have been included in any certificate, open up, review & revise and determine all matters in dispute as if no such certificate, etc had been given 9.4

Arbitrator ceases to act — No

Arbitrator ceases to act — Yes → Parties or person in Appendix must appoint another arbitrator who may not disregard previous directions or vary previous awards except with parties' agreement, by law or as previous arbitrator could under JCT Arbitration Rules 9.8

Reference cannot be opened until after practical completion, alleged practical completion, termination, alleged termination of M.C's employment or abandonment of the project except by written agreement 9.3

STOP

6: The JCT Fixed Fee Form of Prime Cost Contract

6.01   Introduction

The Fixed Fee Form of Prime Cost Contract was first published in 1967; the last revision was carried out in 1976.

It is intended for use where the works cannot be precisely defined at tender stage. The basis of the contract is that, although the works cannot be measured even to the extent of producing approximate bills of quantities, sufficient is known about the work to enable the contractor to produce an estimate of the likely prime cost of the works. This estimate is inserted in the third schedule of the printed conditions. The contractor is to be paid a fixed fee for his services and this fee is inserted in the second schedule. By the time the contract is complete, the contractor will have been paid his actual costs of carrying out the work (the prime cost defined in the first schedule) together with the prearranged fixed fee.

The form of contract is particularly useful if work is required to commence urgently on such projects as renovations, alterations and the repair of fire damage.

One serious disadvantage levelled against this type of contract is that the contractor has no real incentive to work quickly and efficiently to complete the work in good time because his fee is assured together with his actual costs. On the other hand, a tardy contractor would be liable for liquidated damages in the usual way, and, unless the contractor were actually to be paid by the hour, it is always in his best interests to complete work as quickly as possible.

If the amount and type of work is almost totally unknown, the contractor may, quite understandably, show reluctance to enter into a contract by which he receives only a fixed fee even if the amount of work is far more than envisaged. In such a case, the parties might usefully enter into a somewhat different form of contract, by which the contractor receives a fee expressed as a percentage of the actual prime cost expended. This type of contract does have serious dangers in that the greater the prime cost, the higher the fee. Thus the contractor has no incentive to save money. Several devices have been adopted to overcome this problem, notably the sliding scale, by which the contractor is rewarded if he saves on the original target cost. There is no reason why this contract cannot be adapted provided proper care and advice is taken.

Although it is clear that the architect must have power to issue instructions, particularly in the case of a contract in this form, the contractor would be seriously disadvantaged if the work was greatly altered or increased. A curb, therefore, put on the architect's powers in clause 3 which expressly prevents him from issuing any instruction altering the nature or scope of the works.

As might be expected, the contract is closely related to JCT 63 (1976 revision) in layout and wording. There are, however, a number of significant differences, most notably the absence of any provision for valuation of variations, since all architect's instructions will fall to be valued under the payments provisions as a necessary part of the philosophy of this particular contract. **Table 5.01 summarises the contents of the form.**

6.02 Contractor's Obligations

The basic obligations of the contractor are stated in clause 2. He must "carry out and complete the Works in compliance with the Specification and this Agreement, using materials and workmanship of the quality and standards therein specified".

There follows the proviso embodied in all current JCT contracts to the effect that where standards of materials or workmanship are made subject to the architect's opinion, they are to be to his reasonable satisfaction. Although it is clearly difficult, in this type of contract, to avoid reserving some things for the architect's approval, the use of any sweeping phraseology that "all work must be to the architect's satisfaction" should be avoided because the final certificate is conclusive evidence that in such instances the standards of materials and workmanship are to the architect's satisfaction. This could prevent the employer being able to recover damages from the contractor at a later stage.

6.03 Contract Documentation and Information

The contract documentation is very simple. It consists of the printed form together with a specification. Drawings may be included if required. In most cases, some drawings at least will be needed, if only to identify the precise location of the work.

Clause 4(1) requires the architect to issue, from time to time, such drawings and details as are reasonably necessary to explain and amplify the specification or to enable the contractor to carry out and complete the works in accordance with the contract. Although this is a common clause in JCT contracts, it is of special significance in relation to the Fixed Fee Form because of the lack of precise knowledge at tender stage. It is crucial that the architect issues sufficient further information as the work proceeds or the contractor's progress will be seriously impeded. Failure to issue the required information would amount to a serious breach of contract for which the employer would be responsible. The architect's obligation does not depend upon any application by the contractor and, although the contractor could not claim loss and/or expense through clause 20(1)(a) of the contract, he would have a very clear case for damages at common law. Since there is no provision for the architect to issue an extension of time in such a case (unless the contractor has made application in due time) the result might well be that liquidated damages become unenforceable. We are of the opinion that this clause would be interpreted very strictly in the context of this particular contract by the courts. The architect should watch his obligations under this clause with great care.

The contract does not state who is to hold the contract documents. Since whichever party holds them, the other will have a copy (although there is no specific provision for this either) the matter is not of prime importance.

The absence of any provision regarding discrepancies between drawings and specification is again a reflection of the type of work to be carried out and the imprecision to be expected at tender stage. Clause 3 is broad enough to allow the architect to settle all such matters by means of an instruction and valuation is automatic. There is no clause in this contract (unlike JCT 80) giving priority to the printed conditions, and therefore the normal rules of legal interpretation apply, ie the printed conditions can be amended by an item in the specially prepared specification, and in case of conflict the specially drafted provision will prevail.

The contract makes no mention of the contractor's programme, and in many cases it may be difficult to produce a programme which details the work with any precision. However, a programme, even if general, is always useful, so the architect should be sure to insert a suitable clause requiring the contractor to produce one. The programme should not be made subject to the architect's approval.

6.04 Commencement and Completion

Clause 17 states that possession of the site must be given to the contractor on the date noted in the appendix. He must begin the works immediately and proceed "regularly and diligently" in order to complete them *on or before* the date for completion. Failure to give possession on the due date is a serious breach of contract on the part of the employer for which the contractor can obtain damages at common law. If the breach were to continue, it may amount to a repudiation of the contract on the part of the employer. The difficulty cannot be overcome by the award of an extension of time and it is something for negotiation and agreement between the parties.

If completion is delayed beyond the completion date or any extended date, the contractor becomes liable to pay liquidated damages. The employer may either deduct them from monies becoming due to the contractor (ie on certificates) or he may, although the contract does not specifically state this, recover them as a debt. In most cases the employer will opt for the first course of action since it is more straightforward and poses least problems. It should be noted that in this contract, although the architect's certificate of failure to complete by the due date is a precondition to the deduction of liquidated damages, the wording of clause 18 follows that of JCT 63. The issue of the architect's certificate is dependent upon the architect's opinion that the work "ought reasonably so to have been completed". If the contractor has been delayed because of the employer's default, for which no specific provision is made in the list of events in clause 19, it is considered that the architect can withhold his certificate on non-completion or even date it to take account of such default. The question is debatable and the point has been resolved very clearly in JCT 80.

The architect is not given any express power to postpone work, but it is thought that his powers under clause 3 are sufficiently wide to enable him to do so giving the contractor a claim for extension of time under clause 19(e). There are no powers of acceleration. If acceleration is required, the two parties to the contract must agree on the measures to be adopted and the payment to be made. Clause 11 stipulates that "when in the opinion of the Architect the Works are practically completed" he must issue a certificate to that effect. Among other things, the certificate signals the date on which:

● The contractor's liability for liquidated damages ends (clause 18)
● The defects liability period begins (clause 11(2))
● The contractor's liability to insure ends (clause 15)
● Regular certificates cease to be issued (clause 27)
● Reference to arbitration may be opened on any matter (clause 31A).

The length of the defects liability period is to be as stated in the appendix (normally six months) and the contractor is to make good defects, shrinkages and other faults (like defects and shrinkages) which may appear during the period. The defects must be due to materials, goods or workmanship not being in accordance with the contract or to frost occurring before practical completion. They are to be made good entirely at the contractor's own cost, but there is a proviso: "unless the Architect shall otherwise instruct in which case the work involved shall be treated as an addition required by the Architect to the items of work described in the Specification". This appears to give the architect power to include in the schedule items which are not defects, but items of additional work; which is curious and probably not what was intended. When all defects have been made good, the architect is to issue a certificate to that effect.

Clause 12 provides for the situation which might arise if the employer, with the contractor's consent, takes possession of part of the works. Practical completion is deemed to have taken place, for the particular part, on the date of possession and the architect must issue a certificate to that effect, stating his estimate of the approximate prime cost of the relevant part. The liquidated damages provision and any insurance for which the contractor is responsible must be reduced proportionately.

6.05 Extensions of Time

Clause 19 is virtually word for word the same as clause 23 of JCT 63. The grounds for extension listed are either the fault of the employer or the architect or beyond the control of either party to the contract. Not all employer's possible defaults are listed, and therefore if the contractor is delayed due to, for example, the employer failing to give access to the site, the architect will be unable to grant any extension, time will become at large and liquidated damages will not be enforceable. The contractor is required to:

- Give written notice to the architect as soon as it becomes reasonably apparent that the progress of the works is being delayed or is likely to be delayed beyond the date for completion
- Use his best endeavours to prevent delay
- Do all the architect may reasonably require to his satisfaction to proceed with the works.

The contractor is not required to "claim" nor to make any estimate of the period of delay, but clearly it is in his own interests to co-operate fully with the architect if he expects to receive a satisfactory extension of time. The obligation to use best endeavours and to do all the architect requires is thought to be no more than an obligation to continue to proceed regularly and diligently and to make such reprogramming arrangements as the architect thinks desirable. The contactor cannot, however, be expected to expend additional money unless he is properly recompensed.

There is no provision for any review of extensions and it is vital that the architect grants all extensions "so soon as he is able to estimate the length of delay beyond" the previous completion date. As a general rule, extensions of time should be granted before the date for completion. This is particularly the case where employer's acts or defaults are concerned. In other cases, it is permissible to grant extensions after completion date if, for example, the delay is ongoing and it is not reasonable to grant an extension until the total extent of delay is seen. Even in these circumstances, it is good practice to grant an interim extension when it is clear that a delay to the completion date is involved.

6.06 Architect's Instructions

The architect's power to issue instructions is of fundamental importance to this contract and the provisions are contained in clause 3. It is envisaged that the architect will issue a great many instructions throughout the progress of the work to supplement and clarify the information on the drawings and in the specification.

The architect's power is to issue such instructions as he thinks fit. This apparently limitless power is in fact limited, first, by the necessary implication that all instructions will be within his authority and be related to the subject matter of the contract and, second, by a proviso within the clause itself. He "shall not by virtue of this sub-clause be enabled to issue an instruction requiring an alteration in the nature of the scope of the Works". A footnote to the clause reinforces the statement and makes the point that if such an alteration is desired, it must be agreed and embodied in a separate or supplemental contract. This is a sensible and essential safeguard for the contractor engaged on somewhat uncertain works of this type. The precise meaning of an alteration in the nature or scope of the works is something which will depend on all the circumstances. It may well be a question of degree. Clause 3(1) goes on to state quite clearly that an instruction requiring the contractor to execute either an item of work which is specified in the fourth or sixth schedules (work by nominated sub-contractors or by other persons) or an item substituted for such an item is deemed to be an instruction or an alteration in the scope of the works.

The contractor must forthwith comply with all instructions and there is no provision for him to challenge its validity. Clause 31A(2) enables the contractor to seek immediate arbitration if he considers that any instruction is not empowered.

Failure to comply can be dealt with by the architect under clause 3(2). If the contractor continues his failure after the operation of the 7 days notification procedure, the employer can engage others to carry out the work at the contractor's expense. Despite the fact that all instructions are to be in writing, the contract gives detailed provisions regarding the procedure to be adopted if oral instructions are issued. Either the architect or the contractor may confirm instructions at any time prior to the issue of the final certificate.

There is no provision for variations to be valued, since all the work will be valued at prime cost for payment.

6.07 Contractor's Claims

Clause 20 provides for the contractor to claim "direct loss and/or expense" if the "regular progress" of the works has been materially affected by any of a series of matters included in the clause. The matters all come under the general heading of employer or architect default, but it is important to note that not all possible defaults are included (unlike, for example, the ACA 2 form of contract) and the architect is only empowered to deal with those defaults expressly stated. The fact that a particular default is not included does not preclude the contractor from claiming damages at common law and his rights are expressly protected by clause 20(2).

A point to note is that, following the decision in *F G Minter Ltd v Welsh Technical Services Organisation* (1981) 13 BLR 1, finance charges are allowable as an item of direct loss and/or expense, but only from the time of accrual to the time the claim is made. Therefore, under this form of contract, it is necessary for the contractor to make very regular (some commentarors have suggested daily!) applications in order to secure that payment of interest charges is secured. JCT 80 has a revised form of wording which makes more than one application for any one occurrence unnecessary.

The contractor's application must be in writing and must be made within "a reasonable time" of the matter becoming apparent. These are conditions precedent. If they are not fulfilled the architect must reject the claim. The contractor can, however, make the same claim at common law as an alternative to his contractual claim, where the event relied on is a breach of contract at common law. The contract does not expressly require the contractor to supply any particular information to enable the ascertainment to take place. However, an ascertainment cannot be made if relevant information is not provided and it is to be implied that the contractor will provide it so as to substantiate his claim.

A further ground for paying the contractor loss and/or expense is contained in clause 30(3) if the contractor's compliance with the provisions regarding antiquities involve him in direct loss and/or expense for which he would not be reimbursed by payment under any other contract provision. The contractor is not obliged to make any formal claim under this clause. The architect may carry out the ascertainment himself or he may instruct the quantity surveyor to do it. The architect cannot delegate his duty to decide the validity of the claim.

6.08 Certificates and Payment

Clause 26 deals with a number of general matters. In particular, it is expressly stated that the fixed fee covers and includes "all items of cost, charge, expense, insurance and profit which are not included in the definition of prime cost contained in the First Schedule". The fixed fee is not deemed to include any items of loss and/or expense. The contractor is also charged with keeping full and accurate accounts of all invoices and records relating to payments made and work carried out. The contractor's strict observance of this provision is, of course, crucial to the efficient administration of the payments clause.

Clause 27 states that interim certificates shall be issued at the period of interim certificates noted in the appendix (normally one month). All certificates are to be issued to the contractor. Interim valuations need only be made when the architect considers them to be necessary although, in practice, it is difficult to see how a realistic certificate can be issued without a valuation. If a valuation is carried out, it must take place no more than 7 days before the date of issue of the certificate. The employer must pay within 14 days (or such other period as is stated in the appendix) from presentation by the contractor. However, it has been held (*C M Pillings & Co Ltd* v *Kent Investments Ltd* (1986) 4 ConLR 1) that payment of the amount of an interim certificate is not a condition precedent to arbitration under this form of contract. Each certificate must include:

- The prime cost of the work properly executed and of materials or goods delivered to site provided that they are adequately stored and protected. Off-site materials may be included at the discretion of the architect (clause 27(3)). Great care should be exercised when dealing with any unfixed materials because of the prevalence of "retention of title" clauses in suppliers' contracts
- An instalment of the fixed fee proportioned to the prime cost expended compared to the estimate in the third schedule
- Any amount of loss and/or expense ascertained and not already paid.

The employer is entitled to retain a percentage of all monies certified until the certificate of practical completion is issued when half the percentage retained must be released. The release of the balance of the retention must take place after the issue of the certificate of making good defects.

Before the end of the period of final ascertainment of prime cost named in the appendix, the architect or the quantity surveyor must ascertain the prime cost and supply the information to the contractor. This is subject to the contractor submitting all additional documents required by the architect within a reasonable time after practical completion. The architect must issue his final certificate within three months from the latest of the following:

- The end of the defects liability period
- The completion of making good defects (clause 11)

- Receipt by the architect of all documents necessary for ascertainment of the prime cost of the works.

The final certificate is conclusive evidence:
- That where quality and standards are to be to the satisfaction of the architect, they are to his satisfaction
- All the provisions of the contract requiring payment have been complied with *unless* either party commences arbitration or other proceedings within 14 days after the issue of the final certificate. Clause 27(9) makes clear that no other certificate has any degree of conclusiveness.

6.09 Sub-Contractors and Employer's Licensees

Clause 13 states that neither party may assign the contract without the written consent of the other.

The contractor may not sub-let any portion of the works without the written consent of the architect. Because of the nature of the contract, any consent must expressly approve the method of charge and be subject to whatever conditions the architect may see fit to impose. The provision is to safeguard the employer who has to pay the prime cost. The architect, however, must not unreasonably withhold his consent to the prejudice of the contractor.

The contract provides for nomination of sub-contractors in clause 23. Sub-contractors may be nominated in respect of items of work included in the fourth schedule, items substituted for such items already described in the specification. The clause sets out procedures for payment and extension of time. There is no express provision for renomination if the original sub-contractor fails, but it is clear that the employer is under a duty to renominate in those circumstances (*Percy Bilton* v *Greater London Council* (1982) 20BLR 1) and must do so within a reasonable time of the contractor applying for a renomination instruction.

The architect may not nominate any sub-contractor to whom the contractor makes reasonable objection or who will not enter into a sub-contract including the terms set out in clause 23(a). Clause 23(b) sets out the payment procedure. Amounts due to the sub-contractor are to be included in interim certificates and the contractor and sub-contractor must be notified. The architect has power to require proof from the contractor that such sums have been discharged before issuing a further certificate. If the contractor fails to provide proof, the employer may, but need not, pay the sub-contractor direct.

The contractor may grant extensions of time to the nominated sub-contractor with the written consent of the architect (clause 23(d)). The architect must issue a certificate of non-completion if he is satisfied that the sub-contractor has failed to complete the sub-contract works by the due date and the contractor has correctly applied the procedures for extension of time.

Clause 23(f) stipulates that the employer is in no way liable to the nominated sub-contractor. Thus responsibility for the performance of the nominated sub-contractor rests firmly on the shoulders of the contractor, subject of course to the requirements of re-nomination in the event of the sub-contractor's failure. Although there is no specific provision, it is for the architect to advise the employer on the prudence of entering into some form of direct agreement with the nominated sub-contractor. In most cases it appears to be an essential safeguard.

Work not forming part of the contract may be carried out by the employer's own contractors. The contractor's agreement is not required. The contract clearly envisages that such contractor's work will be listed in the sixth schedule, but the drafting of the clause (25) does not appear to limit the employer to work on this list. Exercise of the employer's power may, and probably will, give rise to claims for extension of time and loss and/or expense under clauses 19(h) and 20(1)(c) respectively.

6.10 Statutory Obligations

Clause 5(1) places an obligation on the contractor to comply with all statutory obligations connected with the works. There is no express obligation to pay fees and charges, but if he has any to pay, they will fall to be valued in accordance with clause 27. If the contractor finds any divergence between any of the contract documents or any architect's instruction and statutory requirements, he must notify the architect in writing (clause 5(2)). If the architect receives such a notice or otherwise discovers a divergence, he has 7 days in which to issue an instruction dealing with the matter. Provided the contractor carries out his obligations under clause 5(2), he cannot be held liable to the employer if work carried out in accordance with the contract does not comply with statutory requirements. This does not affect the contractor's own direct liability and duties in complying with statutory requirements, eg building regulations. Provision is made under clause 5(4) in the case of an emergency. The contractor must supply only such limited materials and provide such limited work as is required to secure immediate compliance and he must forthwith inform the architect.

6.11 Injury, Damage and Insurance

The insurance provisions are contained in clauses 14, 15 and 16. They are similar to the insurance provisions contained in most standard forms. The contractor must insure against and indemnify the employer against all claims arising from injury or death due to the carrying out of the works and insure against and indemnify the employer against all claims arising from damage to property caused by the carrying out of the works and due to the contractor's or sub-contractor's negligence. The sum to be insured is to be inserted in the appendix and the contractor must produce policies and premium receipts as requested by the employer. The employer may himself insure if the contractor makes default.

Damage caused to adjacent property otherwise than through the contractor's negligence or certain other listed exceptions is covered by clause 14(2).

Insurance of new building work is covered by clause 16A and existing works and alterations thereto by clause 16B. In each case, it is the employer who has the responsibility to insure and the contractor has power to take out insurance himself should the employer default. A footnote to this clause states that if it is the intention that the contractor should insure a new building, both clause 16 A and B should be struck out and clause 20(A) of JCT 63 Private Edition Without Quantities (or something similar) should be inserted.

6.12 Determination

Clauses 21 and 22 provide for determination of the contractor's employment.
Two situations are envisaged:
- Determination by the employer (clause 21)
- Determination by the contractor (clause 22).

Among the reasons for which the employer may determine are total suspension, without reasonable cause, of the works before completion, failure of the contractor to proceed regularly and diligently and the contractor's persistent refusal to remove defective work or goods by which refusal the work is materially affected. The contractor may determine if he does not receive payment properly due, if the employer obstructs the issue of any certificate or if substantial suspension of the works is caused for a period noted in the appendix by a series of events listed in clause 22(1)(c). Either party may determine if the other becomes bankrupt or goes into liquidation.

Except in the case of the contractor's bankruptcy, the architect must first issue a default notice and allow 7 days for remedial measures to begin before the employer may issue a notice determining the contractor's employment. The contractor is only obliged to follow this procedure in respect of overdue payment; in other cases he may determine forthwith.

There are the normal provisions for payment and clearing the site after determination. The party who determines may claim loss and/or expense and, in the case of the contractor, this can include loss of anticipated profits, which would appear to mean that the contractor could claim the whole of the fixed fee even if the contract had just begun.

6.13 Disputes

The disputes procedure is covered by clause 31. All disputes are to be referred to arbitration. The parties are to agree upon an arbitrator, but if they fail to agree within 14 days of a request by either party, either party may apply to the President or Vice-President of the Royal Institute of British Architects to appoint a suitable person. There is no specific provision for related arbitrations to be joined (as in JCT 80), but there is no reason why this could not be done provided that both parties agree.

The arbitrator has wide powers to direct measurements and valuations, to ascertain and award any amount which should have been included in a certificate and to open up, review and revise any certificate, opinion, decision, requirement or notice. Arbitration must take place after the practical completion, termination or abandonment of the work except as regards the following matters:
- The identity of the architect or quantity surveyor
- Whether an instruction is within the architect's powers
- Whether a certificate has been improperly withheld
- Whether a certificate is in accordance with the contract
- Failure to agree a rate or an addition required for the purposes of the first schedule
- Refusal to authorise payment or an item of expense such as mentioned in s A(b)(ii) or (c) or s CIII(q) of the first schedule

• Disputes of differences with regard to clause 28 (hostilities) and 29 (war damage).

The arbitrator's award is said to be final and binding and is made subject to the Arbitration Act 1950. The 1979 Act was not on the statute book when this contract was drafted but it nonetheless applies.

Table 6.01:   Contents of JCT Fixed Fee Form of Prime Cost Contract 76 Summarised

Clause	Content
1	Definitions
2	Contractor's general obligation
3	Architect's instruction
4	Drawings and certificates
5	Statutory obligations and notices
6	Levels and setting out of the works
7	Labour, materials, goods and workmanship
8	Materials and goods unfixed or off-site
9	Access for architect to the site
10	Clerk of works
11	Practical completion and defects liability
12	Partial possession by employer
13	Assignment and sub-letting
14	Injury to persons and property and employer's indemnity
15	Insurance against injury to persons and property
15A	Excepted risks: nuclear perils etc
16	Insurance of the works against fire
17	Possession and completion
18	Damages for non-completion
19	Extension of time
20	Loss and expense caused by disturbance of regular progress of the works
21	Determination by employer
22	Determination by contractor
23	Nominated sub-contractors
24	Nominated suppliers
25	Work by other persons
26	Payment
26A	Value Added Tax – supplemental agreement
27	Method of payment
27B	Finance (No 2) Act 1975 – statutory tax deduction scheme
28	Outbreak of hostilities
29	War damage
30	Antiquities
31A	Arbitration (England and Wales)
31B	Arbitration (Scotland)

First schedule
Second schedule
Third schedule
Fourth schedule
Fifth schedule
Sixth schedule
Appendix:
Supplemental agreement

Table 6.02: JCT Fixed Fee Form of Prime Contract 76 – Time Chart

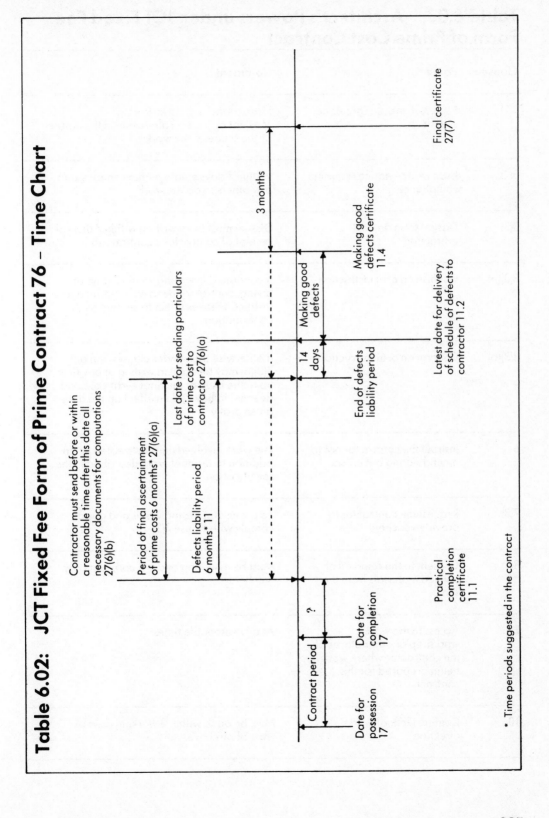

* Time periods suggested in the contract

Table 6.03: Architect's Powers under JCT Fixed Fee Form of Prime Cost Contract

Clause	Power	Comment
3(1)	Issue such instructions as he sees fit	Instructions must be in writing May not require an alteration in the nature or the scope of the works
3(2)	Issue written notice requiring compliance	Within 7 days employer may employ and pay others to do the work
3(3)	Dissent from an oral instruction	Dissent must be in writing within 7 days of receipt of contractor's confirmation
3(3)(a)	Confirm an oral instruction	If confirmed in writing within 7 days of giving, contractor need not confirm and instruction takes effect from date of confirmation
3(3)(b)	Confirm an oral instruction	If otherwise than under clauses 3(3) or 3(3)(a) may be done in writing at any time up to the issue of the final certificate and deemed to have taken effect on the date given orally
6	Instruct the contractor not to amend setting out errors	The work involved must be treated as an addition to terms of work described in the specification
7(3)	Request the contractor to provide vouchers	To prove that the materials and goods comply with clause 7(3)
8(1)	Consent to the removal of unfixed materials from the site	Must be in writing and not unreasonably withheld
9	Access to the works, workshop or other places of the contractor where work is being prepared for this contract	At all reasonable times
10	Confirm clerk of works' direction	Must be done within 2 working days of issue of directive

Table 6.03:   Architect's Powers under JCT Fixed Fee Form of Prime Cost Contract – (continued)

Clause	Power	Comment
11(2)	Instruct that defects, etc in the schedule of defects are not to be made good	Work involved must be treated as an addition to items of work described in the specification
11(3)	Issue instructions requiring any defects etc appearing during the defects liability period to be made good	Contractor must comply within a reasonable time Instructions must not be issued after the later of: Delivery of schedule of defects 14 days from end of defects liability period
	Instruct that defects etc appearing, within the defects liability period are not to be made good	Work involved must be treated as an addition to items of work described in the specification
11(5)	Certify that frost damage appearing after practical completion is due to injury which took place before practical completion	Otherwise the contractor is not liable for the cost of making good such frost damage
13(3)	Consent to sub-letting	Must not be unreasonably withheld May be subject to reasonable conditions Employment of sub-contractor under the sub-contract shall determine immediately upon the determination, for any reason, of the contractor's employment
15(2)(a)	Issue an instruction requiring contractor to maintain insurances in joint names against claims due to damage to property other than the works by collapse etc	Except damage which is: Caused by contractor's negligence Caused by design errors Reasonably foreseeable At risk of employer under clauses 16A or 16B Arising from nuclear risk or war risk
16B(c)(ii)	Issue instructions requiring the contractor to remove and dispose of any debris	After loss or damage affects the works etc at the sole risk of the employer; and Neither party determines the contractor's employment
18	Certify in writing that, in his opinion, the works ought to have been completed	If the contractor fails to complete the works by the date for completion

Table 6.03: Architect's Powers under JCT Fixed Fee Form of Prime Cost Contract – (continued)

Clause	Power	Comment
19	Require the contractor to proceed with the works to the architect's satisfaction	The contractor cannot be made to incur additional expenditure without reimbursement
21(1)	Serve a default notice on the contractor	If the contractor: Suspends the work without reasonable cause; or Fails to proceed regularly and diligently; or Refuses or persistently neglects to remove defective work, etc and thereby the works are materially affected; or If he fails to comply with the provisions of clause 13
21(3)(c)	Require the contractor to remove from the works temporary buildings etc belonging to or hired by him	If the contractor does not comply within a reasonable time, the employer may remove and sell them The contractor must not remove them before receipt of architect's instruction
23	Instruct that items of work are to be carried out by nominated sub-contractors	The items of work must be: either Specified in the fourth schedule; or Substituted for such items; or In addition to items already described in the specification
23(c)	Request the contractor to furnish reasonable proof that all amounts included in certificates and due to nominated sub-contractors have been discharged	If contractor fails to comply, architect must issue a certificate to that effect and the employer may pay direct and deduct from monies due to the contractor
23(d)(i)	Consent to contractor's grant of extension of time to a nominated sub-contractor	Contractor must inform architect of nominated sub-contractor's representations and consent must not be unreasonably withheld
23(e)	Include an amount in an interim certificate to cover a final payment to a nominated sub-contractor	If: The architect wishes; and The sub-contractor has indemnified the contractor against latent defects The contractor is thereupon discharged from all liability for the work, materials or goods supplied by such sub-contractor except for latent defects

Table 6.03: Architect's Powers under JCT Fixed Fee Form of Prime Cost Contract – (continued)

Clause	Power	Comment
24	Instruct that materials are to be supplied by nominated suppliers	The materials must be: Specified in the fifth schedule; or Substituted for such items; or In addition to those items already described in the specification
	Instruct that the provisions of this clause will not apply	As far as materials in the fifth schedule or materials substituted for them are concerned
27(1)	Carry out interim valuations	When the architect considers them to be necessary
27(3)	Include the prime cost of any off-site materials in any interim certificate	Provided that: Materials are intended for inclusion Nothing remains to be done to them They have been set apart and marked with employer's name and destination Provision is made for the passing of property if ordered by contractor or sub-contractor They are in accordance with the contract Contractor provides proof of passing of property Contractor provides proof of insurance
28(2)	Issue instructions requiring protective work or continuation of work up to specified point of stoppage	Within 14 days of determination issued under clause 28(1)
29(1)(b)	Issue instructions requiring the contractor to remove and/or dispose of debris etc and execute specified protective work	If the works sustain war damage as defined in clause 29(4)

Table 6.04:   Architect's Duties under JCT Fixed Form of Prime Cost Contract

Clause	Duty	Comment
3(3)	Issue all instructions in writing	
4(1)	Provide the contractor, without charge, with 2 copies of such drawings etc reasonably necessary to explain and amplify the specification or to enable the contractor to carry out and complete the works in accordance with the contract	From time to time as necessary
4(2)	Preserve the confidentiality of the figure in the second schedule	
4(3)	Issue all certificates to the contractor	
5(3)	Issue instructions regarding divergence between statutory requirements and contract documents or architect's instructions	If contractor submits written notice or If the architect otherwise discovers Instruction must be issued within 7 days and the contractor is entitled to payment
6	Determine levels which may be required and provide accurately dimensioned drawings	The contractor is responsible for setting out the works
11(1)	Certify practical completion	When the architect is of the opinion that it has been achieved
11(2)	Deliver a schedule of defects to the contractor specifying defects etc which appear during the defects liability period	Not later than 14 days after the end of the defects liability period The defects must be due to defect etc due to materials or workmanship not in accordance with the contract or frost before practical completion
11(4)	Certify making good defects	When the architect is of the opinion that defects etc he required to be made good have been so made good

Table 6.04: Architect's Duties under JCT Fixed Fee Form of Prime Cost Contract – (continued)

Clause	Duty	Comment
12(a)	Certify his estimate of the approximate prime cost of the relevant part	If, before practical completion, the employer with contractor's consent takes possession of part of the works Certificate must be issued within 7 days of taking possession
12(c)	Certify making good of defects	When the architect is of the opinion that defects etc in the relevant part which he required to be made good have been so made good
19	Make, in writing, a fair and reasonable extension of time	If it is reasonably apparent that progress is being delayed; and Contractor has given required notice; and The delaying events are listed; and Completion of the works is likely to be delayed beyond completion date New date must be fixed so soon as the architect is able to estimate the length of the delay
20(1)	Ascertain or instruct the quantity surveyor to ascertain the amount of loss and/or expense incurred by the contractor	If the contractor has applied in writing within a reasonable time of it becoming apparent that progress has been affected
21(3)(d)	Certify the amount of expenses properly incurred by the employer and the amount of any direct loss and/or expense caused to the employer by determination	The employer is not bound to make any further payment until after completion of the work
23(b)	Direct the contractor as to the amount of each payment to nominated sub-contractors included in each interim certificate. Forthwith inform each nominated sub-contractor of the amounts	On the issue of each interim certificate
23(c)	Issue a certificate stating that the contractor has failed to provide reasonable proof of payment of nominated sub-contractors	If the architect has requested proof and the contractor has so failed The employer may then pay the nominated sub-contractors direct and deduct from monies due to the contractor

Table 6.04: Architect's Duties under JCT Fixed Fee Form of Prime Cost Contract – (continued)

Clause	Duty	Comment
23(d)(i)	Not to unreasonably withhold consent	To the granting of an extension of time by the contractor to the nominated sub-contractor
23(d)(ii)	Certify sub-contractor's failure to complete sub-contract works within the specified or any extended period	If the nominated sub-contractor so fails Copy of the certificate must be sent to the sub-contractor
27(1)	Issue interim certificates stating the amount due to the contractor from the employer according to the rules in clause 27(2)	At the frequency stated in the appendix but not less than 1 calendar month, to practical completion. Thereafter, as and when further amounts are due
27(5)(b)	Issue a certificate releasing half the retention monies	On the issue of the certificate of practical completion
27(5)(c)	Issue a certificate releasing the residue of the retention monies	On the later of: The expiration of the defects liability period; or The issue of the certificate of making good defects
27(6)(a)	Ascertain or instruct the quantity surveyor to ascertain the prime cost of the works Supply particulars to the contractor	Within the period of final ascertainment of prime cost stated in the appendix Not later than the end of the period and before the issue of the final certificate
27(7)	Issue the final certificate	Within 3 months from the latest of: The end of the defects liability period; or Completion of making good clause 11 defects; or Receipts of all documents necessary for computations required by the contract
29(1)(c)	Grant a fair and reasonable extension of time	After war damage has been sustained
30(2)	Issue instructions regarding antiquities	On receipt of the contractor's notification

Table 6.04: Architect's Duties under JCT Fixed Fee Form of Prime Cost Contract – (continued)

Clause	Duty	Comment
30(3)	Ascertain loss and/or expense in connection with antiquities	If the contractor's compliance with architect's instructions has involved the contractor in loss and/or expense for which he will not be reimbursed under any other provision of the contract

Table 6.05: Contractor's Powers under JCT Fixed Fee Form of Prime Cost Contract

Clause	Power	Comment
12	Consent to the employer taking possession of part of the works before practical completion	Within 7 days the architect must issue his certificate stating his estimate of the prime cost of the part. Defects liability period for the part starts on the date of possession. Liquidated damages are to be reduced by the appropriate amount
13(1)	Consent to assignment of the contract by the employer	
13(2)	Assign the contract	With the employer's consent
15(1)(a)	Choose a greater sum than that stated in the appendix	In respect of personal injury or death, or injury or damage to property insurance
16A	Insure all work executed etc against loss or damage due to insurance contingencies	If the employer fails to produce policy receipts on request
16B	Insure existing structures etc against loss or damage due to insurance contingencies Right of entry and inspection to existing structures for the purpose of inventory	If the employer fails to produce policy receipts on request
16B(b)(i)	Determine his employment	Within 28 days of occurrence of clause 16B loss or damage It must be just and equitable to do so; and 7 days notice must be given during which time either party may request arbitration
20(1)	Make written application to the architect for loss and/or expense	Must be made within a reasonable time of it becoming apparent that progress has been materially affected
22(1)(a)	Serve a default notice on the employer	If he does not pay the contractor the amounts due on any certificate within the period for honouring named in the appendix
22(1)	Forthwith determine his employment under the contract	If: The employer does not comply with the default notice under clause 22(1)(a) within 7 days; or

Table 6.05: Contractor's Powers under JCT Fixed Fee Form of Prime Cost Contract – (continued)

Clause	Power	Comment
		The employer interferes with or obstructs any certificate; or The carrying out of substantially the whole of the works is suspended for a period stated in the appendix by reason of: ● *Force majeure*; or ● Insurance losses; or ● Civil commotion; or ● Architect's instructions in regard to addition, omission, substitution or postponement of any item of work; or ● Late instructions; or ● Employer's men; or ● Opening up or testing The employer becomes bankrupt
22(2)	Take possession of and have lien upon all unfixed materials and goods which may have become the property of the employer under clause 8	After the contractor has determined and until payment of all monies due to the contractor
23(a)	Make reasonable objection to a proposed sub-contractor	No such person may be nominated
23(d)(i)	Grant extension of time to a nominated sub-contractor	With the architect's written consent
24(a)	Agree to the nomination as supplier of a person who will not enter into a contract of sale in accordance with the terms set out in this clause	
24(c)	Refuse to enter into a contract with a nominated supplier	Until the architect has specifically approved in writing any restrictions, limitations or exclusions upon the liability of the supplier and included in the contract of sale
28(1)	Determine his employment under the contract	If 28 days has elapsed from the date of general mobilisation; *and* Practical completion has not occured (unless war damage has been sustained)
28(2)	Abandon protective work etc ordered by the architect	If prevented from completing within 3 months for reasons beyond his control

Table 6.06: Contractor's Duties under JCT Fixed Fee Form of Prime Cost Contract

Clause	Duty	Comment
2	Carry out and complete the works in accordance with the specification and agreement	If approval of materials and workmanship are to be for the architect's opinion, they are to be to his reasonable satisfaction
3(2)	Forthwith comply with architect's instructions Comply with architect's written notice	Oral instructions are of no immediate effect, but must be confirmed in writing If the contractor does not comply within 7 days, the employer may employ and pay others to do the work
3(3)	Confirm in writing to the architect within 7 days	If the architect purports to issue an oral instruction If he does not dissent within 7 days it takes effect forthwith
4(2)	To use the specification and any other details only for the purposes of the contract	
5(1)	Comply with and give all notices required by statutory requirements	
5(2)	Immediately give the architect a written notice	If he finds any divergence between statutory requirements and contract documents or AIs
5(4)(a)	Supply such limited materials and workmanship as reasonably necessary	If the contractor has to comply with the statutory requirements as an emergency measure
5(4)(b)	Forthwith inform the architect	Of the emergency and the steps being taken
6	Set out the works	Architect must provide levels and accurately dimensioned drawings Contractor must correct errors at his own cost unless architect instructs otherwise
7(1)	Provide all labour, materials, goods, plant, stores and services required for the	Subject to clauses 13, 23 and 24 must not make greater provision than reasonably required or he does so at his own cost

Table 6.06: Contractor's Duties under JCT Fixed Fee Form of Prime Cost Contract – (continued)

Clause	Duty	Comment
	carrying out and completion of the works	
7(2)	Constantly keep a competent foreman-in-charge upon the works	Instructions given to him are deemed to have been given to the contractor
7(3)	Provide materials, goods and workmanship of kinds and standards described in the specification	Only so far as is procurable
7(3)	Provide vouchers to prove that goods etc comply with this sub-clause	If the architect so requests
8(1)	Not to allow unfixed goods etc intended for the works to be removed therefrom	Unless the architect gives written consent. If goods etc have become the property of the employer, the contractor remains responsible for loss or damage
9	Give access to the architect and his representatives to the works and workshops and by a term in the sub-contract give a similar right in respect of sub-contract works and do all things reasonably necessary to make such rights effective	At all reasonable times
10	Give every reasonable facility to enable the clerk of works to carry out his duties	
11(2)	Make good defects etc in the schedule of defects within a reasonable time	Defects must: Have appeared within the defects liability period Be due to materials or workmanship not in accordance with the contract or frost occurring before practical completion Be notified not later than 14 days after the end of the defects liability period

Table 6.06: Contractor's Duties under JCT Fixed Fee Form of Prime Cost Contract – (continued)

Clause	Duty	Comment
11(3)	Make good defects etc in architect's instructions	As above Architect may issue such instructions whenever he considers it necessary but not later than the delivery of the schedule of defects
11(5)	Make good damage by frost appearing after practical completion	If the architect certifies that it is due to injury taking place before practical completion
14(1)	Indemnify the employer against any claim, etc in respect of personal injury or death	Arising out of the carrying out of the contract unless due to employer's act or neglect
14(2)	Indemnify the employer against any claim, etc in respect of injury or damage to real or personal property	Must arise out of the carrying out of the contract and be due to contractor's negligence etc Not applicable if damage is at risk of the employer under clause 16A and 16B
15(1)(a)	Maintain and cause all sub-contractors to maintain insurance against personal injury or death and damage to real or personal property	
15(1)(b)	Produce and cause any sub-contractor to produce evidence of insurance and the policies and premium receipts	If so required by the architect On any occasion required by the employer provided the request is not unreasonable or vexatious
15(2)	Maintain insurance in joint names against claims against employer due to collapse etc of property other than the works Policies and receipts must be placed with the architect	If the architect issues an instruction to that effect Architect must approve insurers
16A	Forthwith give notice to the architect and employer in writing stating extent, nature and location of the damage	On discovering damage caused by clause 16A contingencies

Table 6.06: Contractor's Duties under JCT Fixed Fee Form of Prime Cost Contract – (continued)

Clause	Duty	Comment
16A(b)	With due diligence restore damaged works, etc dispose of debris and carry out and complete the works	After damage under clause 16A Extra work deemed to be addition required by the architect to items in the specification
16B	Forthwith give notice to architect and employer in writing stating extent, nature and location of the damage	On discovering damage caused by clause 16B contingencies
16B(c)(i)	With due diligence reinstate or make good loss or damage and carry out and complete the work	After damage under clause 16B if the contractor's employment is not determined
17	Begin the works, regularly and diligently proceed and complete them on or before the date for completion	On the date for possession and after possession has been given
18	Pay liquidated damages to the employer	If the architect has issued his certificate of non-completion
19	Forthwith give written notice to the architect of the cause of delay Constantly use best endeavours to prevent delay and do all reasonably required to the satisfaction of the architect to proceed with the works	If it becomes reasonably apparent that progress is delayed
21(1)	Comply with default notice from architect	
21(3)(b)	Assign the benefit of any agreement for supply of goods and/or execution of work to the employer without payment	If so required by the employer or architect within 14 days of the date of determination The supplier or sub-contractor to be able to make reasonable objection to any further assignment

Table 6.06: Contractor's Duties under JCT Fixed Fee Form of Prime Cost Contract – (continued)

Clause	Duty	Comment
21(3)(c)	Remove from the works any temporary buildings etc	After the employer has determined and as and when required to do so by the architect in writing
21(3)(d)	Allow or pay to the employer direct loss and/or expense after determination	To be taken into account when the architect makes a final certification of monies after determination
22(2)(a)	Remove from site all temporary buildings etc and give facilities to sub-contractors to do the same	With reasonable dispatch and with due precautions to prevent injury, death or damage
23(b)	Discharge interim payments to nominated sub-contractors	As directed by architect
23(c)	Provide reasonable proof of discharge to nominated sub-contractors	If requested by the architect
23(d)(i)	Request the architect's consent to extension of time for nominated sub-contractors	Architect must be informed of sub-contractor's representations
24(b)	Payments to nominated suppliers must be in full within 30 days of end of month in which delivery made	Less only cash discount of 5% if so paid
25	Permit work not forming part of the contract by other persons engaged by the employer	
26(3)	Keep full and accurate accounts of, and all invoices relating to, all payments made and work performed for the purpose of this contract	

Table 6.06: Contractor's Duties under JCT Fixed Fee Form of Prime Cost Contract – (continued)

Clause	Duty	Comment
27(2)	Send to the architect all documents necessary to ascertain amount to be stated as due in any interim certificate	
27B(3)(a)	Either: Provide evidence to the employer of entitlement to payment without statutory deduction; or Inform employer in writing, copy to architect, that he is not entitled to be paid without deduction	Not later than 21 days: Before first contractual payment; or After the employer has become a "contractor"
27B(4)(a)	Inform employer if he gets tax certificate	If previously not entitled to payment without deduction Deduction not made thereafter
27(4)(b)	Provide evidence to employer of entitlement to payment without statutory deduction Inform the employer in writing of cessation of entitlement after expiry of certificate	If tax certificate expires before final payment due. Contractor must take action at least 28 days before expiry If not satisfied, employer will make deduction
27(4)(c)	Immediately write to employer	If tax certificate is cancelled
28(2)	Comply with instruction after determination	If issued within 14 days after determination under clause 28(1)
29(1)(c)	Reinstate etc war damage and carry out and complete the works	If war damage sustained
30(1)	Leave antiquities undisturbed Take all necessary steps to preserve Inform the architect or clerk of works	

Table 6.07:   Employer's Powers under JCT Fixed Fee Form of Prime Cost Contract

Clause	Power	Comment
3(2)	Employ and pay others and deduct the cost from contractor	If contractor fails to comply with architect's notice regarding instruction
10	Appoint a clerk of works	His duties are purely that of inspector on behalf of the employer under the direction of the architect
12	Take possession of part of the works	With the contractor's consent
13(1)	Assign the contract	With the contractor's consent
13(2)	Consent to the assignment of the contract by the contractor	
15(1)(b)	Require the contractor to produce policies or premium receipts	But not unreasonably or vexatiously
15(1)(c)	Insure and deduct premium amounts from monies due to the contractor	If contractor fails to insure against personal injury or death or injury to real or personal property
15(2)(c)	Insure against damage to property	If the contractor fails to insure
16B	Determine the contractor's employment	Within 28 days of the occurence of clause 16B damage It must be just and equitable to do so and 7 days' notice must be given during which time either party may request arbitration
18	Deduct liquidated damages from monies due or to become due to the contractor	If the architect issues his certificate of non-completion
21	Forthwith determine the contractor's employment	If the contractor continues a default for 14 days after receipt of a default notice from the architect under this clause; or

Table 6.07: Employer's Powers under JCT Fixed Fee Form of Prime Cost Contract – (continued)

Clause	Power	Comment
		If the contractor repeats the default at any time thereafter Notice of determination must be given within 10 days after the continuance or repetition
21(2)	Reinstate the contractor's employment	If the contractor, his liquidator etc agree after automatic determination due to bankruptcy etc
21(3)(a)	Employ and pay other persons to carry out and complete the works	After the employer has determined the contractor's employment The other persons or the employer have the right to enter the site and use all temporary plant etc belonging to the contractor
21(3)(b)	Require the contractor to assign him without payment the benefit of any agreement for goods or work	Must be done within 14 days of the date of determination and the sub-contractors or suppliers have the right of reasonable objection to any further assignment by the employer Does not apply if determination was for bankruptcy etc
21(3)(c)	Remove and sell contractor's property holding the proceeds less all costs to the credit of the contractor	If contractor has not removed temporary buildings etc from site within a reasonable time of the architect requiring him in writing to do so
23(c)	Pay nominated sub-contractors direct	If architect has certified that contractor has failed to comply with a request for proof of payment
25	Carry out work not forming part of the contract with the aid of other persons	
27(4)(a)	Retain a percentage of any interim certificate issued before the issue of the certificate of practical completion	Retention percentage must be 5 % unless a lower rate is agreed between the parties and noted in the appendix

Clause	Power	Comment
27(4)(b)	Retain a percentage equal to half the retention percentage	For certificates issued before the residue of retention is released but after practical completion is certified
27(5)(a)	Recourse to the retention fund for payment of any amount he is entitled to deduct from monies due to the contractor	Otherwise the employer's interest is fiduciary as trustee
28(1)	Determine the contractor's employment under the contract forthwith	If 28 days have elapsed from the date of general mobilisation; *and* Practical completion has not occurred (unless war damage has been sustained)

Table 6.08: Employer's Duties under JCT Fixed Fee Form of Prime Cost Contract

Clause	Duty	Comment
4(2)	Preserve the confidentiality of the figure contained in the second schedule	
13	Not to assign the contract	Without the contractor's consent
16A	Maintain insurance against clause 16A contingencies Produce policy and last premium receipt for inspection by contractor	If so requested by the contractor
16B	Maintain insurance against clause 16B contingencies Produce receipt showing that the policy is effective	If so requested by the contractor
17	Give possession of the site to contractor	On the date for possession
22(1)(a)	Comply with default notice from contractor	
22(2)(b)	Pay the contractor: Prime cost of all the work executed at the date of determination	After the contractor has determined his employment
	Prime cost of materials ordered for the works for which the contractor has paid or is legally bound to pay Fixed fee adjusted to take into account direct loss and/or expense due Reasonable cost of removal of temporary plant, etc from site Any direct loss and/or damage caused to the contractor by the determination after taking into account amounts previously paid	Goods become the property of the employer

Table 6.08: Employer's Duties under JCT Fixed Fee Form of Prime Cost Contract – (continued)

Clause	Duty	Comment
26(1)	Pay to the contractor: The prime cost of the works The fixed fee stated in the second schedule	At times and in the manner stipulated in the contract Fixed fee must be adjusted to take account of loss and/or expense
27(1)	Pay within the period for honouring certificates stated in the appendix	
27B(2)	Notify the contractor	If the employer becomes a "contractor" for the purposes of the Finance (No 2) Act 1975; and The words "was a 'contractor'" have been deleted from para (a)
27(3)(b)	Give written notification to the contractor that he intends to make the statutory deduction from payments due under the contract	If he is not satisfied with the evidence submitted by the contractor that he is entitled to be paid without statutory deduction
27B(5)	Promptly pass all vouchers, submitted by the contractor, to the Inland Revenue	If the employer is a "contractor"
27B(6)(a)	Notify the contractor in writing Require the contractor's statement of the amount to be included representing direct cost, to contractor of any other person, of materials used in carrying out the works	If he considers that the Act requires him to make statutory deduction from payment due to be made Not later than 7 days before each future payment becomes due (or within 10 days of the notification above, if that would be later)
27B(7)	Repay to, or deduct from, payments to contractor to correct errors	If an error has occurred, unless there is a contrary statutory obligation
28(3)	Pay the contractor as though protective work etc instructed by the architect were an addition to items in the specification	If: 14 days has elapsed since determination has occurred following outbreak of hostilities; and Protective works are required by the architect The contractor is also entitled to be paid as though he had determined under clause 22 except that he is not entitled to any loss and/or damage caused by the determination

Table 6.09: Clauses that may Give Rise to Claims under JCT Fixed Fee Form of Prime Cost Contract

Clause	Event	Type
3(1)	Alteration in the scope or nature of the works	CL
3(2)	Employer engages others to do the work without proper procedure	CL
4(1)	Failure to provide information reasonably necessary or failure to provide it at the correct time	CL
4(2)	Employer or architect divulging confidential information	CL
4(3)	Failure to issue certificates to the contractor	CL
5(2)	Divergence between statutory requirements and contract documents or architect's instructions	C
5(3)	Architect's failure to issue instruction within 7 days	CL
6	Failure to provide levels or accurately dimensioned drawings for setting out	CL
7(3)	Materials, goods and workmanship not procurable	C
7(4)	Opening up or testing of works etc found to be in accordance with the contract	C
8(1)	Unreasonably withholding consent to the removal of goods	CL

Table 6.09: Clauses that may Give Rise to Claims under JCT Fixed Fee Form of Prime Cost Contract – (continued)

Clause	Event	Type
10	Clerk of works exceeding contractual duties	CL
11(1)	Failure to issue certificate of practical completion	CL
11(2)	Failure to deliver a schedule of defects	CL
11(3)	Late instructions to make good defects	CL
11(4)	Failure to issue certificate of making good defects	CL
11(5)	Wrongful instruction to make good frost damage	CL
12	Possession without contractor's consent	CL
12(a)	Failure to issue certificate of partial completion	CL
12(b)	Failure to give effect to all the results of the certificate	CL
12(c)	Failure to issue certificate of making good defects	CL
12(d)	Failure to reduce liquidated damages correctly or at all	CL
12(e)(i)	Failure to release half retention on possession	CL
12(e)(ii)	Failure to release remainder of retention	CL

Table 6.09: Clauses that may Give Rise to Claims under JCT Fixed Fee Form of Prime Cost Contract – (continued)

Clause	Event	Type
13(1)	Assignment by employer without consent	CL
13(3)	Unreasonably withholding consent to sub-letting to the prejudice of the contractor	CL
15(2)	Effects of special insurance Special insurance under architect's instruction	CL C
16A(b)	Restoration of damaged work	C
16B(a)	Wrongful computation of amounts payable to the contractor	CL
16B(b)	Invalid determination	C
16B(c)(iii)	Reinstatement of damaged work	C
17	Failure to give possession on due date	CL
18	Wrongful deduction of liquidated damages	CL
19	Architect not carrying out his duties	CL
20	Loss and/or expense	C
21	Invalid determination	CL
22(2)	Payment after determination	C

Table 6.09: Clauses that may Give Rise to Claims under JCT Fixed Fee Form of Prime Cost Contract – (continued)

Clause	Event	Type
23	Nominated sub-contractors	CL
24	Nominated suppliers	CL
25	Work by employer	CL
26(1)	Failure to pay in accordance with the conditions	CL
27(1)	Certificates	C
27	Failure to observe rules	CL
27(5)	Interest on retention monies	CL
28(3)	Payment for protective work	C
29(1)	Making good war damage	C
30(3)	Loss and/or expense regarding antiquities	C

KEY
C = Contractual claims
CL = Common law claims
Contractual claims are usually dealt with by the architect
Common law claims are usually dealt with by the employer

Table 6.10: Certificates to be Issued by the Architect under JCT Fixed Fee Form of Prime Cost Contract

Clause	Certificate
11(1)	Practical
11(4)	Making good of defects
11(5)	That damage by frost which may appear after practical completion is due to injury which took place before practical completion
12(a)	Estimate of approximate prime cost of relevant part
12(c)	Making good of partial possession
18	Non-completion by the due date
21(3)(d)	Expenses incurred by employer on determination of contractor's employment by employer
23(c)	Contractor's failure to comply with request for reasonable proof of payment of nominated sub-contractor
23(d)(ii)	Nominated sub-contractor's failure to complete sub-contract works on the due date
27(1)	Interim certificates
27(5)(b)	Release of first moiety of retention
27(5)(c)	Release of residue of retention
27(7)	Final certificate

Table 6.11: Architect's Instructions Empowered by JCT Fixed Fee Form of Prime Cost Contract

Clause	Instruction
3	As the architect thinks fit except any instruction requiring an alteration in the nature or the scope of the works
5(3)	In relation to divergence between any contract document or architect's instruction and any statutory requirement
6	That errors in setting out are not to be amended
11(2)	That items in the schedule of defects are not to be made good
11(3)	Requiring defects etc to be made good That defects etc are not to be made good
15(2)(a)	Require the contractor to take out special insurance
16B(c)(ii)	Requiring removal and disposal of debris after loss and damage
23	Nominating a sub-contractor
28(2)	Requiring execution of protective work or continuation of work up to specified point of stoppage after determination on the outbreak of hostilities
29(1)(b)	Requiring removal and disposal of debris and execution of protective work after war damage
30(2)	Regarding antiquities, including excavation, examination or removal by third parties

Flowchart 6.12:   Architect's Instructions

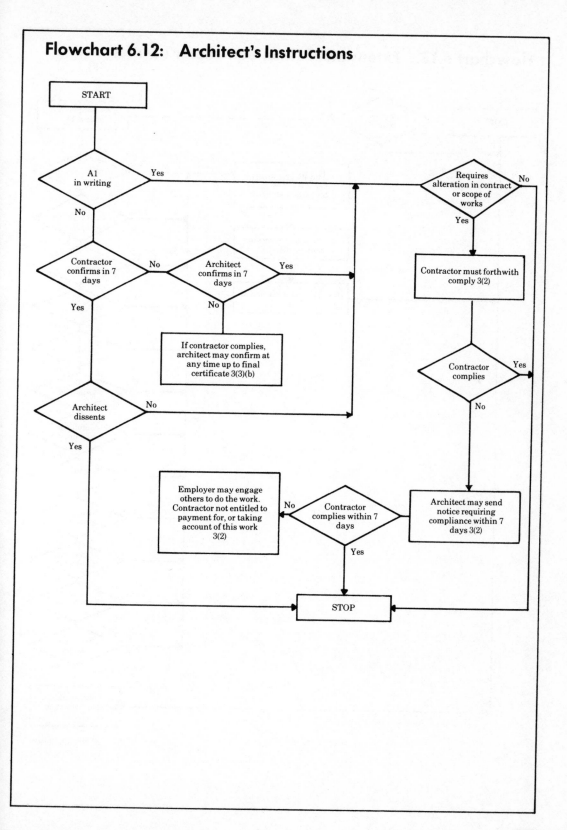

Flowchart 6.13: Extension of Time: Contractor's Duties

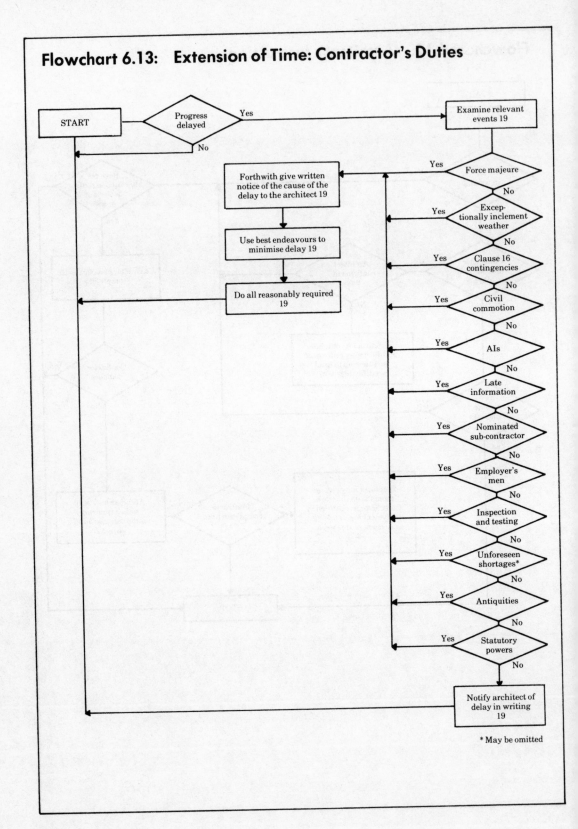

* May be omitted

Flowchart 6.14:   Extension of Time: Architect's Duties

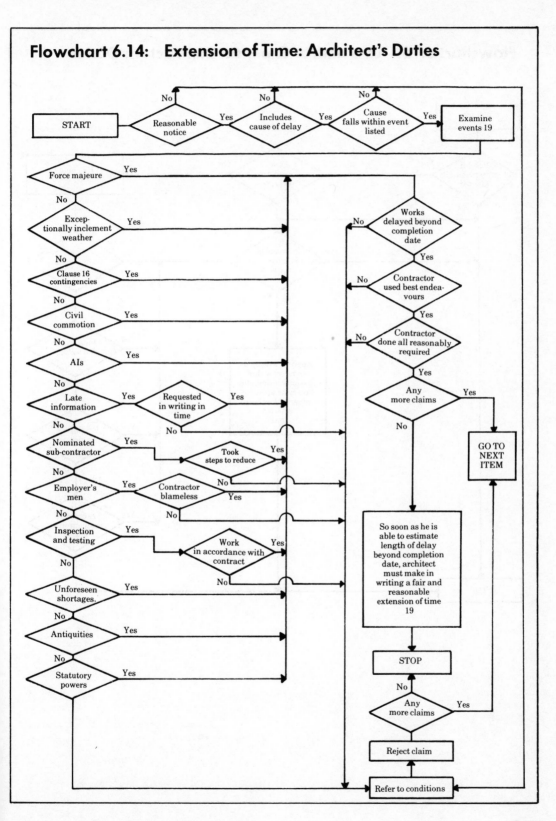

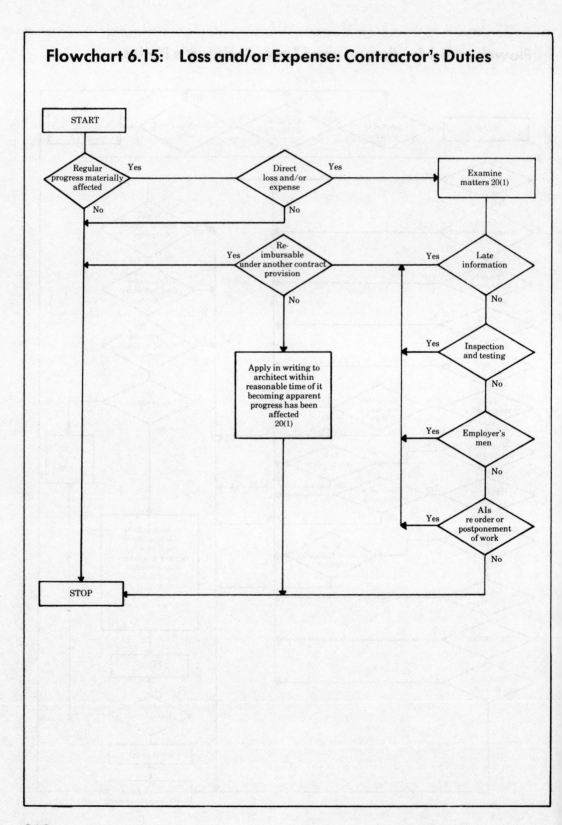

Flowchart 6.15:   Loss and/or Expense: Contractor's Duties

START

Regular progress materially affected

Yes → Direct loss and/or expense — Yes → Examine matters 20(1)

No

No

Re-imbursable under another contract provision — Yes →

No

Late information — Yes →

No

Inspection and testing — Yes →

No

Employer's men — Yes →

No

AIs re order or postponement of work — Yes →

No

Apply in writing to architect within reasonable time of it becoming apparent progress has been affected 20(1)

STOP

Flowchart 6.16: Loss and/or Expense: Architect's Duties

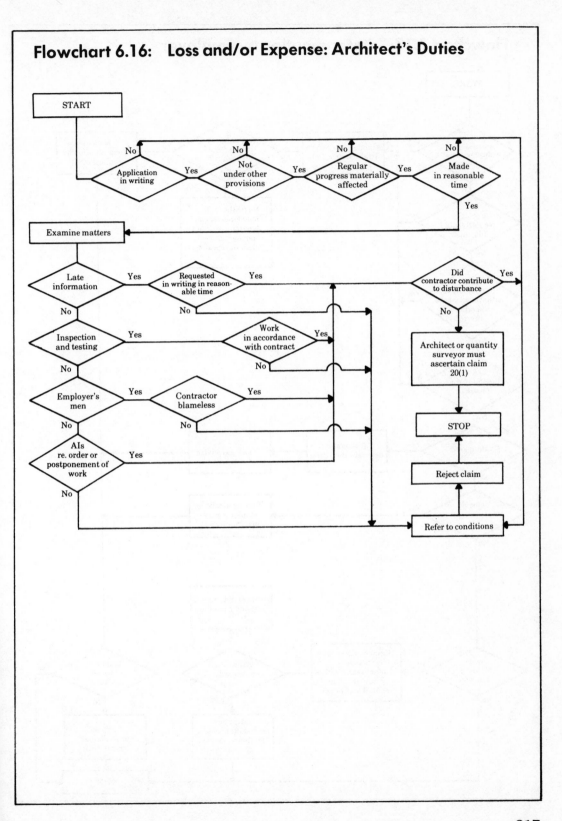

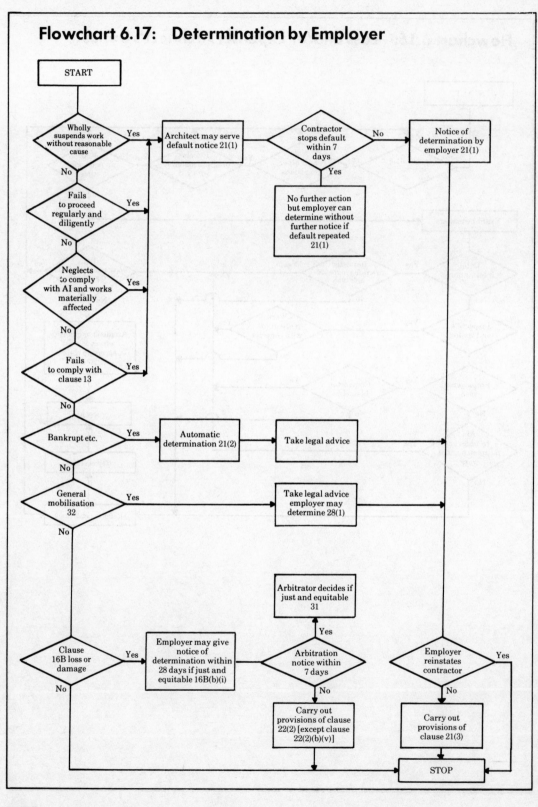

Flowchart 6.17: Determination by Employer

START

Wholly suspends work without reasonable cause — Yes → Architect may serve default notice 21(1) → Contractor stops default within 7 days — No → Notice of determination by employer 21(1)

Contractor stops default within 7 days — Yes → No further action but employer can determine without further notice if default repeated 21(1)

Fails to proceed regularly and diligently — Yes

Neglects to comply with AI and works materially affected — Yes

Fails to comply with clause 13 — Yes

Bankrupt etc. — Yes → Automatic determination 21(2) → Take legal advice

General mobilisation 32 — Yes → Take legal advice employer may determine 28(1)

Clause 16B loss or damage — Yes → Employer may give notice of determination within 28 days if just and equitable 16B(b)(i) → Arbitration notice within 7 days

Arbitration notice within 7 days — Yes → Arbitrator decides if just and equitable 31

Arbitration notice within 7 days — No → Carry out provisions of clause 22(2) [except clause 22(2)(b)(v)]

Employer reinstates contractor — Yes

Employer reinstates contractor — No → Carry out provisions of clause 21(3)

STOP

318

Flowchart 6.18: Determination by Contractor

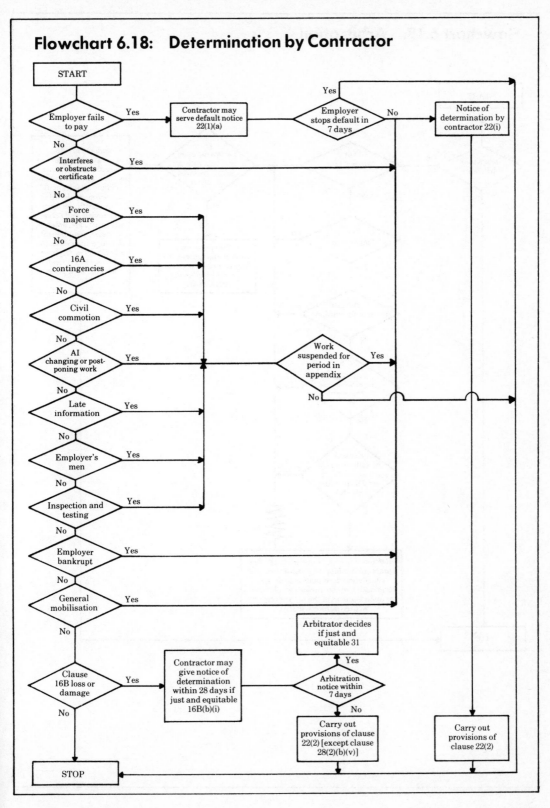

Flowchart 6.19:   Arbitration

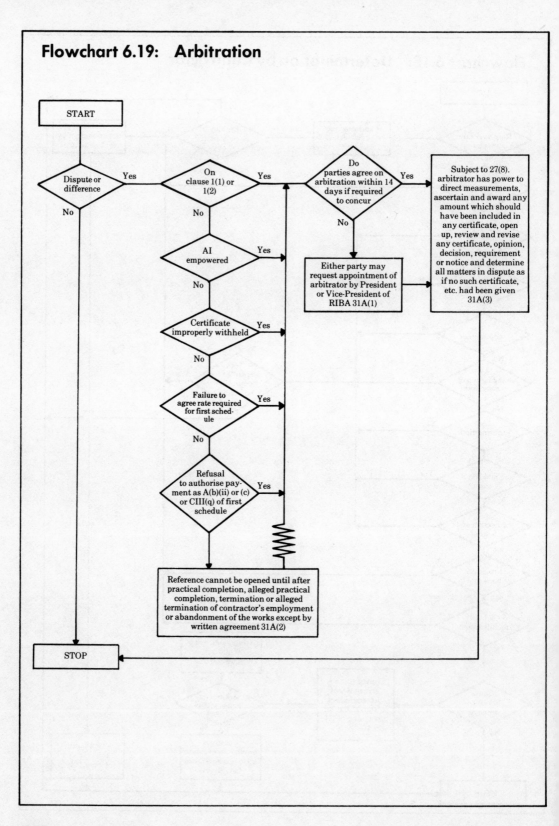

START

Dispute or difference — Yes → On clause 1(1) or 1(2) — Yes → Do parties agree on arbitration within 14 days if required to concur — Yes → Subject to 27(8). arbitrator has power to direct measurements, ascertain and award any amount which should have been included in any certificate, open up, review and revise any certificate, opinion, decision, requirement or notice and determine all matters in dispute as if no such certificate, etc. had been given 31A(3)

Dispute or difference — No

On clause 1(1) or 1(2) — No

AI empowered — Yes

AI empowered — No

Certificate improperly withheld — Yes

Certificate improperly withheld — No

Failure to agree rate required for first schedule — Yes

Failure to agree rate required for first schedule — No

Refusal to authorise payment as A(b)(ii) or (c) or CIII(q) of first schedule — Yes

Do parties agree on arbitration within 14 days if required to concur — No → Either party may request appointment of arbitrator by President or Vice-President of RIBA 31A(1)

Reference cannot be opened until after practical completion, alleged practical completion, termination or alleged termination of contractor's employment or abandonment of the works except by written agreement 31A(2)

STOP

7: JCT Form With Contractor's Design

7.01   Introduction

The JCT Standard Form of Building Contract With Contractor's Design was published in 1981. It has been amended five times, the last amendment being issued in April 1989. Closely modelled on the layout and wording of JCT 80, it is widely used for package deal projects.

The form is intended for use where design details are not to be issued by the employer or the architect on his behalf. It is therefore a true design and build contract. If the architect is to produce and issue design details, leaving only a portion of the works to be designed by the contractor, the separate Contractor's Designed Portion Supplement must be used in conjunction with JCT 80.

The JCT has produced two very useful Practice Notes which are essential reading for users of the form. It should be noted, however, that the notes have no contractual significance if the interpretation of the contract comes before the courts for decision.

Practice Note CD/1A gives a brief introduction to the form and the three vital documents (discussed below) which are required for carrying out the work under its provisions. It also deals with VAT and insurance matters particularly in regard to the contractor's design liability.

Practice Note CD/1B is a brief clause-by-clause commentary on the form with some notes on the Contract Sum Analysis and formula price adjustment.

Because this is essentially a package deal and the contractor is responsible for design and construction, there is no reference to the architect in the form, but provision is made (article 3) for an employer's agent who might well be, and often is, an architect. He is specifically mentioned only twice more. He is given a right of access of the works (clause 11) and the contract and related documents must be made available to him at all reasonable times (clause 5.4). Elsewhere in the form, the reference is to the employer.

Practice Note CD/1D, para 4, makes the point that the employer may wish to use his own architect or quantity surveyor at pre-contract stage and retain him afterwards to advise on the contractor's execution of the works and the amount and timing of payment. The employer certainly requires skilled professional advice throughout the stages because the contract is extremely complex from an administrative point of view and can be compared with JCT 80 in this respect.

In many clauses this contract is virtually identical to JCT 80 in its wording. Therefore, experience gained from using JCT 80 will be relevant to the architect acting as employer's agent. Some minor points of drafting require attention, but these apart it is an exceptionally good form of contract within the parameters set. It gives adequate safeguards to both employer and contractor, but its use requires a great deal of preplanning on the part of the employer and his professional advisers. The key to success lies in good contractor selection procedures and careful drafting of the employer's requirements which are the basis of the contract. A wish to make use of nominated sub-contractors will normally preclude the use of the form, but specialists can be employed, if essential, under the clause 29 provisions (execution of work not forming part of the contract). In addition, amendment 3, issued in February 1988, makes it possible to incorporate in the contract a set of optional provisions which include a provision for the naming of persons as sub-contractors. It is suggested that, although optional, the provisions should commonly be stated to apply. To achieve this, appendix 1 must contain an appropriate entry. Briefly, the optional provisions are as follows:

- *Adjudication*: This provision modifies the arbitration provisions in clause 39. When a dispute arises, it is first to be referred to an adjudicator named in appendix 1 if the dispute concerns any of a list of "adjudication matters". The procedure is designed to be quick. Within 14 days of either party giving notice to the other that a dispute has arisen both parties must make written statements on the matters for the adjudicator. Within a further 14 days (or such other time as may be agreed) the adjudicator must say when he will give his decision and he may ask for more information. The adjudicator's decision is deemed to be a provision of the contract and prevails, if there is a conflict, over any other provision. There is provision for either party to object to the decision within 14 days, but it remains in place until after practical completion when arbitration may take place.

- *Submission of drawings to the employer*: This enables the employer to set out in the employer's requirements, his wishes with regard to the contractor's submission of drawings and the employer's rights to comment. It is made clear that the employer's comments or lack of them will not affect the contractor's responsibility under the contract unless the comments specifically so state.
- *Site manager*: This provision replaces clause 10 if the employer's requirements so state. The contractor must obtain the employer's consent to the appointment of a site manager prior to commencement of work on site. He must not be replaced without the employer's written consent. The site manager and any other servant, agent, supplier or sub-contractor of the contractor must attend a meeting convened by the employer as necessary.
- *Persons named as sub-contractors in employer's requirements*: This provision has many similarities to the naming provisions in IFC 84. The employer may name a person in the employer's requirements who is to be employed as a sub-contractor. The contractor must enter into a sub-contract as soon as reasonably practicable unless there is a bona fide reason not to do so. Then the employer may either remove the reason or omit the work and issue instructions regarding its execution, but may not name another person. The contractor may, however, be required to select another person or the employer may employ a person directly under clause 29. The employer's consent must be obtained before determination of the named person's employment. The contractor must complete the balance of the work and it is treated as a change unless due to the contractor's default. The contractor must account to the employer in respect of amounts he has, or could have, recovered by reasonable diligence provided that the amounts can properly be regarded as due in reduction of the costs to the employer of the change.
- *Bills of quantities*: This provision sets out the way in which bills of quantities are to be prepared and used if they are part of the employer's requirements. In general, the provisions are similar to terms relating to bills of quantities in other JCT contracts.
- *Valuation of change instructions – direct loss and/or expense – submission of estimates by the contractor*: The provision assumes that the number of changes will be small. Clause 12 (changes), clause 25 (extension of time) and clause 26 (loss and/or expense) are modified by this provision. There are similarities to ACA 2 provisions. If it is thought that compliance with an instruction will entail valuation, extension of time or loss and/or expense, the contractor must submit to the employer (normally within 14 days), estimates of the value of any adjustment in cost, additional resources, method statement, length of extension required and amount of loss and/or expense. The contractor need not submit the estimates if the employer states that estimates are not required or the contractor raises reasonable objection within 10 days of receipt of instructions. After submission, all reasonable steps must be taken to agree the estimates. Failing agreement within 10 days, the employer may instruct compliance and this provision will not apply, or may withdraw the instruction, or may refer the matter to the adjudicator. The contractor is not entitled to any additional payment if the instruction is withdrawn unless he had been involved in any additional design work. If the contractor fails to submit an estimate, his compliance with the instruction is to be dealt with in accordance with clauses 12, 25 and 26 of the contract, but any addition to the contract sum will not be made until the final account and no interest or financing charges will be included.

- *Direct loss and/or expense – submission of estimates by the contractor*: This provision modifies clause 26 (loss and/or expense) and makes it similar to the equivalent provision in ACA 2. If the contractor is entitled to direct loss and/or expense, he must submit an estimate to the employer on presentation of the next application for payment. He must continue to submit estimates with subsequent applications for payment so long as the loss and/or expense continues to be incurred. Within 21 days of receipt of the estimate, the employer may request further information, but he must also give written notice that he accepts it, he wishes to negotiate, or the provisions of clause 26 are to apply. An important term provides that an acceptance, agreement or adjudicator's decision is final and no further additions are to be made to the contract sum in respect of that particular matter during the period under consideration. If the contractor fails to submit estimates, the loss and/or expense is to be dealt with under clause 26 and adjustment of the contract sum is not to take place until the final account. No interest or financing charges are claimable in respect of the amounts in such an instance.

The essential feature of the package deal contract is that the contractor takes full responsibility for the whole of the process from initial briefing to completion. This form compares favourably with ACA 2 and it is much to be preferred to the "in-house" contracts produced by specialists in this sort of work. The contents are summarised in **Table 7.01.**

7.02   Contractor's Obligations

The contractor's basic obligation is to carry out and complete the works in accordance with the contract documents "and for that purpose shall complete the design for the Works including the selection of any specifications for any kinds and standards of the materials, goods and workmanship. . .*so far as not described* or stated in the Employer's Requirements or Contractor's Proposals" (clause 2.1).

This must be read in conjunction with clause 2.5, which is the contractor's design warranty and the need, in the interest of the employer, to ensure that the contractor takes out a professional indemnity policy. It should be noted that the contract contains no requirements that the contractor must insure his liabilities under clause 2.5. In this respect, it compares unfavourably with ACA 2 in its design and construct mode. It is crucial that the employer protects his interests in the event of the contractor being unable to meet a claim and provision must be made either in the employer's requirements or by amending the contract itself.

Clause 2.5.1 states, "insofar as the design of the Works is comprised in the Contractor's Proposals and in what the Contractor is to complete under clause 2 and in accordance with the Employer's Requirements and the Conditions", the contractor's design liability is "the like liability ... as would an architect ... or other appropriate professional designer holding himself out as competent to take on work for such design". In other words, liability will depend on proof of negligence and the contractor is not guaranteeing the result. The standard, therefore, is that of the ordinary and reasonably competent professional designer exercising ordinary professional care and skill, although the courts seem keen to impose liability if it is possible to do so.

Clause 2.5.3 restricts the contractor's liability still further where work other than dwellings is involved. In such a case, the contractor's liability for loss of use, loss of profit or other consequential loss due to design failure is limited to whatever amount, if any, is specified in appendix 1. The whole of these provisions are a serious obstacle to the recovery of damages by the employer from a contractor who is negligent. From the contractor's point of view, it is a necessary safeguard and, if removed, the tender price will reflect the contractor's increased liability. It is something which the employer must consider carefully before embarking on this kind of contract. Put simply, and increased protection required by the employer will have to be paid for.

7.03   Contract Documentation and Information

In addition to the printed form, three further documents must be prepared:
● The employer's requirements
● The contractor's proposals
● The contract sum analysis.

Because the definition of the contractor's work is confined to the first two documents, their importance cannot be over-emphasised.

The employer's requirements
Practice Note CD/1A (paras 8 to 10) summarises the main points to be borne in mind in preparing this document. It is suggested in the note that it may range from little more than a description of the accommodation required to anything up to a full "scheme design". The essential point is "to give a sufficient brief to the contractor on the kind of building and accommodation the employer requires" so that the contractor can formulate his proposals. In practice, the employer will often make use of a full-scale and detailed performance specification to ensure that his requirements are properly understood and catered for. Note that:
● There is no provision for nominated sub-contractors or suppliers
● The works cannot be effectively controlled on sparse information.

Critical areas are the related ones of quality and price.
Table 7.11 summarises some of the matters to be taken into account in preparing the brief.

The contractor's proposals
They are the contractor's response to the employer's requirements. As a result of the wording of clause 2.4.1, if there is a discrepancy in the employer's requirements, "the Contractor's Proposals shall prevail. . .without any adjustments in the Contract Sum". It might be the case that the contractor's proposals do not deal with the discrepancy in the employer's requirements. In that situation, the contractor must submit written proposals to deal with the discrepancy. The employer may either agree or decide himself, notifying the contractor in writing. Either case is to be treated as a change in the employer's requirements.
If there is a discrepancy in the contractor's proposals, the contractor must inform the employer in writing of his proposed amendment to remove the discrepancy. The employer is entitled to decide between the items in question or

the contractor's proposed amendment and the contractor must comply at no cost to the employer (clause 2.4.2). The employer will examine the contractor's proposals and, as Practice Note CD/1B observes, "it may therefore be presumed that what is in the proposals is what the employer wishes to be carried out". The employer is advised to amend his own requirements before the contract documents are signed, if he accepts a divergence in the contractor's proposals. Hence the advice given in the footnote to the third recital:

"Where the Employer has accepted a divergence in the Proposals submitted by the Contractor from the Requirements as issued by the Employer to tenderers, the divergence should be removed by deletion or substitution in the Employer's Requirements before the contract documents are signed".

Failure to do this and the subsequent discovery of a discrepancy between employer's requirements and contractor's proposals leaves the contract strangely silent. Stronger wording of the third recital would overcome the difficulty which is sometimes encountered in practice.

The contractor's proposals must, therefore, be scrutinised with the greatest care to ensure that they accord with the brief. Requirements and proposals must be consistent. Practice Note CD/1A (para 23) recommends that the proposals should include the following items "in such detail as the Requirements may state":

● Plans, elevations, sections or typical details and the scales to which they should be drawn
● Information about structural design
● Layout drawings indicating the services to be incorporated
● Specifications for materials and workmanship.

The contract sum analysis

There is no provision for priced bills of quantities or a schedule of rates and therefore, the contract sum analysis forms the basis of valuation of changes (clause 12) and of formula price adjustment, where applicable (clause 38).

The precise form and content of the analysis should be stipulated by the employer in his requirements. It is to be submitted by the contractor and annexed to the contractor's proposals. Practice Note CD/1A points out that "it should allow for including design work in the valuation of changes" (para 26).

The contract, therefore, comprises all three documents together with printed conditions, clause 2.2 of which provides:

"Nothing contained in the Employer's Requirements or the Contractor's Proposals or the Contract Sum Analysis shall override or modify the application or interpretation of that which is contained in the Articles of Agreement, the Conditions or the Appendices".

The printed form is, therefore, given priority. In this, the form closely follows the practice observed in other JCT contracts.

7.04 Commencement and Completion

Very unusually, but sensibly, the contract provides that the employer is to define the boundaries of the site (clause 7). Presumably, he may do it by indicating the boundary clearly on a drawing or, less desirably, on the site itself. Although, in the absence of any express clause, it must be implied that the employer should indicate the extent of the site to the contractor, in order to give business efficacy to the contract, the definition is important because of the wording of clause 23.1. This states that, on the date of possession, the employer must give possession of the site to the contractor, who must then immediately begin "the construction of the Works" and proceed "regularly and diligently" so that the works are completed "on or before" the due or the extended date. A useful provision allows the employer to defer giving possession for up to six weeks, depending on the appendix entry. The meaning of "diligence" was examined in regard to an engineering contract in *GLC* v *Cleveland Bridge & Engineering Co Ltd* (1986) 8 ConLR 30. There is provision for liquidated damages to be payable for delay (clause 24), but the employer, before deduction, must have issued a written notice to the contractor that the contractor has failed to complete before the contractual completion date or any extended date. This is the equivalent of the architect's certificate of delay under JCT 80 clause 24.

The deduction of liquidated damages cannot take place unless:

- The employer has issued a written notice to the contractor of failure to complete by the due date
- The employer has required liquidated damages in writing not later than the date when the final account and final statement become conclusive.

There is the usual provision (under clause 24.2.2) for the employer to repay liquidated damages deducted if a further or any extension of time is granted at a later date.

7.05   Extensions of Time

The extension of time provision is closely modelled on the corresponding and identically numbered provision in JCT 80, clause 25, with the substitution of the word employer for architect. There are fourteen grounds which may give rise to an extension of time and they follow the JCT 80 pattern with the exception of the last ground, which is additional in this contract. It is *delay which the contractor has taken all practicable steps to avoid or reduce consequent upon a change in the Statutory Requirements after the Base Date and which affect the Works or an amendment to the Contractor's Proposals necessitated by a decision of the planning authority*. The reference is, in fact, to Development Control Requirements. It should be noted that this clause must be read in conjunction with clause 6.3, from which it is clear that the change in statutory requirements or in the planning authority's decision must have taken place after the base date. The base date is to be inserted in the appendix and it can be any fixed date agreed by the parties.

In common with other contract forms, failure to grant an extension of the contract completion time for delay caused by any act or default of the employer (or the employer's agent) may result in the completion date becoming unenforceable and the employer losing his right to liquidated damages. Since the employer can only grant such extensions under the express terms of the contract, delay caused by a default of the employer which is not included in the list of relevant events may lead to time under the contract becoming at large.

7.06 Employer's Instructions

Clause 4 deals with employer's instructions. It very closely follows the format and wording of JCT 80. The only instructions which can be given are those expressly empowered by the contract. One of the most interesting powers is contained in clause 23.2, which entitles the employer to issue instructions "in regard to the postponement of any *design or construction* work to be executed under..." the contract. An instruction issued under this clause may entitle the contractor to an extension of time: clause 25.4.5.1. If, as a result of such an instruction, the work is suspended for a period named in the appendix, the contractor may determine his employment under the contract (clause 28.1.2.4). It is debatable whether or not this clause could be used if the employer desired the works to be constructed in a particular order.

An instruction changing the order of construction or imposing fresh obligations may be issued under clause 12.1.2, subject to the contractor's right to make reasonable objection to compliance (clause 4.1.1). Generously interpreted, clause 23.2 could achieve the same result, although at considerable cost. However, it should be noted that the general opinion of lawyers is that clause 23.2 does not give the employer power to defer or postpone giving possession of the whole site if the appropriate deferment entry has been omitted from appendix 1.

It is quite clear that, under traditional forms of contract, the architect has no power to instruct the contractor *how* the work is to be done. It has been suggested that the position is different under this particular form. The argument seems to be based on a misunderstanding of clause 12.1.1 (definition of change in the employer's requirements) because the paragraph (closely following JCT 80) is simply a traditional variation clause, which in fact has a limiting effect. Clause 12.1.2 enables the imposition of obligations or restrictions or a change to be made in respect of "any such obligations or restrictions so imposed or imposed by the employer in the Employer's Requirements in regard to" site access, limitation of working space or hours, or the execution or completion of the work in any specific order – subject to the contractor's right of reasonable objection. In our view this clause cannot be used to enable the employer or his agent to direct operations.

The power to deal with defective work is contained in clauses 8 and 16. Clause 8.4 differs from its JCT 80 counterpart in that it not only empowers the employer to order *removal* of defective work from the site, but also gives the option of ordering *rectification*. This option is missing from JCT 80 and it has been held – under JCT 63 terms – that the architect under that contract has no power to instruct the contractor to rectify defective work during the currency of the contract (*Holland Hannen & Cubitts (Northern) Ltd* v *WHTSO* (1980) 18 BLR 80). In other respects, clause 8.4 is similar to JCT 80 particularly in the power to instruct opening up and testing to check the extent of non-compliance after failure of work. Due regard must be had to a "Code of Practice" which is to be attached to the contract.

Clause 16.3 is limited to defects occurring during the defects liability period. The word used in the clause is "appear". Therefore, defects which are apparent at practical completion but which for one reason or another have not prevented the issue of the written statement, are excluded. Indeed, patent defects would prevent the issue of the written statement: *H W Nevill (Sunblest) Ltd* v *Wm Press & Son Ltd* (1981) 20 BLR 78.

The provisions for valuing variations are contained in clause 12.5. They are very similar to the JCT 80 terms, but somewhat shorter. Reference is to be made to the contract sum analysis rather than the contract bills. If it is not appropriate to value in accordance with the rates set out in the contract sum analysis or derivatives of those rates, a fair valuation is to be made, which may be on a daywork basis. It is expected that the employer will retain the services of a quantity surveyor for valuations.

7.07   Contractor's Claims

Clause 26 is virtually the same as in JCT 80. The nature of the contract, under which the contractor takes responsibility for the whole of the design and build package, means in practice, however, that there should be fewer claims. To set the machinery in motion it is necessary for the contractor to make a written application to the employer. Detailed provisions set out the various matters which can delay progess and cause the contractor to incur direct loss and/or expense. All the matters are acts or defaults of the employer or his agent. Clause 26.3 provides that amounts ascertained "from time to time" are to be added to the contract sum. Since there is no certification requirement in this contract, the contractor must submit applications for payment. Ascertainment is presumably in the hands of the employer and is dealt with by his agent although the contract is silent about the point.

7.08   Payments

The very detailed clause 30 deals with payment. It sets out the scheme of payments, interim and final, and deals with the retention. Payment is to be made in accordance with whichever alternative is stipulated (in appendix 2) to apply. There are two possibilities:
● Stage payments
● Periodic payments.

Under the *stage payments* system (alternative A) applications must be made on the *completion* of each stage as set out in appendix 2. Under the *periodic payments* method (alternative B) the contractor is to make applications at the periods specified in the appendix up to and including the period in which practical completion occurs. The contractor must make further applications after practical completion to accommodate the release of the retention monies. There is a proviso to clause 30.3.1.2, the purpose of which is to prevent the contractor from consistently claiming small payments as the final account is being calculated. It applies to payments occurring after practical completion under alternative B and states that the employer is not required to make any interim payment within one calendar month of having made a previous interim payment.

The employer must pay the amount stated as due in the contractor's application within 14 days, subject to two conditions:
● Each application must be accompanied by such details as are stated in the employer's requirements (clause 30.3.2)

- The employer may dispute the amount if he considers that the amount stated as due is not in accordance with the contract. He does this by notifying the contractor forthwith, stating his reasons and, at the same time, paying the amount which he considers to be properly due (clause 30.3.4).

The first of these vital safeguards emphasises the importance of the employer's requirements giving the requisite amount of detail. The second is a necessary protection for the employer. The contractor has equal protection because clause 30.3.5 states that the payment on account is "without prejudice to the rights of the contractor in respect of any amount which he considers has been improperly withheld". If aggrieved, therefore, he can seek arbitration or sue through the courts.

Following the system under JCT 80, the amounts to be included in the contractor's application are divided into those which are subject to retention and those which are not. The only potential problem area is encountered under alternative A (stage payments) because the contract does not define what is meant by the completion of each stage nor does it state that it is the employer's opinion which decides the issue. It is therefore something which the contractor may challenge. It may well be prudent to opt for alternative B, a situation which seems to exist in practice. It is a matter on which the employer must take professional advice. Completion of a stage is a question of fact and three criteria are relevant:

- Has the particular stage reached completion?
- Has the work been properly executed, including any design work?
- Has the cost of remedying any defective work been determined?

Whichever alternative applies, the contractor may include in his application the value of unfixed goods and materials delivered to the works, although only alternative B specifies this as a separate item (clause 30.2B.1.2) because under alternative A the contractor will presumably make an allowance for it in his calculation of the value of the stage payment. How a stage can be considered to be complete when some materials are not incorporated is left to the imagination. Presumably, what the provisions intend is that the value of a particular stage will include the complete value of that stage plus the value of materials on site ready for future stages. Since the values are to be inserted in the appendix before work begins, it is possible that the materials may not, in the event, be on site, in which case the contractor could be overpaid. In addition, the prevalence of retention of title clauses in suppliers' contracts is a potential danger if the contractor goes into liquidation unless the contractor is, indeed, the true owner of the goods. The provisions bristle with problems and are in need of amendment.

Clause 30.2B.1.3 gives the employer (as JCT 80 does to the architect) a discretion to include the value of off-site materials.

The usual items are deductable from the gross valuation, including retention, following the JCT 80 pattern. The provisions are clear and unexceptional and require no detailed comment.

There are some interesting points to note in regard to the provisions for final payment. The issuing of the written statement of practical completion by the employer triggers off the final account procedures (clause 16.1). Unlike the position under JCT 80, it is the contractor who undertakes the preparation of the final account. He must submit the final account (clause 30.5.1) and final statement within 3 months of practical completion "together with such supporting documents as the employer may reasonably require" (a matter for definition in the employer's requirements), and clause 30.5.3 defines the permitted deductions from and additions to the contract sum so as to enable the adjusted final account figure to be calculated. He is also required to submit a *final statement* with the final account. It must be set out to show:

- The adjusted contract sum
- The sum of amounts already paid by the employer to the contractor.

Any difference between the sums is to be expressed as a balance due to one or other of the parties.

If the employer agrees the final account or if it is not disputed by the employer, it becomes "conclusive as to the balance due between the parties" on the last of the following:

- One month from the end of the defects liability period, *or*
- One month from completion of making good defects under clause 16, *or*
- One month from the submission of the final account and final statement with all necessary supporting documents.

The employer is given useful powers if the contractor does not submit the final account and statement by the due date. The employer may give written notice to the contractor warning that after a further two months from the date of the notice, the employer may himself prepare the final account and final statement. The contractor has until the latest of the following to dispute the account and statement:

- One month from the end of the defects liability period, *or*
- One month from completion of making good defects under clause 16, *or*
- One month from the sending of the employer's final account and final statement to the contractor by the employer.

If the contractor does not so dispute, the employer's final account and final statement is conclusive as to the balance due between the parties.

The final statement is not a "certificate" and its effect is dealt with in clause 30.8. It is conclusive as to satisfaction on four matters. Where the employer's requirements state that the quality of materials or the standard of workmanship are to be to the employer's reasonable satisfaction, then only such items are deemed to be to that satisfaction. This is an excellent reason for drafting the employer's requirements without reference to "reasonable satisfaction" so as to effectively remove any element of conclusiveness, in regard to quality and standards, from the final statement, even though this limited effect is further reduced by the provisions relating to fraud or commencement of proceedings, as under JCT 80.

The second matter is that all extensions of time due under clause 25 have been given. The third matter is that any reimbursement of direct loss and/or expense is in final settlement of all contractor's claims in respect of clause 26 matters. The fourth and final element of conclusiveness is in regard to the balance owing between the parties as referred to above.

Clause 30.9 expressly states that the contractor cannot rely on any payment other than the final payment as conclusive evidence that "any design, work, materials or goods to which it relates are in accordance with this contract".

If fluctuation provisions are applicable, they correspond to those in JCT 80. The contract is for a lump sum price and, in practice, it is suggested that a fixed price is appropriate in tune with the overall philosophy of the contract, whereby the contractor undertakes the main burden of responsibility.

7.09 Sub-Contractors and Employer's Licensees /Agent

Clause 18.2.1 provides that the contractor must not sub-let all or any portion of the works without the employer's reasonable written consent. Clause 18.2.2 reflects the contractor's involvement in the design of the works by making the employer's reasonable written consent a precondition to the contractor sub-letting any portion of the design. In practice, it will be quite common for a contractor without his own design staff to wish to sub-let the design to a firm of architects. Many contractors will base their tenders on just such an arrangement, and a refusal to such sub-letting might well be judged unreasonable provided that the architects proposals were known to the employer or his own professional advisers.

There is no provision for nominating sub-contractors, nor for providing a list of sub-contractors from which the contractor can choose. Given the heavy burden on the contractor, it is a reasonable omission.

Provision is made, in clause 29, for the employer to engage other persons to carry out work not forming part of the contract. The pattern of the identically numbered JCT 80 clause is followed with similar wording. There are two situations:

- Where the work is indicated in the employer's requirements and the contractor must permit its execution
- Where the work is not indicated in the employer's requirements, in which case the contractor may not unreasonably withhold his consent to the execution.

The employment of other persons by the employer does however leave the avenue open for the contractor to claim an extension of time (clause 25.4.8.1) and direct loss and/or expense (clause 26.2.3.1).

The "Employer's Agent" is the only person referred to in the contract other than the employer and the contractor, and the express references to him are sparse. He is referred to in article 3 of the articles of agreement as a named individual or firm "or such other persons as the employer shall nominate in his place...and, save to the extent which the employer may otherwise specify by written notice" he is the employer's agent "for the receiving or issuing of such applications, consents, instructions, notices, requests or statements or for otherwise acting for the employer" under the contract.

The role of the employer's agent is in effect the dual role fulfilled by the architect and the quantity surveyor under JCT 80. Obviously in practice it will be desirable for an employer to designate an architect (or other appropriate professional, depending on the nature of the works) as his agent for the general purposes of the contract, and to give written notice to the contractor of the appointment of a quantity surveyor for the traditional QS functions.

If an employer's agent is appointed, he has both powers and duties under the contract. It is important to note that, in common with other standard form contracts, failure by the employer's agent to carry out his duties will be a breach of contract for which the employer will be liable in damages. This elementary principle was re-emphasised by the Court of Appeal upholding His Honour Judge Newey QC in *Croudace Ltd* v *London Borough of Lambeth* (1986) 6 ConLR 70 where the architect's failure to ascertain or instruct the quantity surveyor to ascertain the contractor's claim for direct loss and/or expense was held to be a breach of contract for which Lambeth Borough was liable.

There is no provision for the appointment of a clerk of works. Despite the JCT's view (Practice Note CD/1B) that it is "considered that the provisions of clause 11 suffice", if a clerk of works is to be appointed, the contract should be amended accordingly. Clause 11 merely provides for the employer's agent "and any other person authorised by the employer or the employer's agent" to have access to the works. At the very least the matter of the clerk of works' appointment and his functions should be covered in the employer's requirements, because clearly someome authorised under clause 11 would have no power to issue even "directions". Ideally, the contract itself should be amended by an appropriately worded clause.

7.10 Statutory Obligations

Clause 6 covers statutory obligations, and is somewhat different in emphasis from JCT 80 provisions. The contractor is to comply with and give all notices required by Act of Parliament, etc, and specifically including planning requirements unless the employer has specifically stated in the employer's requirements that they comply with statutory requirements. All approvals received by the contractor must be passed to the employer, a provision not found in JCT 80, but necessary in this contract. The contractor must also pay and indemnify the employer against all fees or charges for which he is not to be reimbursed except that provisional sum items are to be adjusted (clause 6.2).

A duty is placed on each party by clause 6.1.2 to give the other written notice if a divergence is found between the statutory requirements and the employer's requirements (including any change) or the contractor's proposals. However, it is for the contractor to propose amendments in order to remove the divergence and, after he has obtained the employer's consent, he must put it into effect at his own cost. The exception to this is if the relevant part of the employer's requirements have been stated to comply with statutory requirements. Then the employer must issue an instruction for a change. A most curious provision states that the amendments are to be noted by the employer on the contract documents. Presumably, the intention is to ensure that the amendment can be said to be "in accordlance with the contract".

There is the usual JCT provision for the contractor to use limited materials and execute limited work in the case of an emergency. A provision not found in JCT 80 (clause 6.3) states that changes in statutory requirements or decisions of the planning authority after the date of tender are to be treated as employer's instructions effecting a change in the employer's requirements. In other words, the contractor is entitled to payment.

7.11 Injury, Damage and Insurance

The insurance provisions are unremarkable and follow very closely the provisions of JCT 80. The contractor must indemnify the employer and insure against injury and death arising out of the carrying out of the works and against claims arising from damage to property caused by carrying out the works and due to the contractor's or his sub-contractor's negligence (clauses 20 and 21).

Clause 21.2 directs the contractor to maintain insurance in joint names against collapse, etc, of property other than the works not due to negligence if the employer's requirements so state. The amount of insurance required must be stated in appendix 1.

There are the usual provisions for insuring the works against all risks in three forms:

- 22A if the contractor is to insure new works
- 22B if the employer is to insure new works
- 22C if works to existing buildings are involved, in which case the works are to be insured against all risks by the employer and he is to insure the existing structure against specified perils. All insurance is to be in joint names.

Like JCT 80, provision is made for the employer to require insurance against the loss of liquidated damages.

A notable omission from the insurance provisions is insurance for the contractor's design liability. It is recommended that the omission be corrected by a suitable amendment.

7.12 Determination

The provisions for determination follow the numbering and wording of JCT 80 provisions. Only two points call for comment:

- There is no provision for the contractor to determine his employment if the employer interferes with or obstructs the issue of any certificate, for the obvious reason that the employer is in the general position of the architect under JCT 80 and he (or his agent) deals directly with all notices etc, under the contract. No certificates are required under this form.
- An additional ground for determination by the contractor is given in clause 28.1.2.8 if the works are delayed for a continuous period of the length named in appendix 1 by reason of delay in receipt of planning approvals or permissions which the contractor has taken all practicable steps to reduce.

7.13 Disputes

Clause 39 deals with the procedure to be adopted in the case of any difference or dispute arising between the parties. It follows closely the wording of JCT 80 with the exception that, for obvious reasons, the provision for joining nominated sub-contract disputes is omitted.

Table 7.01:   Contents of JCT 81 with Contractor's Design Summarised

Clause	Content
1	Interpretation, definitions
1.1	Method of reference to clauses
1.2	Articles to be read as a whole
1.3	Definitions
2	Contractor's obligations
2.1	Contractor to carry out and complete the works in accordance with the documents
2.2	Employer's requirements: relation to articles, conditions and appendices
2.3	Divergences between documents – treatment of errors
2.4	Discrepancies within documents
2.5	Contractor's design warranty and limit of design liability
3	Contract sum – additions or deductions – adjustment – interim payments
4	Employer's instructions
4.1	Compliance with employer's instructions
4.2	Provisions empowering instructions
4.3.1	Instructions to be in writing
4.3.2	Procedure if instructions given otherwise than in writing
5	Custody and supply of documents
5.1	Custody of employer's requirements and contractor's proposals
5.2	Copies of documents
5.3	Drawings etc of contractor – provision to employer
5.4	Availability of certain documents
5.5	Supply by contractor of "as built" drawings etc
5.6	Limits to use of documents
6	Statutory obligations, notices, fees and charges
6.1	Statutory requirements
6.2	Fees or charges
6.3	Addition to or deduction from contract sum – changes in statutory requirements after date of tender – decision of relevant authority under development control requirements
7	Site boundaries
8	Materials, goods and workmanship to confirm to description – testing and inspection
8.1	Kinds and standards
8.2	Vouchers – materials and goods
8.3	Inspection – tests
8.4	Powers of employer – work not in accordance with the contract
8.5	Samples – employer's requirements or contractor's proposals

Table 7.01:   Contents of JCT 81 with Contractor's Design Summarised – (continued)

Clause	Content
9	Copyright, royalties and patent rights
9.1	Treatment of royalties etc – indemnity to employer
9.2	Employer's instructions – treatment of royalties, etc
10	Person-in-charge
11	Access for employer's agent, etc to the works
12	Changes in the employer's requirements and provisional sums
12.1	Definition of change in the employer's requirements
12.2	Instruction requiring a change
12.3	Instruction on provisional sums
12.4	Valuation of changes and provisional sum work
12.5	Valuation rules
13	Contract sum
14	Value added tax – supplemental provisions
14.1	Definitions: VAT agreement
14.2	Contract sum: exclusive of VAT
14.3	Possible exemption from VAT
15	Unfixed materials and good
16	Practical completion and defects liability period
16.1	Employer's written statement: practical completion
16.2	Defects, shrinkages or faults
16.3	Defects: employer's instructions
16.4	Notice of completion of making good defects
17	Partial possession by employer
17.1	Estimate of value
17.1.2	Practical completion: relevant part
17.1.3	Defects etc: relevant part
17.1.4	Insurance: relevant part
17.1.5	Liquidated damages: relevant part
18	Assignment and sub-contracts
18.1	Assignment
18.2	Sub-contracts: work or design
18.3	Sub-letting – determination of employment of sub-contractor

Table 7.01: Contents of JCT 81 with Contractor's Design Summarised – (continued)

Clause	Content
19	[Number not used]
20	Injury to persons and property and indemnity to employer
20.1	Liability of contractor – personal injury – indemnity to employer
20.2	Liability of contractor – injury or damage to property – indemnity to employer
20.3	Injury or damage to property – exclusion of the works and site materials
21	Insurance against injury to persons and property
21.1	Contractor's insurance – personal injury or death – injury or damage to property
21.2	Insurance – liability, etc of employer
21.3	Excepted risks
22	Insurance of the works
22.1	Insurance of the works – alternative clauses
22.2	Definitions
22.3	Sub-contractors – benefit of joint names policies – specified perils
22A	Erection of new building – all risks insurance of the works by the contractor
22A.1	New buildings – contractor to take out and maintain a joint names policy for all risks insurance
22A.2	Single policy – insurers approved by employer – failure by contractor to insure
22A.3	Use of annual policy maintained by the contractor – alternative to use of clause 22A.2
22A.4	Loss or damage to works – insurance claims – contractor's obligations – use of insurance monies
22B	Erection of new building – all risks insurance of the works by the employer
22B.1	New buildings – employer to take out and maintain a joint names policy for all risks insurance
22B.2	Failure of employer to insure – rights of contractor
22B.3	Loss or damage to works – insurance claims – contractor's obligations – payment by employer
22C	Insurance of existing structures – insurance of the works in or extensions to existing structures
22C.1	Existing structures and contents – specified perils – employer to take out and maintain joint names policy
22C.2	Works in or extensions to existing structures – all risks insurance – employer to take out and maintain joint names policy
22C.3	Failure of employer to insure – rights of contractor
22C.4	Loss or damage to works – insurance claims – contractor's obligations – payments by employer
22D	Insurance for employer's loss of liquidated damages – clause 25.4.3

Table 7.01: Contents of JCT 81 with Contractor's Design Summarised – (continued)

Clause	Content
23	Date of possession, completion and postponement
23.1	Date of possession – progress to completion date
23.2	Employer's instructions – postponement
23.3	Possession by contractor – use or occupation by employer
24	Damages for non-completion
24.1	Notice of employer
24.2	Payment or allowance of liquidated damages
25	Extension of time
25.1	Interpretation of delay
25.2	Notice of contractor of delay to progress
25.3	Fixing completion date
25.4	Relevant events
26	Loss and expense caused by matters materially affecting regular progress of the works
26.1	Matters materially affecting regular progess of the works – direct loss and/or expense
26.2	List of matters
26.3	Amounts ascertained – added to the contract sum
26.4	Reservation of rights and remedies of the contractor
27	Determination by employer
27.1	Default by contractor
27.2	Contractor becoming bankrupt
27.3	Corruption
27.4	Determination of employment of contractor – rights and duties of employer and contractor
28	Determination by contractor
28.1	Acts, etc giving ground for determination by contractor
28.2	Determination of employment by contractor – rights and duties of employer and contractor
28A	Determination by employer or contractor
29	Execution of work not forming part of contract
29.1	Information in employer's requirements
29.2	Information not in employer's requirements
30	Payments
30.1	Interim payments
30.2A	Gross valuation for alternative A – stage payments

Table 7.01:   Contents of JCT 81 with Contractor's Design Summarised – (continued)

Clause	Content
30.2B	Gross valuation for alternative B – periodic payments
30.3	Application for interim payment
30.3.3	Payment by employer
30.4	Retention – rules for ascertainment
30.4.3	Employer's right of deduction under this contract
30.5	Final account
30.5.4	Final statement
30.5.6	Failure by contractor to submit final account and final statement – rights of employer
30.6	Balance stated in final statement – debt due to contractor or employer
30.7	Notice of deduction
30.8	Effect of final account and final statement
30.9	Effect of payments other than of final statement
31	Finance (No 2) Act 1975 – statutory tax deduction scheme
31.1	Definitions
31.2	Whether employer a "contractor"
31.3	Provision of evidence – tax certificate
31.4.1	Uncertificated contractor obtains tax certificate
31.4.2	Expiry of tax certificate
31.4.3	Cancellation of tax certificate
31.5	Vouchers
31.6	Statutory deduction – direct cost of materials
31.7	Correction of errors
31.8	Relation to other clauses
31.9	Application of arbitration agreement
32	Outbreak of hostilities
32.1	Notice of determination of the contractor's employment
32.2	Protective work etc
32.3	Payment
33	War damage
33.1	Effect of war damage
33.2	Relation with clause 32
33.3	Use of compensation for war damage
33.4	Definition of war damage
34	Antiquities
34.1	Effect of finding of antiquities
34.2	Employer's instructions on antiquities found
34.3	Direct loss and/or expense
35	Fluctuations
35.1	Choice of fluctuations provisions – entry in appendix

Table 7.01: Contents of JCT 81 with Contractor's Design Summarised – (continued)

Clause	Content
36	Contribution, levy and tax fluctuations
36.1.1	Deemed calculation of contract sum – types and rates of contribution, etc
36.1.2	Increases or decreases in rates of contribution, etc – payment or allowance
36.1.3	Persons employed on site other than "workpeople"
36.1.5	Refunds and premiums
36.1.8	Contracted-out employment
36.1.9	Meaning of contributions, etc
36.2	Materials – duties and taxes
36.3	Fluctuations – work sub-let
36.1.1	Sub-let work – incorporation of provisions to like-effect
36.1.2	Sub-let work – fluctuations – payment to or allowance by the contractor
36.4–6	Provisions relating to clause 36
36.4.1	Written notice by contractor
36.4.2	Timing and effect of written notices
36.4.3	Agreement – employer and contractor
36.4.4	Fluctuations added to or deducted from Contract Sum
36.4.5	Evidence and computations by Contractor
36.4.6	No alterations to Contractor's profit
36.4.7	Position where Contractor in default over completion
36.5	Work, etc to which clauses 36.1 to .3 not applicable
36.6	Definitions for use with clause 36
36.7	Percentage addition to fluctuation payments or allowances

Clause	Content
37	Labour and materials cost and tax fluctuations
37.1	Deemed calculation of contract sum – rates of wages, etc
37.1.2	Increases or decreases in rates of wages, etc – payment or allowance
37.1.3	Persons employed on site other than "workpeople"
37.1.5	Workpeople – wage-fixing body – reimbursement of fares
37.2	Contributions, levies and taxes
37.3	Materials, goods, electricity and fuels
37.4	Fluctuations – work sub-let
37.4.1	Sub-let work – incorporation of provisions to like effect
37.4.2	Sub-let work – fluctuations – payment to or allowances by the contractor
37.5–7	Provisions relating to clause 37
37.5.1	Written notice by contractor
37.5.2	Timing and effect of written notices
37.5.3	Ageement – employer and contractor
37.5.4	Fluctuations – added to or deducted from contract sum
37.5.5	Evidence and computations by contractor
37.5.6	No alteration to contractor's profit
37.5.7	Position when contractor in default over completion
37.6	Work, etc to which clause 37.1 to .4 not applicable
37.7	Definitions for use with clause 37
37.8	Percentage addition to fluctuation payments or allowances

Clause	Content
38	Use of price adjustment formulae
38.1	Adjustments of contract sum – price adjustment formulae for building contracts – formulae Rules
38.2	Application for payment – schedule of values
38.3	Fluctuations – articles manufactured outside the UK

Table 7.01:   Contents of JCT 81 with Contractor's Design Summarised – (continued)

Clause	Content
38.4	Power to agree – employer and contractor
38.5	Position where monthly bulletins are delayed etc
38.6	Formula adjustment – failure to complete
39	Settlement of disputes – arbitration

Appendices 1, 2, 3

Supplemental provisions (the VAT agreement)

Table 7.02: JCT 81 With Contractor's Design – Time Chart

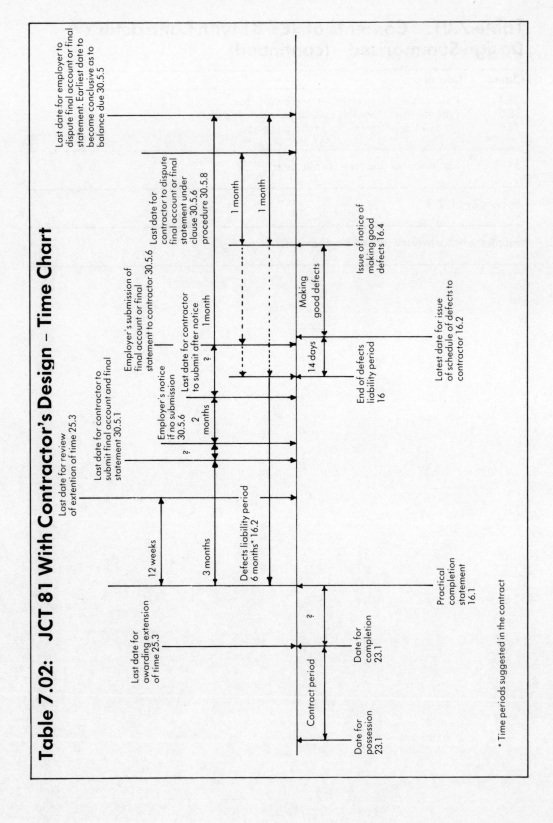

* Time periods suggested in the contract

Table 7.03: Employer's/Employer's Agent's Powers under JCT 81 WCD

Clause	Power	Comment
2.4.1	Agree contractor's proposed amendment or decide how discrepancy must be dealt with	After contractor has notified employer of proposed amendment to deal with discrepancy within Employer's Requirements not dealt with by Contractor's Proposals
2.4.2	Decide between discrepant items or accept the contractor's proposed amendment	After contractor has notified employer of proposed amendment to remove discrepancy within Contractor's Proposals
4.1	Issue instructions to the contractor on any matter in respect of which he is empowered to do so by the contract	The contractor must immediately comply with such instructions *except* One requiring a change within clause 12.1.2, in which case he has a right of reasonable objection to compliance
	Issue a written notice to the contractor requiring compliance with an instruction Employ and pay others to give effect to the instruction Recover all costs incurred in connection therewith by deduction from monies due or to become due to the contractor under the contract or as a debt	If the contractor fails to comply with the notice requiring compliance within seven days of its receipt
4.2	Request the contractor to concur in the appointment of an arbitrator	If the employer wishes a decision as to whether the specified clause provision in fact authorises the instruction. The request for arbitration must be made before the contractor complies with the instruction
4.3	Confirm in writing any non-written instruction which has been given	Within seven days of its issue
	Confirm any oral instruction in writing at any time before the final statement and account becoming conclusive as to the balance due under the contract	This is a long-stop provision

Table 7.03: Employer's/Employer's Agent's Powers under JCT 81 WCD – (continued)

Clause	Power	Comment
6.1	Consent to any amendment proposed by the contractor for removing the divergence and note the amendment on the specified documents*	Consent must not be unreasonably withheld
8.2	Request the contractor to provide vouchers to prove that materials and goods comply with clause 8.1	
8.3	Issue instructions requiring the contractor to open up for inspection, testing, etc of work, goods and materials	The cost will be added to the contract sum unless the tests, etc prove adverse to the contractor or where such costs have been provided for in the employer's requirements or contractor's proposals
8.4	Issue instructions requiring removal from site or rectification of any work, materials or goods	Not in accordance with the contract
8.4.2	Issue reasonably necessary instructions re change following 8.4.1 instruction	After consulting contractor no addition is to be made to the contract sum and no extension of time given
8.4.3	Issue reasonable instructions to open up work or carry out tests to establish to employer's satisfaction the likelihood of further similar non-compliance	After having due regard to the code of practice appended to the conditions
11	Have access to the works and to the workshops and other places of the contractor where work is being prepared for the contract	This refers to "the employer's agent and any other person authorised by the employer or the employer's agent". The right is exercisable at reasonable times, that is, during normal working hours
12.2	Issue instructions effecting a change in the employer's requirements	A change is a variation. No change may be effected (unless the contractor consents) which is or will make necessary an alteration or modification in the design element of the works

Table 7.03: Employer's/Employer's Agent's Powers under JCT 81 WCD – (continued)

Clause	Power	Comment
15	Consent in writing to the removal of unfixed materials and good delivered to, placed on or next to the works	Consent must not be unreasonably withheld
16.2	Issue instructions that defects, etc be not made good	An appropriate deduction must then be made from the contract sum
16.3	Issue instruction that defects, etc be made good	No such instructions can be issued after delivery of the schedule of defects or after 14 days from the expiry of the defects liability period
17.1	Take practical possession of the works before practical completion*	With the contractor's consent
18.1.1	Assign the contract*	Only if the contractor consents in writing
18.1.2	Assign to any transferee or lessee the right to bring proceedings in the employer's name or enforce any contractual terms made for the employer's benefit*	If employer transfers leasehold or freehold interest or grants a leasehold interest in the whole of the works
	The assignee is estopped from disputing enforceable agreements reached between employer and contractor related to the contract	If made prior to the date of the assignment
18.2	Consent in writing to sub-letting all or part of the works, including design*	Consent must not be unreasonably withheld or delayed
21.1.2	Require the contractor to produce documentary evidence that clause 21.1.1.1 insurances are properly maintained*	The power must not be exercised unreasonably or vexatiously
21.1.3	Effect the necessary insurance if the contractor has failed to insure or continue to insure*	The premiums may be deducted from monies due or to become due to the contractor or can be recovered as a debt

Table 7.03: Employer's/Employer's Agent's Powers under JCT 81 WCD – (continued)

Clause	Power	Comment
21.2.2	Approve insurers*	In regard to insurance against damage to property other than the works – employer's liability
21.2.3	Insure against damage to property other than the works – employer's liability*	If the contractor fails to insure when so stated in the Employer's Requirements
22A.2	Approve the contractor's insurers and accept deposit of policies and premium receipts* Insure against all risks and deduct sums from monies due or recover them as a debt	In regard to insurance against all risks to be taken out by the contractor If the contractor has failed to insure or continue to insure
22A.3.1	Inspect documentary evidence or the policy*	If the contractor maintains a policy independently of his obligations under the contract and it is in joint names
22C.4.3.1	Determine the contractor's employment under the contract* Request concurrence in appointment of an arbitrator*	If the works are damaged by clause 22C.4 risks and it is just and equitable to do so If the contractor serves notice determining his employment
22D.1	Require the contractor to accept the quotation in respect of liquidated damages insurance*	The employer must so instruct
23.1.2	Defer giving possession for not more than 6 weeks	Where clause 23.1.2 is stated in the appendix to apply
23.2	Issue instructions regarding the postponement of any design or construction work to be executed under the contract	
23.3.2	Use or occupy the site of the works before issue of practical completion certificate*	With contractor's written consent
24.2	Deduct liquidated damages for late completion*	The employer's notice under clause 24.1 must have been issued and the employer must have

Table 7.03: Employer's/Employer's Agent's Powers under JCT 81 WCD – (continued)

Clause	Power	Comment
		required liquidated damages by writing to the contractor no later than the date when the final statement and account becomes final and conclusive as to the balance due between the parties
25.3	Fix an earlier completion date than that previously fixed under clause 25.2 if it is fair and reasonable to do so in the light of any subsequently issued omission instructions	This can only be done after an extension of time has been granted under clause 25.2
25.3.3	Review extensions of time granted and fix a new completion date or confirm existing*	May be carried out at any time after completion date if this occurs before practical completion, but no later than 12 weeks after practical completion
27.1	Serve written notice on the contractor by registered post or recorded delivery specifying a default*	If the contractor, without reasonable cause, wholly suspends the design or construction of the works before completion; or Fails to proceed regularly and diligently with the performance of his contractual obligations; or Refuses or neglects to comply with a written notice requiring him to remove defective work, etc and as a result the works are materially affected; or Fails to comply with clause 18 (sub-contracting, etc)
	Determine the contractor's employment by written notice served by registered post or recorded delivery*	The notice must not be given unreasonably or vexatiously. It can be served only if the contractor continues his default for 14 days after receipt of the preliminary notice or if he repeats that default at any time thereafter. The notice must be served within 10 days of the continuance or repetition
27.2	Reinstate the contractor's employment in agreement with the contractor and his trustee in bankruptcy, etc	If the contractor becomes insolvent, etc his employment under the contract is said to be determined automatically
27.3	Determine the contractor's employment under this or any other contract*	Where the employer is a local authority and the contractor is guilty of corrupt practices. No procedure is prescribed but determination should be effected by written notice served by

Table 7.03: Employer's/Employer's Agent's Powers under JCT 81 WCD – (continued)

Clause	Power	Comment
		recorded delivery or registered post as a precaution
27.4	Employ and pay others to carry out and complete the design and construction of the works and make use of the contractor's equipment, etc*	
	Require the contractor to assign to him the benefit of any sub contracts, etc	Not where the contractor's insolvency was the cause of determination
	Pay direct any supplier or sub-contractor*	Not where the contractor's insolvency was the cause of determination
	Require the contractor to remove from the works his temporary buildings, etc and in default to remove and sell the contractor's property*	
28A.1	Forthwith determine the contractor's employment under the contract*	If the carrying out of substantially the whole of the works is suspended for a period named in appendix 1 by reason of: ● force majeure ● loss by specified perils ● civil commotion
29	Have work not forming part of the contract carried out by the employer or his licensees	If the employer's requirements so provide and give the contractor the necessary information. If not, the contractor's consent is required under clause 29.2
30.4	Deduct and retain the retention percentage, holding the same as trustee*	
30.5.6	Give written notice to contractor 3 months after practical completion	If the contractor does not submit final account and statement within 3 months of practical completion
	Prepare or have prepared a final account and statement	If the contractor does not so submit
32.1	Determine the contractor's employment by written notice served by registered post or	Notice of determination cannot be given before the expiry of 28 days of the date of the general mobilisation order nor after practical

Table 7.03: Employer's/Employer's Agent's Powers under JCT 81 WCD – (continued)

Clause	Power	Comment
	recorded delivery if there is an outbreak of hostilities*	completion of the works unless they have sustained war damage
32.2	Issue instructions requiring the contractor to carry out protective works*	Within 14 days after notice under clause 32.1 has been given or received
33.1	Issue instructions requiring the contractor to remove and/or dispose of debris, damaged work, etc and to execute protective work	If the works sustained was damage as defined

* Those powers which are personal to the employer, fluctuations clauses are not covered in this table

Table 7.04: Employer's/Employer's Agent's Duties under JCT 81 WCD

Clause	Duty	Comment
2.3	Issue instructions on divergences between the employer's requirements and the definition of the site boundary. The instruction is deemed to be a change and is valued accordingly Give written notice to the contractor specifying the divergence	If such a divergence is found
2.4	Decide between discrepant items or otherwise accept contractor's amendments proposed Give the contractor written notice specifying any discrepancy	Where there is a discrepancy within the contractor's proposals and the contractor has informed him of it. If such a discrepancy is found. The notice must be given immediately.
4.2	Specify in writing the contract clause empowering the issue of an instruction	On the contractor's written request
4.3	Issue all instructions in writing	There is a procedure for confirmation of oral instructions
5.1	Be custodian of the employer's requirements, contractor's proposals and contract sum analysis*	These documents must be made available for the contractor's inspection at all reasonable times
5.2	Provide the contractor with a copy of the contract, the employer's requirements, contractor's proposals and contract sum analysis certified on behalf of the employer	This must be done immediately after the contract is signed or sealed unless the contractor has previously been provided with the documents
5.6	Not to divulge to third parties or use any of the specified documents supplied by the contractor other than for the purposes of the contract*	

Table 7.04: Employer's/Employer's Agent's Duties under JCT 81 WCD – (continued)

Clause	Duty	Comment
6.1	Immediately give written notice to the contractor of any discrepancy between the statutory requirements and either the employer's requirements or the contractor's proposals	The employer's requirements include any change (clause 12) and the duty arises if such a discrepancy is found
7	Define the boundaries of the site*	
8.1	Consent in writing to alterations of kinds and standards of materials, goods, workmanship, etc	If the contractor so requests because the goods, etc are not procurable. Consent must not be unreasonably withheld or delayed
12.3	Issue instructions to the contractor on the expenditure of provisional sums included in the employer's requirements	
16.1	Give the contractor a written statement of practical completion	When the works have reached practical completion. The statement must not be unreasonably withheld or delayed
16.2	Deliver to the contractor a schedule of defects which appear within the defects liability period	The defects specified must be due to the contractor's failure to comply with his contractual obligations or to frost occurring before practical completion. The schedule of defects must be issued as an instruction not later than 14 days after the defects liability period expires
16.4	Issue a notice that the contractor has discharged his defects liability – not notice of completion of making good defects	Once the contractor has discharged his liability. The notice must not be unreasonably withheld or delayed
22.3	Ensure that the joint names policies referred to in clauses 22C.1 or 22C.2 *either:* ● provide for recognition of each nominated sub-contractor	If clause 22B or clause 22C applies In respect of specified perils

Table 7.04:   Employer's/Employer's Agent's Duties under JCT 81 WCD – (continued)

Clause	Duty	Comment
	as an insured or: ● includes insurers' waiver of rights of subrogation*	
22A.4.4	Pay insurance monies received to the contractor*	By instalments under clause 30 alternative B
22B.1	Maintain proper insurances against all risks* Produce receipts etc to the contractor at his request*	Where the employer has undertaken the risk in the case of new works
22C.1	Maintain adequate insurances against specified perils*	In the case of existing structures
22C.2	Maintain insurance against all risks for the works of alterations or extention*	In joint names
22C.3	Produce insurance receipts etc	If the contractor so requests
22D.1	Either inform contractor that insurance is not required or instruct him to obtain quotations* Instruct contractor whether or not employer wishes quotation to be accepted*	If Employer's Requirements and appendix states liquidated damages insurance may be required
23.1	Give possession of the site to the contractor on the date of possession*	
23.3.2	Notify insurers under clause 22A or 22B or 22C.2 to .4 and obtain confirmation that use or occupation will not prejudice insurance	
24.1	Issue a written notice to the contractor stating that the contractor has failed to complete the construction of the works by the completion date	

Table 7.04: Employer's/Employer's Agent's Duties under JCT 81 WCD – (continued)

Clause	Duty	Comment
24.2	Pay or repay liquidated damages to the contractor	Where a later completion date is fixed under clause 25.3.3
25.3	Make in writing a fair and reasonable extension of time for completion by fixing a later date as the completion date and stating which of the relevant events have been taken into account and the extent to which regard has been given to any omission instruction issued since the fixing of the previous completion date	It must become apparent that the progress of the works is being or is likely to be delayed; and The contractor must give written notice of the cause of the delay and supply supporting particulars and estimate; and The reasons for the delay must fall within the list of relevant events If reasonably practicable having regard to the sufficiency of the contractor's notice, etc the extension must be granted not later than 12 weeks from receipt of the particulars, etc or not later than the current completion date if that is less than 12 weeks away.
	Notify contractor in writing	If it is not fair and reasonable to fix a later date. Notice must be given not later than 12 weeks from receipt or before completion date whichever is the earlier
	Write to the contractor either fixing a later completion date than that previously fixed if it is fair and reasonable to do so having regard to the relevant events; or Fixing an earlier completion date, likewise in the light of any omission instructions issued subsequently; or Confirming the completion date previously fixed	It is a duty to review the situation whether the relevant event has been notified or not. No decision under clause 25.3 can fix a date earlier than the date for completion stated in appendix 1
26.1	Reimburse the contractor for any direct loss and/or expense caused by matters affecting regular progress of the works*	If the contractor makes written application within a reasonable time of it becoming apparent, and the necessary procedural and other conditions of the clause are satisfied. It is implied that an ascertainment will be made as under JCT 80 – which should be dealt with in the employer's requirements
27.4	Pay to the contractor any amount due to him after completion of the works by others, less expenses, damages, etc	

353

Table 7.04: Employer's/Employer's Agent's Duties under JCT 81 WCD – (continued)

Clause	Duty	Comment
28.2	Pay to the contractor the total value of work completed at the date of termination plus the value of work begun and executed but not completed at that date. Pay sums ascertained as direct loss and/or expense, cost of materials or goods properly ordered for the works and for which the contractor has paid or is legally bound to pay. Pay the reasonable cost of removal from site of temporary buildings, etc and any direct loss and/or expense caused to the contractor by the determination*	Where the contractor has determined his own employment for employer default under clause 28.1. Amounts previously paid are taken into account. Direct loss and/or expense includes loss of profit.
30.3	Pay amounts stated as due in applications for interim payment within 14 days of each application* Notify the contractor (with reasons) in writing if he considers that amounts claimed are not in accordance with the contract and at the same time pay such amount as he considers to be properly due as an interim payment*	This must be done on receipt of the contractor's application
30.4	Place the retention in a separate designated banking account as trust money and inform the contractor in writing that the amount has been so placed*	If the contractor so requests. The retention is to be banked at the date of each interim payment. The employer gets the interest
30.6	Pay the amount due in the final statement within 14 days of the agreement of the final account*	
31.3	Notify the contractor in writing that he intends to make the statutory deduction from payments due under the contract and give reasons for his decision*	If the contractor fails to provide a tax certificate

Table 7.04: Employer's/Employer's Agent's Duties under JCT 81 WCD – (continued)

Clause	Duty	Comment
31.5	Promptly send to the Inland Revenue any voucher given to him by the contractor*	
31.6	Notify the contractor of statutory tax deductions which he proposes to make*	The Inland Revenue regulations should be referred to in this complicated procedure
31.7	Correct any errors or ommissions in calculations or statutory deductions by repayment to or deduction from the contractor as appropriate*	
32.3	Pay the contractor sums due to him ascertained in accordance with the provisions of the subclause*	See clause 28.2 above for details except that in this case the contractor gets no payment in respect of direct loss and/or expense suffered as a result of the determination. The loss lies where it falls
33.1	Make in writing to the contractor a fair and reasonable extension of time	If the contractor makes good the war damage and proceeds with the works
34.2	Issue instructions on antiquities found Reimburse the contractor for any direct loss and/or expense in which he is involved in consequence of a find of antiquities*	If the contractor reports a find of antiquities, etc under clause 34.1
39.1	Give written notice to the contractor*	If employer requires a dispute to be referred to arbitration
39.7	Together with the contractor, forthwith appoint another arbitrator	If the arbitrator ceases to act

* Those duties which are personal to the employer, fluctuations clauses are not covered in this table.

Table 7.05: Contractor's Powers under JCT 81 WCD

Clause	Power	Comment
4.2	Request the employer to specify in writing which contract provision empowers the issue of an instruction	
5.1	Inspect the employer's requirements and the contractor's proposals	These documents are kept by the employer
8.1	Substitute materials, goods and workmanship for those described in the employer's requirements or contractor's proposals or specification	Only if the original goods, etc are not procurable; *and* The employer consents in writing
12.2	Consent to a change in the employer's requirements which is or makes necessary any alteration or modificaton in the design of the works	Consent must not be unreasonably delayed or withheld
12.4	Agree with the employer the valuation of changes and provisional sum work	
17.1	Consent to the employer taking partial possession before practical completion	
18.1	Assign the contract	With the written consent of the employer
18.2	Sub-let all or any part of the works or their design	With the written consent of the employer
21.1.1.2	Choose a greater sum than that stated in the appendix	In respect of personal injury or death, or injury or damage to property insurance
22B.2	Require the employer to produce for inspection the insurance policy and the premium receipts	Where the works are to be insured in joint names by the employer
	Insure in joint names all work executed, etc against all risks	If the employer fails to produce receipt on request

Table 7.05: Contractor's Powers under JCT 81WCD – (continued)

Clause	Power	Comment
22C.3	Request employer to produce receipt showing that he has an effective policy under clauses 22C.1 and 22C.2	Applies to existing structures where employer is to insure in joint names
	Insure in the employer's name and on his behalf and for that purpose enter the premises to make an inventory and survey	If the employer fails to produce the premium receipt when requested unless employer is a local authority
22C.4.3.1	Determine his employment under the contract if it is just and equitable to do so	This must be done within 28 days of the occurrence of the loss or damage, and is effected by a written notice to that effect served on the employer
	Request the employer to concur in the appointment of an arbitrator	If the employer serves notice determining the contractor's employment; and The contractor alleges that it is not just and equitable to do so
22D.1	Require information from the employer	To obtain quotation under this clause
23.3.2	Consent to the employer using or occupying the site of works before the issue of practical completion certificate	If insurers confirm that insurance will not be prejudiced, consent must not be unreasonably withheld
26.1	Write to the employer stating that he has incurred or is likely to incur direct loss and/or expense not reimbursable under any other contract provision	If it becomes or should have become reasonably apparent that regular progress has been or is likely to be affected by one or more of the specified matters
28.1	Determine his employment under the contract by written notice served by registered post or recorded delivery	The notice must not be given unreasonably or vexatiously. The right to determine employment is in addition to the contractor's other rights and remedies. In the case of the default alleged being the employer's failure to pay to the contractor any interim amount properly due, it is a precondition that the contractor should first have served on the employer a default notice under clause 28.1.1 and the employer must have continued his default for seven days thereafter. The grounds for

Table 7.05:   Contractor's Powers under JCT 81WCD – (continued)

Clause	Power	Comment
		determination are traditional but there is an additional ground: delay in receipt of any permission or approval for the purposes or development control requirements necessary for the works to be carried out or proceed and which delay the contractor has taken all practicable steps to avoid or reduce
28A.1	Forthwith determine his employment under the contract	If the carrying out of substantially the whole of the work is suspended for a period named in appendix 1 by reason of: <ul><li>*force majeure*</li><li>loss by specified perils</li><li>civil commotion</li></ul>
29.2	Consent to the carrying out of such work by others	If the employer so requests where the employer's requirements do not so provide Consent must not be unreasonably withheld
32.1	Determine forthwith his employment under the contract by serving notice on the employer by registered post or recorded delivery	If war, etc breaks out during the contract. The determination notice cannot be served – before the expiry of 28 days from the date of the government order for general mobilisation; or After practical completion unless the works or part of them have suffered war damage

Table 7.06: Contractor's Duties under JCT 81 WCD

Clause	Duty	Comment
2.1	Carry out and complete the works referred to in the employer's requirements, the contractor's proposals and the other contract documents and in accordance therewith complete the design for the works including the selection of any specifications for any kinds and standards of materials, goods and workmanship so far as not described or stated in the employer's requirements or contractor's proposals	
2.3	Give the employer written notice immediately on finding any divergence between the employer's requirements and the definition of the site boundary	
2.4.1	Inform the employer in writing of proposals to deal with the discrepancy	If Contractor's Proposals do not deal with a discrepancy within the Employer's Requirements
2.4.2	Inform the employer in writing of his proposed amendment where there is a discrepancy within the contractor's proposals	
2.4.3	Give the employer written notice immediately, specifying any discrepancy discovered in the documents	
2.5	Design the works using the same standard of skill and care as would an architect or other appropriate professional adviser holding himself out as competent to take on work for such a design	

Table 7.06:   Contractor's Duties under JCT 81 WCD – (continued)

Clause	Duty	Comment
4	Forthwith comply with all instructions issued by the employer	The instructions must be in writing *and* Expressly empowered by the contract The contractor need not comply where the instruction requires a change under clause 12.1.2 to the extent that he makes reasonable objection in writing to the employer
4.3	Confirm to the employer in writing any oral instruction issued by the employer	
5.3	Provide the employer free of charge two copies of the drawings, specifications, details, levels and setting out dimensions which he prepares or uses for the works	
5.4	Keep available to the employer's agent at all reasonable times one copy of the employer's requirements, contract sum analysis, contractor's proposals and documents referred to in clause 5.3	
5.5	Supply the employer with "as built" drawings free of charge	This must be done before the defects liability period begins
6.1.1.	Comply with statutory requirements, give all notices, etc and pass statutory approvals to the employer when they are received	This includes making planning and related applications
6.1.2	Notify the employer immediately in writing on finding any diverence between the statutory requirements and the employer's requirements or the contractor's proposals Inform the employer in writing of his proposed amendment for	

Table 7.06: Contractor's Duties under JCT 81 WCD – (continued)

Clause	Duty	Comment
	removing the divergence Complete at his own cost the design and construction of the work in accordance with the amendment	With the employer's consent, which must not be unreasonably delayed or withheld. This is subject to clause 6.3
6.1.3	Supply such limited materials and execute such limited work as are reasonably necessary to secure immediate compliance with statutory requirements Forthwith inform the employer of the emergency and the steps he is taking under clause 6.1.3.1	In an emergency and if this is necessary before receiving the employer's consent
6.2	Pay all statutory fees and charges and indemnify the employer against liability in respect of them	No adjustment is made to the contract sum unless such fees are stated as a provisional sum in the employer's requirements
8.1.1	Provide materials and goods of standards described in Employer's Requirements or Contractor's Proposals	So far as procurable If not so described
8.1.2	Provide workmanship of standards described in Employer's Requirements or in Contractor's Proposals or appropriate to the works	To extent not so described
8.2	Provide the employer with vouchers to prove that the goods comply with clause 8.1	If the employer requests
8.3	Open up for inspection any work covered up and arrange for the testing of any materials or goods or executed work	If the employer so instructs. The cost will be added to the contract sum unless the tests, etc are adverse

Table 7.06: Contractor's Duties under JCT 81 WCD – (continued)

Clause	Duty	Comment
8.4	Remove from site or rectify any work, material or goods not in accordance with the contract	If the employer so instructs
8.5	Provide samples of goods and workmanship as specifically referred to in the Employer's Requirements or the Contractor's Proposals	Before carrying out work or ordering goods
9.1	Indemnify the employer against liability in respect of copyright, royalties and patent rights	If the employer instructs the use of patented articles, etc the contractor is not liable in respect of infringement, and all royalties, damages, etc are added to the contract sum (clause 9.2)
10	Constantly keep a competent person in charge on site	
11	Allow the employer's agent and any person authorised by the employer access to the works, workshops, etc at all reasonable times and ensure a similar right of access in any sub-contract	
16.2	Make good at his own cost all defects, shrinkages and other faults specified in the schedule of defects	The defect, etc must be due to the contractor's failure to comply with his contractual obligations or to frost occurring before practical completion. The employer's schedule of defects must be delivered to the contractor not later than 14 days after the expiry of the defects liability period. The contractor must remedy the defects, etc within a reasonable time of receipt of the schedule
16.3	Comply with any instruction issued by the employer requiring the remedying of defects, shrinkages and other faults	This is in addition, to clause 16.2. No such instruction can be issued after the delivery of the schedule of defects or after 14 days from the expiry of the defects liability period

Table 7.06: Contractor's Duties under JCT 81 WCD – (continued)

Clause	Duty	Comment
17.1	Issue a written statement to the employer identifying the part of the works taken into possession and giving the date of possession	If employer with contractor's consent takes possession of part of the works
20.1	Indemnify the employer against any expense, liability, loss, claim or proceedings whatsoever in respect of personal injury to or death of any person	If the claim arises out of or in the course of or is caused by the carrying out of the works *unless* and to the extent that the claim is due to any act or neglect of the employer or of any person for whom he is responsible.
20.2	Indemnify the employer against any expense, liability, loss, claim or proceedings whatsoever in respect of injury or damage to any property	In so far as the injury or damage arises out of or in the course of or by reason of the carrying out of the works; *and* Is due to the negligence, omission or default of the contractor or any sub-contractor or of their respective servants or agents
21.1.1.1	Maintain necessary insurances for injury to persons or property	The obligations to maintan insurance is without prejudice to the contractor's liability to indemnify the employer
21.1.2	Produce documentary evidence of insurance cover	When reasonably required to do so by the employer who may (but not unreasonably or vexatiously) require production of the policy or policies and premium receipts
21.2	Maintain in joint names of the employer and the contractor insurances for such amounts of indemnity as are specified in the employer's requirements and recorded in appendix 1 for damage to property other than the works caused by collapse, subsidence, etc Deposit with the employer the policy(ies) and premium receipts	Employer must approve insurers
22.3	Ensure that the joint names policies referred to in clause 22A.1 or 22A.3 *either*	If clause 22A applies

Table 7.06: Contractor's Duties under JCT 81 WCD – (continued)

Clause	Duty	Comment
	● provide for recognition of each nominated sub-contractor as insured or ● include insurers' waiver of rights of subrogation	In respect of specified perils
22A.1	Insure the works in joint names against all risks for their full reinstatement value	Applicable to new buildings – the obligation continues until the date of the statement of practical completion or date of determination. The insurance is to be placed with insurers approved by the employer. Clause 22A.3.1 enables this cover to be by means of the contractor's all-risks policy
22A.2	Deposit the policy(ies) and premium receipts with the employer	
22A.4.1	Give written notice to the employer	Upon discovering loss or damage caused by risks covered by the joint names policy in clause 22A.1 or 22A.2 or 22A.3
22A.4.3	With due diligence restore any work damaged, replace or repair any unfixed materials or goods that have been destroyed or damaged, remove and dispose of debris and proceed with the carrying out and completion of the works	After insurance claim under clauses 22A.1 or 22A.2 or 22A.3 and any inspection required by the insurers
22A.4.4	Authorise insurers to pay insurance money to employer	Acting also on behalf of sub-contractors recognised pursuant to clause 22.3
22B.3.1	Notify forthwith the employer of the extent, nature and location of any loss or damage affecting the works etc	Upon discovering the loss or damage caused by risks covered by joint names policy in clause 22B.1
22B.3.3	With due diligence restore work damaged, replace or repair any unfixed materials	The restoration of damaged work, etc, is to be treated as a change in the employer's requirements and valued under clause 12.2

Clause	Duty	Comment
	or goods that have been destroyed or injured Remove and dispose of debris and proceed with the carrying out and completion of the works	
22B.3.4	Authorise insurers to pay insurance money to employer	Acting also on behalf of sub-contractors recognised pursuant to clause 22.3
22C.4	Notify forthwith the employer of the extent, nature and location of any loss or damage affecting the works, etc	The contractor must do this upon discovering the loss, etc
22C.4.2	Authorise insurers to pay insurance monies to employer	Acting also on behalf of sub-contractors recognised pursuant to clause 22.3
22C.4.4.1	With all due diligence reinstate and make good loss or damage and proceed with the carrying out and completion of the work	If no notice of determination is served or if the arbitrator decides against the notice of determination
22D.1	Send quotation to the employer Forthwith take out and maintain the relevant policy and send to employer for deposit with premium receipts	If the Employer's Requirements state and it is recorded in appendix 1 that liquidated damages insurance may be required and the employer has so instructed If so instructed by the employer
23.1	Begin the construction of the works when given possession of the site Regularly and diligently proceed with the works and complete them on or before the completion date	This is subject to the provision for extension of time in clause 25

Table 7.06:   Contractor's Duties under JCT 81 WCD – (continued)

Clause	Duty	Comment
23.3.2	Notify insurers under clause 22A or 22B or 22C.2–.4 and obtain confirmation that use or occupation will not prejudice insurance	Before giving consent to use or occupation
24.2	Pay or allow to the employer liquidated damages at the rate specified in appendix 1	If the contractor fails to complete the works by the completion date; *and* If the employer has notified him in writing to that effect; *and* If the employer has required liquidated damages in writing not later than the date when the final account and statement become conclusive
25.2	Notify the employer in writing forthwith of the material circumstances (including the cause or causes of delay), identifying any event which in his opinion is relevant	If and when it becomes reasonably apparent that the progress of the works is being or is likely to be delayed. The duty is in respect of any cause of delay and is not confined to the "relevant events" specified in clause 25.4
	Give particulars of the expected effects of any relevant event and estimate the extent, if any, of the expected delay to completion beyond the currently fixed completion date	If practicable, this must be done in the above notice, but otherwise in writing as soon as possible thereafter
	Keep the particulars and estimate up to date by further written notices as may be reasonably necessary	
25.3	Constantly use his best endeavours to prevent delay in progress to the works and to prevent the completion of the works being delayed or further delayed beyond the completion date; *and*	
	Do all that may be reasonably required to the satisfaction of the employer to proceed with the works	The second part of this duty does not require the contractor to spend money
26.1	Submit to the employer such information as is reasonably necessary to ascertain the	Upon request by the employer

Table 7.06: Contractor's Duties under JCT 81 WCD – (continued)

Clause	Duty	Comment
	amount of direct loss and/or expense	
27.4	Provide the employer with two copies of all drawings, details or descriptions, etc as he has prepared or previously provided relating to the works before determination of his employment. Assign to the employer without payment the benefit of any sub-contracts, etc within 14 days	In the event of determination by the employer under clause 27.1, 27.2 or 27.3 If so required by the employer. Not applicable where determination was on grounds of insolvency
	Remove from the works any temporary buildings, plant tools, equipment, goods and materials belonging or hired to the contractor	As and when so required by the employer in writing
	Pay or allow to the employer any direct loss and/or damage caused to the employer by the determination	
28.2	With all reasonable dispatch and taking necessary precautions to prevent injury, damage, etc remove from site all temporary buildings, plant, tools, equipment, goods and materials and give facilities to his sub-contractors to do the same	
	Provide the employer with two copies of all drawings, details or descriptions, etc as he has prepared or previously provided relating to the works before determination of his employment	
29.1	Permit the execution of work not forming part of the contract to be carried out by the employer or by persons employed or otherwise engaged by him	If the employer's requirements provide the contractor with such information as is necessary to enable him to carry out and complete the works in accordance with the contract

Table 7.06: Contractor's Duties under JCT 81 WCD – (continued)

Clause	Duty	Comment
30.3	Apply for interim payment, accompanied by such details as may be stated in the employer's requirements	Under alternative A the applications are to be made on completion of each stage Under alternative B applications are to be made at the period stated in appendix 2 up to and including the end of the period during which the day named in the statement of practical completion occurs and thereafter as and when further amounts are due. The employer is not required to make any such interim payment within one calendar month of having made a previous interim payment
30.5	Submit to the employer the final account and the final statement for the employer's agreement Supply such supporting documents as the employer may reasonably require	Within three months of practical completion
31.3	Provide the employer with evidence that the contractor is entitled to be paid without statutory tax deduction or inform him in writing that he is not so entitled	Where the employer is stated to be a "contractor" for the purposes of the Finance (No 2) Act 1975 in appendix 1. The tax certificate must be provided not later than 21 days before the date of first payment under the contract
31.4	Immediately inform the employer if he obtains a tax certificate Provide the employer with evidence that he is entitled to be paid without statutory deduction or inform him that he is not so entitled Immediately from the employer in writing if the contractor's current tax certificate is cancelled, giving the date of cancellation	Where the contractor is uncertified and then obtains a tax certificate Where tax certificate expires before final payment. The evidence must be provided not later than 28 days before expiry of the certificate
32.2	Comply with the employer's instructions as to protective work, etc	If the employer issues the requisite instructions within 14 days after the determination notice

Table 7.06: Contractor's Duties under JCT 81 WCD – (continued)

Clause	Duty	Comment
34.1	Use his best endeavours not to disturb any fossils, antiquities, etc found on site and cease work if its continuance would endanger the object found or impede its excavation or removal Take all necessary steps to preserve the object in the exact position and condition in which it was found Inform the employer of the discovery and precise location of the object	
34.2	Permit the examination or removal of the object by a third party	If the employer so instructs
39.1	Give written notice to the employer	If the contractor requires a dispute to be referred to arbitration
39.7	Together with the employer forthwith appoint another arbitrator	If the arbitrator ceases to act

Table 7.07: Clauses that may Give Rise to Claims under JCT 81 WCD

Clause	Event	Type
2.3.1	Divergence between employer's requirements and definition of site boundary	C
2.4	Discrepancies between employer's requirements and the contractor's proposals	CL
3	Failure to take ascertainment into account in the computation of the next interim payment	CL
4.1.1	Additions, omissions, alterations in goods, workmanship, order of work	C
4.1.2	Employer employs others to do the work without proper procedure	CL
4.3.2	Oral instructions by employer	CL
6.3	Changes in statutory requirements and decisions of development control authority after the date of tender	C
7	Failure to define site boundaries	CL
8.3	Opening up or testing of work found to be in accordance with the contract	C
8.4	Wrongly worded instruction or failure to have regard to Code of Practice	CL

Table 7.07:   Clauses that may Give Rise to Claims under JCT 81 WCD – (continued)

Clause	Event	Type
9.2	Royalties and patent rights	C
12.2	Changes	C
12.3	Expenditure of provisional sums	C
12.4	Failure to value	CL
12.5.1–5	Failure to follow valuation rules	CL
12.5.6	Valuations not otherwise included	C
14	Recovery of VAT or loss of input tax	C
16.1	Failure to issue statement at practical completion	CL
16.2	Failure to deliver schedule of defects	CL
16.3	Late instructions to make good defects	CL
16.4	Failure to issue notice at making good of defects	CL
17.1	Possession without contractor's consent	CL
17.1.3	Failure to issue notice at making good of defects	CL
17.1.5	Failure to reduce liquidated damages correctly or at all	CL

Table 7.07: Clauses that may Give Rise to Claims under JCT 81 WCD – (continued)

Clause	Event	Type
18.1	Assignment by employer without contractor's written consent	CL
18.2	Unreasonably withholding consent to sub-letting	CL
21.2	Effects of special insurances	CL
22A.4.2	Accepted insurance claims	C
22B.3.5	Restoration of damaged work	C
22C.4.4.2	Restoration of damaged work	C
23.1.1	Failure to give possession on due date if no deferment	CL
23.2	Postponement of work	C
24.2.2	Repayment of liquidated damages	C
25	Employer not carrying out his duties	CL
26	Loss and/or expense	C
27.1	Invalid determination	CL
28.2	Payment after determination	C
29	Work by employer	C

Table 7.07:   Clauses that may Give Rise to Claims under JCT 81 WCD – (continued)

Clause	Event	Type
30	Payments Failure to observe rules Interest on retention	C CL CL
31	Failure to observe requirements of this clause	CL
32.1	Invalid determination	CL
32.3	Payment for protective work	C
33.1	Making good war damage	C
34.3	Loss and/or expense regarding antiquities	C
35–38	Fluctuations	C

KEY
C = Contractual claims
CL = Common law claims
Common law claims are usually dealt with by the employer
In this contract, contractual claims will usually be dealt with by the
employer's agent (depending on the extent of his authorisation) or by the
employer

Table 7.08: Statements and Notices to be Issued by the Employer under JCT 81 WCD

Clause	Statement of notice
2.3	Notice of divergence
2.4.3	Notice of discrepancy
4.1.2	Notice requiring compliance with instruction
6.1.2.	Notice specifying divergence between statutory requirements and employer's requirements or contractor's proposals
16.1	Statement of practical completion
16.4	Notice of making good of defects
17.1.2	Notice of making good of defects
22C.4.3.1	Notice of determination
24.1	Notice of failure to complete on due date
27.1	Notice of default
	Notice of determination
30.3.4	Notice that the amount stated in the application for interim payment is not in accordance with the contract
32.1	Notice of determination

Table 7.09: Employer's Instructions Empowered by JCT 81 WCD

Clause	Instruction
2.3.1	In regard to discrepancy between employer's requirements and definition of the site boundary
8.3	To open up for inspection or carry out testing
8.4.1	Removal from site or rectification of work, materials or goods
8.4.2	Reasonably necessary change after defective work
8.4.3	Reasonably necessary to open up and establish likelihood of non-compliance
12.2	Effecting a change in the employer's requirements
12.3	Expenditure of provisional sums included in the employer's requirements
16.2	Schedule of defects
16.3	Requiring defects etc to be made good
22D.1	To obtain and accept liquidated damages insurance
23.2	Postponing work
32.2	Requiring the execution of protective work or continuation of work up to a specified point of stoppage after determination on the outbreak of hostilities
33.1.2	Requiring removal and disposal of debris and execution of protective work after war damage
34.2	Regarding antiquities, including excavation, examination or removal by third parties

Table 7.10: Adjustment of the Contract Sum under JCT 81 WCD

Clause	Adjustment
2.3.1	Divergencies between employer's requirements and definition of the site boundary
3	Contract sum adjustments
6.2	Fees legally demandable by Act of Parliament, etc *and* Stated by way of a provisional sum
6.3	Change in statutory requirements or decision of the development control authority after the date of tender
8.3	Opening up and testing
9.2	Royalties and patent rights
12	Changes
13	Adjustment of contract sum
16.2 & 16.3	Defects, shrinkages and other faults
22B.2	Contractor insuring if employer defaults
22C.3	Contractor insuring if employer defaults
26.3	Loss and/or expense
28.2.3.2	Work begun but not completed at date of determination
30.5.2	Final adjustment of the contract sum
32.3	Works required after outbreak of hostilities
33.1.4	Removal of debris and protective work after war damage
34.3.1	Loss and/or expense due to antiquities
35–38	Fluctuations

Table 7.11: Matters for Inclusion in Employer's Requirements under JCT 81 WCD

	Source or comment
Details of the site Details of accommodation requirements Purposes for which building is to be used Any other matter likely to affect preparation of contractor's proposals or his price	CD/1A para 14
Statement of functional and ancillary requirements ● Kind and number of buildings ● Density and mix of dwellings and any height limitations ● Schematic layout and/or drawings ● Specific requirements as to finishes, etc	CD/1A para 15
Statement of planning and other constraints, eg restrictive covenants Statement of site requirements The extent to which the contractor is to base his proposals on information supplied Availability of public utilities Statement of extent and detail of information to be included in contractor's proposals regarding: Plans, elevations, and scale of drawings Information about structural design Services to be specified and indicated on layout drawings Specification notes for judging quality of proposed works	Copies of permissions, etc should be annexed Care is needed: information supplied may give rise to liability CD/1A para 15
Data for conditions of contract Requirements as to form and content of contractor's proposals and contract sum analysis Details of proposed arbitrator Any other requirements "The employer should state how the Date for Completion of the Whole of the Works is to be fixed for insertion in the contract" Detail functions of employer's agent, quantity surveyor and clerk of works if required	See text: essential that details required. The form in which the contract sum analysis is required should always be stated This is vital

Flowchart 7.12: Employer's Instructions

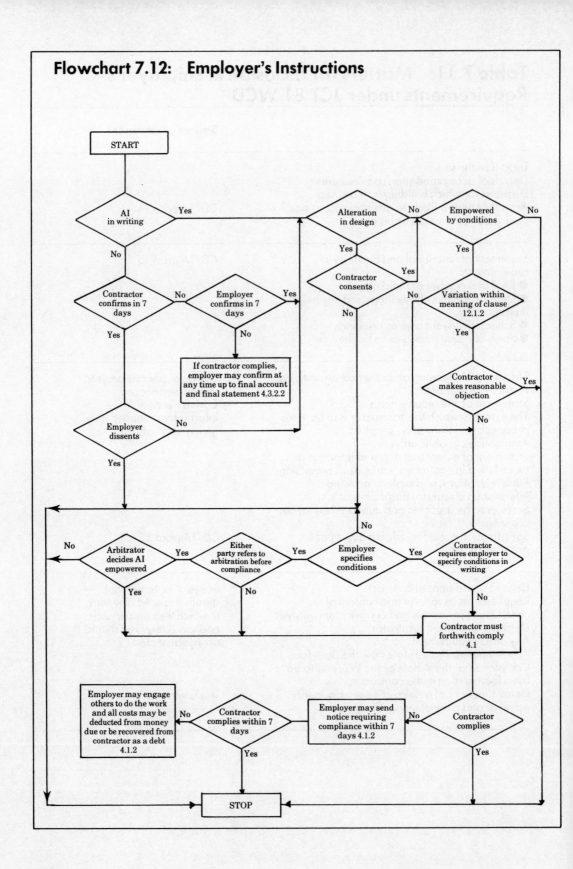

Flowchart 7.13: Valuation of Variations

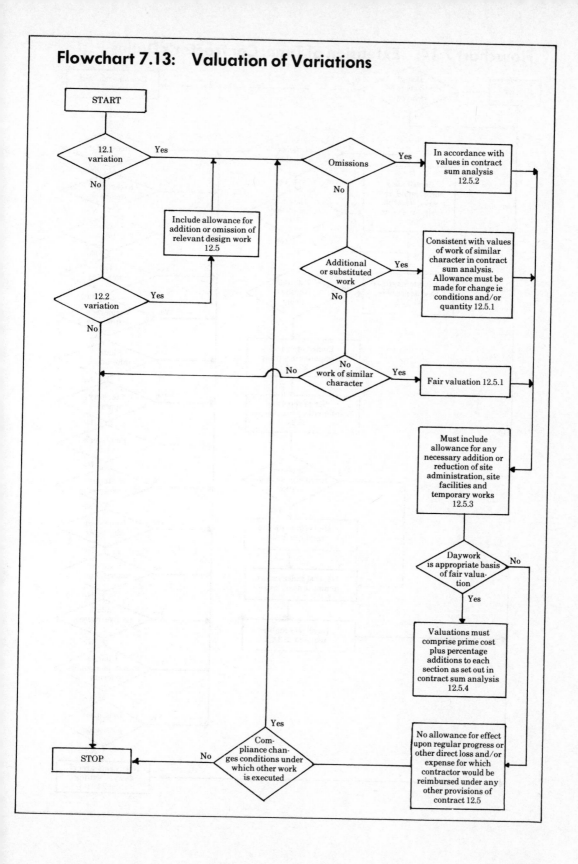

Flowchart 7.14: Extension of Time: Contractor's Duties

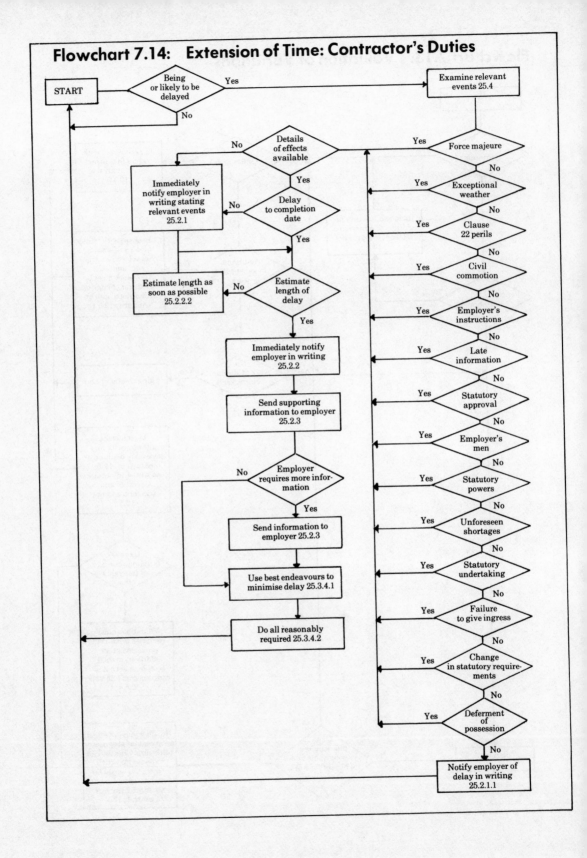

Flowchart 7.15: Extension of Time: Employer's Duties

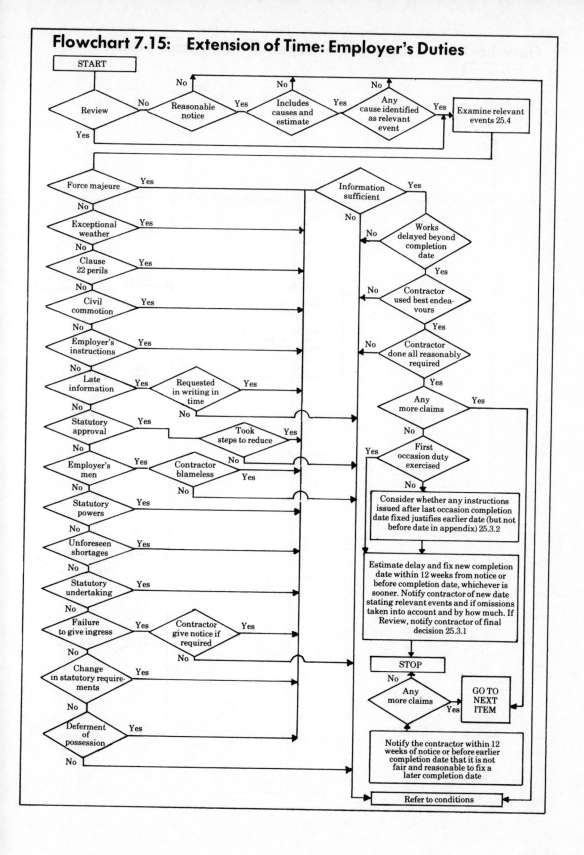

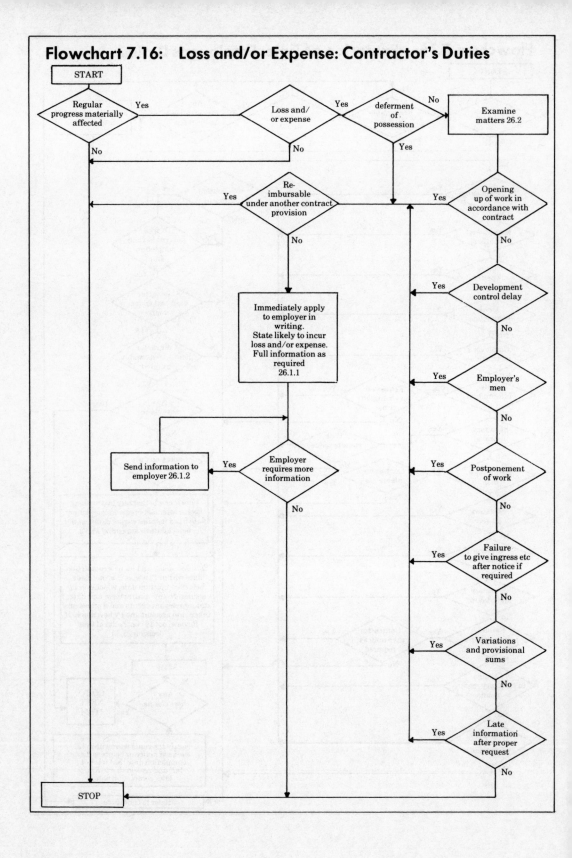

Flowchart 7.16:   Loss and/or Expense: Contractor's Duties

START

Regular progress materially affected — Yes

Loss and/or expense — Yes

deferment of possession — No

Examine matters 26.2

No (Regular progress materially affected → No)

No (Loss and/or expense → No)

Yes (deferment of possession → Yes)

Re-imbursable under another contract provision — Yes

Opening up of work in accordance with contract — Yes

No (Re-imbursable under another contract provision → No)

No (Opening up of work in accordance with contract → No)

Immediately apply to employer in writing. State likely to incur loss and/or expense. Full information as required 26.1.1

Development control delay — Yes

No (Development control delay → No)

Employer's men — Yes

No (Employer's men → No)

Send information to employer 26.1.2 ← Yes — Employer requires more information

Postponement of work — Yes

No (Postponement of work → No)

No (Employer requires more information → No)

Failure to give ingress etc after notice if required — Yes

No (Failure to give ingress etc after notice if required → No)

Variations and provisional sums — Yes

No (Variations and provisional sums → No)

Late information after proper request — Yes

No (Late information after proper request → No)

STOP

Flowchart 7.17: Loss and/or Expense: Employer's Duties

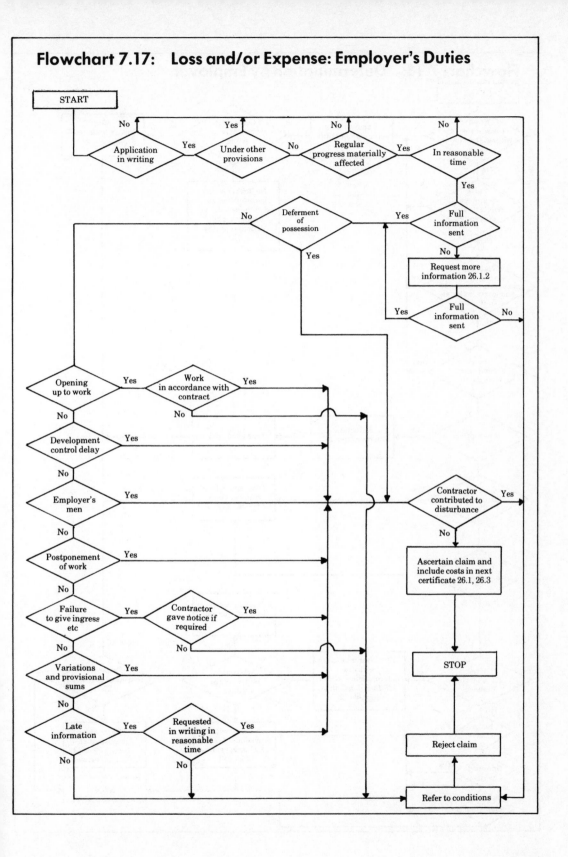

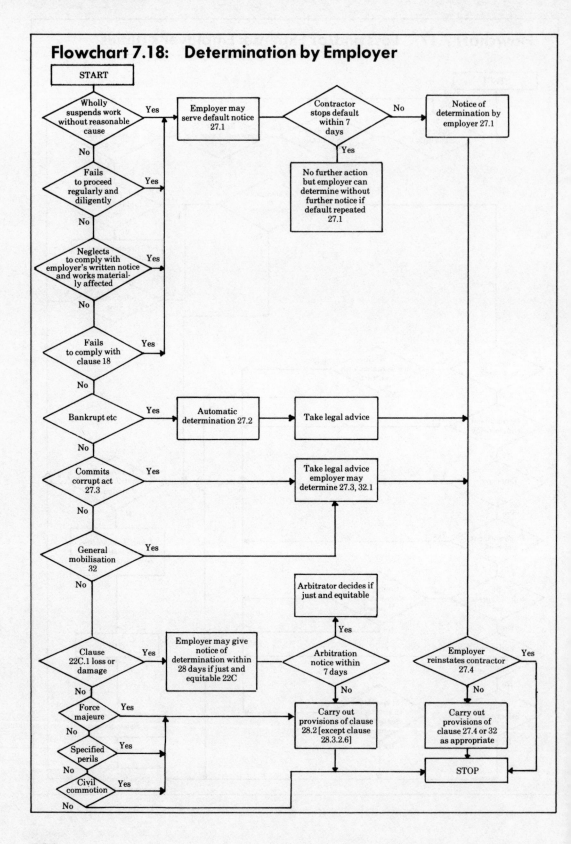

Flowchart 7.18: Determination by Employer

START

Wholly suspends work without reasonable cause — Yes → Employer may serve default notice 27.1 → Contractor stops default within 7 days — No → Notice of determination by employer 27.1

Contractor stops default within 7 days — Yes → No further action but employer can determine without further notice if default repeated 27.1

No

Fails to proceed regularly and diligently — Yes

No

Neglects to comply with employer's written notice and works materially affected — Yes

No

Fails to comply with clause 18 — Yes

No

Bankrupt etc — Yes → Automatic determination 27.2 → Take legal advice

No

Commits corrupt act 27.3 — Yes → Take legal advice employer may determine 27.3, 32.1

No

General mobilisation 32 — Yes

No

Arbitrator decides if just and equitable

Clause 22C.1 loss or damage — Yes → Employer may give notice of determination within 28 days if just and equitable 22C → Arbitration notice within 7 days — Yes → Arbitrator decides if just and equitable

Employer reinstates contractor 27.4 — Yes

No

Arbitration notice within 7 days — No → Carry out provisions of clause 28.2 [except clause 28.3.2.6]

Force majeure — Yes

No

Specified perils — Yes

No

Civil commotion — Yes

No

Employer reinstates contractor 27.4 — No → Carry out provisions of clause 27.4 or 32 as appropriate

STOP

384

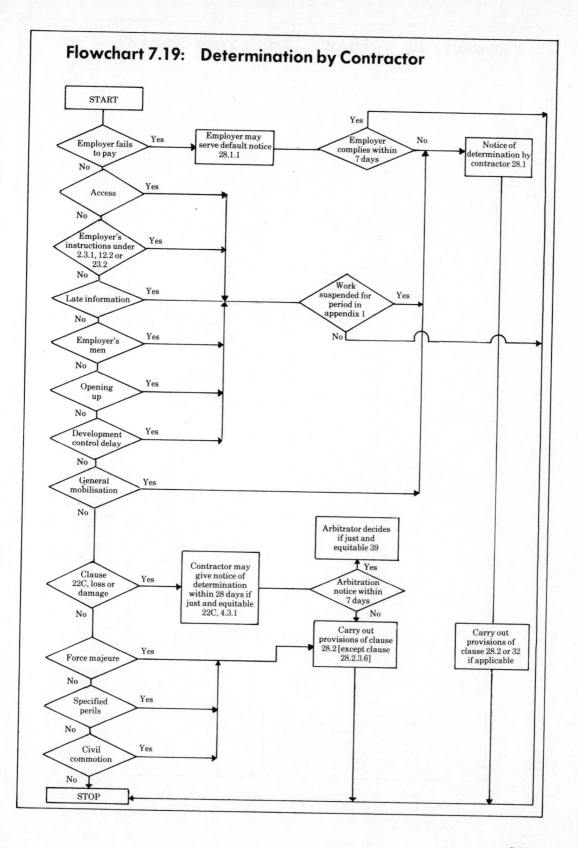

Flowchart 7.19:   Determination by Contractor

START

Employer fails to pay — Yes → Employer may serve default notice 28.1.1 → Employer complies within 7 days — Yes → Notice of determination by contractor 28.1

Employer complies within 7 days — No → Notice of determination by contractor 28.1

Access — Yes →

Employer's instructions under 2.3.1, 12.2 or 23.2 — Yes →

Late information — Yes → Work suspended for period in appendix 1 — Yes →

Work suspended for period in appendix 1 — No →

Employer's men — Yes →

Opening up — Yes →

Development control delay — Yes →

General mobilisation — Yes →

Clause 22C, loss or damage — Yes → Contractor may give notice of determination within 28 days if just and equitable 22C, 4.3.1 → Arbitration notice within 7 days — Yes → Arbitrator decides if just and equitable 39

Arbitration notice within 7 days — No → Carry out provisions of clause 28.2 [except clause 28.2.3.6]

Force majeure — Yes →

Specified perils — Yes →

Civil commotion — Yes →

Carry out provisions of clause 28.2 or 32 if applicable

STOP

Flowchart 7.20: Arbitration (Article 5 and Clause 39)

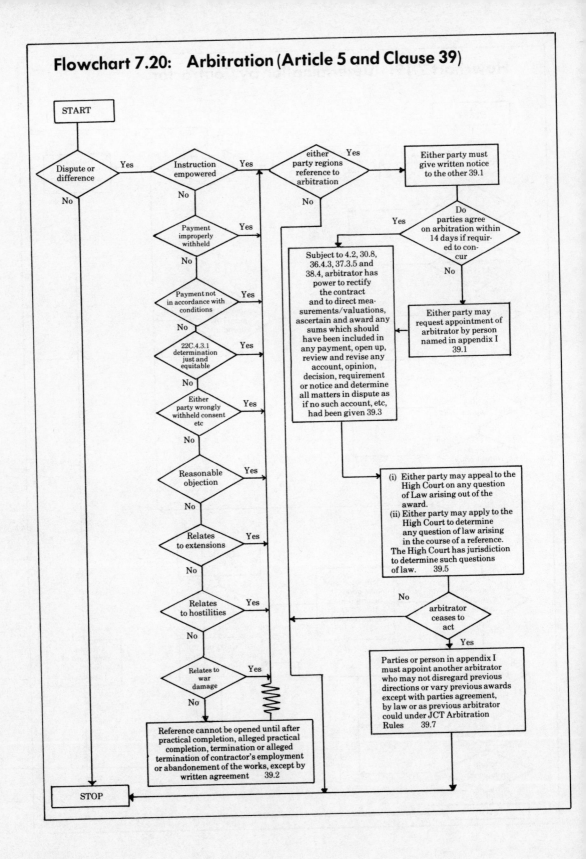

START

Dispute or difference — No → STOP
Yes →

Instruction empowered — No ↓
Yes →

Payment improperly withheld — No ↓
Yes →

Payment not in accordance with conditions — No ↓
Yes →

22C.4.3.1 determination just and equitable — No ↓
Yes →

Either party wrongly withheld consent etc — No ↓
Yes →

Reasonable objection — No ↓
Yes →

Relates to extensions — No ↓
Yes →

Relates to hostilities — No ↓
Yes →

Relates to war damage — No ↓
Yes →

either party regions reference to arbitration — No ↓
Yes →

Either party must give written notice to the other 39.1

Do parties agree on arbitration within 14 days if required to concur — Yes →
No ↓

Either party may request appointment of arbitrator by person named in appendix I 39.1

Subject to 4.2, 30.8, 36.4.3, 37.3.5 and 38.4, arbitrator has power to rectify the contract and to direct measurements/valuations, ascertain and award any sums which should have been included in any payment, open up, review and revise any account, opinion, decision, requirement or notice and determine all matters in dispute as if no such account, etc, had been given 39.3

(i) Either party may appeal to the High Court on any question of Law arising out of the award.
(ii) Either party may apply to the High Court to determine any question of law arising in the course of a reference. The High Court has jurisdiction to determine such questions of law.   39.5

arbitrator ceases to act — No →
Yes ↓

Parties or person in appendix I must appoint another arbitrator who may not disregard previous directions or vary previous awards except with parties agreement, by law or as previous arbitrator could under JCT Arbitration Rules   39.7

Reference cannot be opened until after practical completion, alleged practical completion, termination or alleged termination of contractor's employment or abandonement of the works, except by written agreement   39.2

STOP

8: The ACA Form of Building Agreement (ACA 2)

8.01 Introduction

The ACA Form of Building Agreement was first published in October 1982 in response to widespread dissatisfaction with JCT 80 expressed by members of the Association of Consultant Architects. A second edition, incorporating many revisions to the original text and layout, was published in October 1984.

The ACA has also issued a useful *Guide to the ACA Form of Building Agreement Second Edition* and a supporting (optional) form of sub-contract, together with various administrative documents.

An important feature of ACA 2 (as it is widely known) is the provision of standard alternative clauses which, in the appropriate combination, can be used to produce a variety of contractual arrangements to suit the parties. Thus, the form can be used as a contract in the traditional mould, in which the architect takes responsibility for all the design and the production of constructional drawings and the contractor is responsible for building. Alternatively, the architect's design role can be reduced to a minimum and the contractor given all the responsibility for detailed design *and* construction. Careful deletion of the alternative clauses allows a wide variation between these two extremes. **The contents of the form are summarised in Table 7.01.**

There is also a British Property Federation edition of ACA 2, specially adapted to suit the requirements of the BPF system of building procurement.

The main differences between BPF variant and the ordinary ACA form are:

- Fewer alternative clauses
- Absence of provisional sums
- Only one method of disputes settlement: mandatory adjudication followed by arbitration
- The substitution of the term "client's representative" for "architect".

The client's representative might well be an architect; equally he could be a project manager or someone from another relevant discipline.

Moreover, the BPF edition introduces the concept of a *Schedule of Activities* as the main pricing document, but in response to suggestions from the industry the Federation has made provision for bills of quantities to be used as an alternative.

8.02 Contractor's Obligations

The contractor's basic obligation is stated in clause 1.1. It is to "execute and complete the works in strict accordance with the contract documents". The contract documents are:

- The contract drawings
- The time schedule
- *Either* a schedule of rates *or* bills of quantities *or* schedule of activities
- A specification (optional).

The contractor must "comply with and adhere strictly to the architect's instructions" issued under the agreement. He is entitled to be paid for so doing unless the matter is already covered by the contract sum or is a result of his default.

8.03 Contract Documentation and Information

There are two alternatives in clause 2 which deals with contract documentation. Alternative 1 requires the architect to issue such further information and drawings as is necessary to amplify or explain the contract drawings or as is necessary to enable the contractor to progress. This is the traditional position.

Alternative 2 usefully provides for the contractor to undertake the supply of all further drawings and information. They must be submitted to the architect for his comments in accordance with the period set down in the time schedule or, otherwise, within 10 working days. If the architect has no comments to make, he must endorse the drawings "no comment," in which case they become part of the works (clause 2.5).

The time schedule sets out the important stages of the job:
- Possession of the site
- Taking-over of the works
- Rate of liquidated damages
- Maintenance period.

An alternative (2) provides for sectional possession or completion.

A list is to be completed to show dates and details of information to be provided. The completion is optional under ACA 2, but mandatory under BPF/ACA. It is clearly envisaged that the list will always be completed. If, for some reason, the information flow is not specified, it is for the contractor to apply for the information in time to allow the architect to carry out his duties under clause 2.3 (**see Table 7.04**).

The contractor is recognised as an expert, and therefore he warrants under clause 3.1 that:
- The works will comply with any performance specification or requirement contained in the contract documents
- Any part of the works to be designed by him will be fit for its purpose.

Clause 1.2 lays down that, in carrying out his obligations, the contractor must exercise a high degree of skill and care, to the standard of a properly qualified and competent contractor experienced in carrying out similar projects. If he is responsible for the design of the whole or any part of the design, an optional clause (6.6) requires him to take out professional indemnity insurance in respect of negligent design or that of his sub-contractors, suppliers etc.

8.04   Commencement and Completion

Clause 11.1 stipulates that immediately possession of part or the whole of the site is given, the contractor must begin the works and proceed regularly and diligently and in accordance with the time schedule so that the works are completed fit and ready for taking-over by the employer by the due or any extended date. If taking-over is delayed, either liquidated or general (unliquidated) damages are payable by the contractor depending upon the alternative clause chosen. The BPF/ACA version has provision for liquidated damages only. Whichever option is chosen, the architect's certificate of delay under clause 11.2 must have been issued before liability arises.

If the liquidated damages option is chosen, the employer has no discretion whether or not the contractor is to pay or allow the damages, but he has the option of requiring the architect to deduct them or of recovering them himself as a debt. Under the unliquidated damages option the employer, although entitled to deduct, may decide not to do so.

8.05 Extensions of Time

Grounds for extension of time are covered by clause 11.5 which is in alternative forms. Only one of them, that with a wider range of grounds, is available in the BPF/ACA version. Alternative 1 limits the grounds to "any act, instruction, default or omission of the employer or of the architect on his behalf" whether authorised by the agreement or not. Alternative 2 lists such things as *force majeure* and insurance contingencies, hostilities and defaults by governmental agencies as well as employer's acts or defaults. For the clause to operate:

- It must become reasonably apparent to the contractor that completion of the works is likely to be prevented *and*
- The contractor must notify the architect in writing immediately, specifying the circumstances; *and*
- As soon as possible after the notice, the contractor must submit full and detailed particulars of the extension of time required; *and*
- The contractor must update such particulars as necessary or if the architect so requests.

The above sequence of notifications must be observed by the contractor before the architect can discharge his duty to grant a "fair and reasonable" extension of time *unless* the cause of the delay is an act, omission or default of the employer or the architect (clause 11.6).

If the architect is of the reasonable opinion that the taking-over will be delayed, he must grant a suitable extension *either*:

- As soon as practicable, but in any case not later than 60 working days from receipt of the contractor's particulars; *or*
- At any time, in the case of acts, omissions or defaults of the employer or the architect and where the contractor has failed to give notice.

The architect may take into account any omissions from the work, provided he does so before taking-over, but failure to grant an extension of time which is properly due may result in the contract completion date becoming unenforceable in which case the employer would lose his rights to deduct liquidated or other damages.

Clause 11.7 makes an important provision for a mandatory review of extensions. Within a reasonable time after taking-over, the architect must confirm the date previously fixed or fix a later date, *either*:

- As a result of reviewing previous decisions given under clause 11.6 and given before the date stated in his clause 11.2 certificate of delay; *or*
- As a result of any act, instruction etc, of the employer or of the architect which has occurred after the date stated in the clause 11.2 certificate.

This clarifies a situation which is debatable under some other contract forms. Note that the architect is not entitled to fix an earlier date for completion.

Clause 11.8 gives power to the architect to order postponement or acceleration of the whole or any part of the works. If the power is exercised, the architect must "ascertain and certify a fair and reasonable adjustment (if appropriate) to the contract sum" for the contractor's compliance. Damage, loss and/or expense suffered or incurred by the contractor as a direct result is also to be included. The architect's decisions may be referred to adjudication or arbitration depending upon which version of clause 25 applies.

If the contract period is extended or if acceleration or postponement is authorised, the contractor must submit a revised time schedule to the architect for his consent (clause 11.9).

8.06 Architect's Instructions

Clause 8 empowers the architect to issue instructions. They must be in writing. The only exception to this is that, in an emergency, he may issue oral instructions provided that they are confirmed in writing within 5 working days. All instructions may be issued up to taking-over, but certain instructions (clause 8.1) may be issued at any time up to the completion of the contractor's obligations in regard to outstanding defective work.

The instructions in question are:
- Removal of any work, materials or goods not in accordance with the contract
- Dismissal of incompetent or negligent personnel from the works
- Opening up for inspection and testing
- Variations in regard to site access and use, working space and working hours.

The contractor is entitled to be paid for all instructions unless they require him to do something provided for in, or to be reasonably inferred from, the contract documents, or because they have arisen because of his default or that of any sub-contractor or supplier of his or those for whom he is or they are responsible in law.

Clause 17 deals with the procedures to be adopted for valuations. The contractor must submit to the architect written estimates of:
- The value of the instruction
- Any extension of time required
- Any damage, loss and/or expense (including interest if appropriate).

The architect may dispense with the need to follow this procedure (clause 17.5). Unless he does, non-compliance by the contractor results in loss of entitlement to payment until the final certificate; rights to interest and finance charges are also forfeit in respect of the intervening period.

If the correct notice is given, the contractor and the architect have 5 working days in which to agree estimates. If no agreement is reached, the architect may:
- Instruct the contractor to comply and ascertain a fair and reasonable adjustment and extension of time; *or*
- Instruct him *not* to comply, in which case the contractor has no claim arising out of the instruction or failure to reach agreement; *or*
- Refer the estimates to the adjudicator, if appointed.

8.07 Contractor's Claims

Clause 7 is very broad in its scope and is wider than comparable JCT clauses. It provides that "Any act, omission, default or negligence of the employer or the architect" which disrupts the regular progress of the work or any section, or delays their execution in accordance with the time schedule, shall give rise to a claim, provided that, in consequence, the contractor suffers or incurs damage, loss and/or expense. It amounts to giving the architect authority to settle common law claims. The results of architect's instructions are excluded and are covered in clause 17.

The contractor is entitled to be reimbursed in interim certificates provided that he:

- Gives written notice to the architect immediately it becomes reasonably apparent that an event giving rise to a claim has occurred or is likely to occur; *and*
- Submits an estimate of the adjustment required with supporting documentation. This must be done with his next interim application for payment following the notice; *and*
- Submits further estimates in respect of continuing losses (if any).

Failure to submit notices and estimates as required by clause 7.2 or 7.3 will result in loss of entitlement to reimbursement until the final certificate and forfeiture of any claim to interest.

The architect has 20 working days in which to give notice to the contractor that he accepts the estimates or wishes to negotiate an appropriate adjustment. Curiously, the architect is not given power to reject the estimate, but, if agreement cannot be reached within 20 working days of the architect's notice to negotiate, either party may refer the matter to the adjudication (if appointed).

8.08   Certificates and Payment

A very simple and clear system of payments is contained in clauses 16 and 19. On the last working day of each calendar month up to and including the month in which taking-over occurs, the contractor must submit interim applications for payment with supporting documentation. He must continue to do this thereafter as and when further amounts become due to him.

Within 10 working days of the contractor's application, the architect must issue his interim certificate which may include, if provided for in the contract documents, the value of goods and components manufactured for the works and stored off-site. The employer must make payment of the amount due within 10 working days of the date of the certificate. Failure to pay is grounds for determination under clause 20.2(a).

The contractor must submit his final account, complete with all vouchers, documents and receipts within 60 workings days of the end of the maintenance period (clause 19.1). The architect may request additional information as necessary to assist him to compute the final contract sum. The architect has 60 working days to issue his final certificate after compliance by the contractor with all his obligations under the agreement (clause 19.2). The obligations are compliance with clause 19.1 and the return of all drawings and documents under clause 19.4. Once again, the employer has 10 working days in which to make payment. Clause 19.5 makes clear that neither the issue of the final certificate nor any other certificate relieves the contractor of any liability under the contract. This is not the case with JCT 80. Moreover, the architect may "by any certificate delect, correct or modify any sum previously certified by him".

8.09   Sub-Contractors and Employer's Licensees

Clause 9.3 and 9.4 deal with named sub-contractors and suppliers who can arise in three ways:
- A person is named in the contract documents and his work or goods and materials are priced by the contractor (clause 9.3)

- A person or list of people is given in the contract documents and the work is covered by a provisional sum (clause 9.4). This is not applicable under the BPF edition.
- A provisional sum is given in the contract documents for work to be executed by a firm yet to be instructed by the architect (clause 9.5). In this case, the contractor has a right of reasonable objection to the person named. Once again, this provision does not appear in the BPF edition.

"Named sub-contractors and suppliers" under the ACA contract differ from those under IFC 84. In particular, it should be noted that under the terms of clause 9.6 the contractor is required to find his own equivalent sub-contractor if, for reasons beyond his control, he cannot negotiate a satisfactory sub-contract. The architect must be invited to all negotiations, thus safeguarding the employer's interests. If negotiations fail then it is for the contractor to select someone else for the approval of the architect, and the contractor is also under a duty to keep proper and detailed accounts and records of all payments to sub-contractors and suppliers and make them available for the architect's inspection.

Responsibility for all sub-contractors – named or otherwise – is that of the contractor and, interestingly, if a named sub-contractor fails and his sub-contract is terminated or discharged, it is the contractor's obligation to select a substitute (clause 9.7).

Work not forming part of the contract may be carried out by the employer's own contractors either:

- If the contract documents so provide, *or*
- If the architect issues an instruction requiring the contractor to permit the carrying out of such work by others. The contractor has the right to make reasonable objection.

Any resultant disruption or delay is reimbursable, unless reasonably foreseeable at the date of the agreement, by a contractor using the appropriate standard of skill and care. This provision cannot be used to take away work from the contractor and reallocate it to others. That would be against the general law.

Clause 5 obliges the contractor to provide for proper management of the works, appoint a site manager, and employ only appropriately skilled and qualified people on the works.

Clause 8.1(b) provides that the architect may require the dismissal from the works of any incompetent person.

8.10 Statutory Obligations

Unless the architect instructs otherwise, the contractor's obligation is to make all applications, pay all fees and give all notices and fully comply with statutory requirements.

If it becomes apparent that carrying out the work in accordance with the contract documents, any drawings issued by the architect or architect's instructions will cause an infringement or if the contractor so notifies the architect, the architect must issue an instruction stating how the infringement is to be resolved (clause 1.6). This provision does not apply, however, if the contractor is to supply details under BPF/ACA or under clause 2, alternative 2 of ACA 2, where clause 2.5 makes the contractor responsible for ensuring that work shown on his drawings complies with statutory requirements.

If the architect certifies that the contractor has properly paid fees, they are to be added to the contract sum unless already provided for in the contract documents. Fees included for and not used on the instructions of the architect are to be deducted from the contract sum.

8.11 Injury, Damage and Insurance

Clause 6 deals with vesting of property, contractor's indemnity and insurance. Property in goods and materials passes to the employer when they have been incorporated into the works. If there is provision for payment before incorporation, property is to pass at that stage. This clause, however will not defeat a retention of title clause in a supplier's contract of sale. Although property passes on incorporation, risk of damage does not pass from the contractor until taking-over (clause 6.2).

The insurance provisions are very much in common form. The contractor is to insure and indemnify the employer against injury and death due to the carrying out of the works and against damage to property arising from the works and due to contractor's or sub-contractor's negligence.

There are two provisions for insurance of the works against contingencies:
- Clause 6.4, alternative 1: where the contractor is to insure
- Clause 6.4, alternative 2: where the employer is to insure.

One of the alternatives is to be deleted.

If the contract documents so require, the contractor must maintain insurance in joint names against collapse, etc, of adjacent property due to the carrying out of the work excepting:
- Damage caused by contractor's negligence
- Damage due to design errors
- Foreseeable damage
- Damage arising from nuclear or war risk or sonic boom.

If the contractor undertakes the preparation of any production information, he must take out design indemnity insurance (clause 6.6) for an amount to be not less than a sum stated in the contract documents, in respect of negligence. This clause is mandatory in the BPF/ACA edition. The employer has the right to approve all insurers and inspect policies and insure himself if the contractor defaults on any insurance under this clause 6. It should be noted that the contractor has no such express remedy under the contract if the employer fails to insure under clause 6.4 alternative 2, but the contractor would, of course, have his common law remedies in the case of such breach.

8.12 Termination

Clause 20 provides for termination of the contractor's employment. There are three situations envisaged:
- Termination by the employer
- Termination by the contractor
- Termination due to causes outside the control of both parties.

Among the reasons for which the employer may determine are substantial suspension of the works by the contractor without reasonable cause before taking-over, failure of the contractor to proceed regularly and diligently and the contractor's refusal to comply with any instruction of the architect. The contractor may terminate if he does not receive amounts properly due, if the employer obstructs the issue of any certificate or if the employer is otherwise in breach of the agreement and the contractor has been prevented from carrying out his obligations for a continuous period of 20 working days.

In all these cases, the party wishing to terminate must issue a default notice and allow 10 working days for remedial measures to begin before issuing notice of termination. Either party may terminate forthwith if the other becomes insolvent.

Causes outside the control of either party include *force majeure*, clause 6.4 contingencies, hostilities.

If the employer terminates, he is entitled to claim damage, loss and/or expense. If the contractor terminates, he has no contractual right to loss and/or expense or loss of anticipated profit. Common law rights of both parties are unaffected. A sensible provision (clause 22.4) requires the contractor to deliver up possession of the site immediately upon termination "notwithstanding that the validity of such termination is disputed by the contractor". The employer is entitled to receive all the benefits of any sub-contracts without payment.

8.13 Disputes

A unique and important feature of this contract is the optional provision for the settlement of disputes by a named adjudicator. The provision is mandatory in the BPF/ACA version, but one of three options in ACA 2; the alternatives are arbitration or litigation. If litigation is adopted (clause 25 alternative 3), the contract attempts to confer on the courts "full power to open up, review and revise" the architect's opinions. In the absence of that provision, they have no such power (*Northern Regional Health Authority* v *Derek Crouch Ltd* [1984] 2 All ER 175 CA). However, it is doubtful whether the clause is effective, and only in the rarest of circumstances should the litigation option be chosen.

If there is an adjudicator, he is named in the contract, but he may delegate his powers to someone else provided he gives written notice to the employer, the architect and the contractor (clause 25.1). The following disputes are referable to the adjudicator:

- Adjustment or alteration of the contract sum
- Entitlement to and length of any extension of time
- Whether the works are being executed in accordance with the contract documents
- Either party's entitlement to terminate the contractor's employment under the contract
- The reasonableness of any contractor's objections to a change of architect, architect's instruction requiring sub-letting, or in relation to work carried out by the employer's own contractors.

The adjudicator can call for evidence and he has wide powers. He must give his decision within 5 working days of the reference to him. In practice, this is a very short period. He is specifically stated to be acting as expert and not as arbitrator which means that he is open to the charge of negligence by either party. His decision, however, is given temporary finality and both parties must give effect to it. They do have the right to give notice to refer the matter to arbitration by an independent arbitrator if they do so within 20 working days of receipt of the adjudicator's decision. In default of agreement between the parties, the arbitrator is to be appointed by the president of the Chartered Institute of Arbitrators. Failing such notice, the adjudicator's decision becomes final and binding.

The adjudication option is one of the best features of this contract. In our view, it is an option which should be taken in all but the smallest projects because it provides for immediate settlement of disputes which often threaten the good working relationship between the parties. The real difficulty lies in the availability of sufficient numbers of suitably qualified and experienced adjudicators.

Table 8.01: Contents of ACA 2 Summarised

Clause	Content
1	Contractor's general obligations
2	Drawings, details, documents and information
3	Obligations in respect of drawings, details, documents and information
4	Visits to the works by the architect
5	Supervision of the works by the contractor
6	Vesting of property, contractor's indemnity and insurance
7	Employer's liability
8	Architect's instructions
9	Assignment and sub-letting
10	Employer's licensees
11	Commencement and delays in the execution of the works
12	Taking-over and defective work
13	Taking-over of part of the works
14	Antiquities
15	The contract sum
16	Payment
17	Valuation of architect's instructions
18	Fluctuations
19	Payment of the final contract sum
20	Termination
21	Termination due to causes outside the control of both parties
22	Consequences of termination
23	Notices and interpretation
24	Finance (No 2) Act, 1975
25	Disputes – alternative 1 – adjudicator
25	Disputes – alternative 2 – arbitration
25	Disputes – alternative 3 – litigation
	The time schedule

Table 8.02: ACA 2 and BPF/ACA – Time Chart

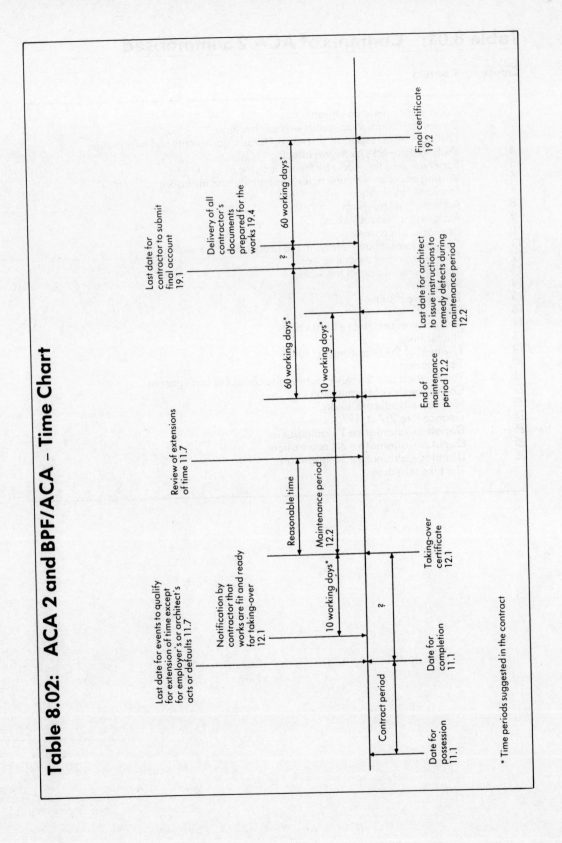

* Time periods suggested in the contract

Table 8.03: Architect's Powers under ACA 2 and BPF/ACA

Clause	Power	Comment
1.4	Give consent to revised schedule of activities	BPF edition only where alternative 1 applies
1.5	Issue instructions regarding ambiguities or discrepancies in the contract documents	
1.7	Issue instructions to the contractor not to make statutory applications etc	If the fees are included in the contract sum, they must be deducted on an interim certificate and the contract sum reduced accordingly
3.5	Instruct contractor to provide samples of quality of goods and/or materials or standards of workmanship to be used in works	
4.2	Visit site and workshops, etc from time to time or as specified in contract documents	
4.3	Delegate all or any of his duties in connection with the works to any number of persons or firms	Only applies to the BPF edition Contractor must be notified of the names and authority Contractor has right of reasonable objection
5.2	Consent in writing to the appointment of site manager or substitute	Notification by contractor
5.3	Request contractor's site manager, employees, sub-contractors or suppliers to attend meetings	
7.4	Require contractor to submit vouchers, receipts, etc necessary for computing the contractor's estimate of the adjustment of the contract	

Table 8.03: Architect's Powers under ACA2 and BPF/ACA – (continued)

Clause	Power	Comment
	sum as a result of disturbance to regular progress	
8.1	Issue written instructions at any time up to take-over in respect of any matter connected with the works; *and* Issue instructions at any time up to completion of all defective outstanding work in respect of: removal from site of defective work, etc; dismissal from the works of incompetent people; opening up of work for inspection and testing; altering obligations or restrictions as regards working hours, space or site access or use	
8.3	Issue oral instructions	Oral instructions can only be issued in an emergency
9.2	Consent in writing to subletting any portion of the works	If so requested by contractor
9.4	Issue instructions requiring contractor to sublet work to person named	Not applicable to BPF edition Contract documents must provide that work priced as provisional is to be carried out by person(s) named
9.5	Issue instructions requiring subletting	As above, but sub-contractor or supplier need not be named
9.6	Attend negotiation meetings between contractor and named sub-contractor; *and* Inspect and check accounts and payment records in respect of named sub-contractors and suppliers	Not applicable to BPF edition The sub-contractor or supplier must be named in the contract documents or under clause 9.5
10.2	Issue instructions in relation to employer's contractors	Contractor is not bound to comply if he makes reasonable objection within 5 working days

Table 8.03: Architect's Powers under ACA2 and BPF/ACA – (continued)

Clause	Power	Comment
11.3	Deduct damages from amount otherwise payable to contractor on any certificate	Does not apply where ACA alternative 2 used Certificate under 11.2 is a prerequisite to deduction
11.8	Instruct contractor to accelerate or postpone dates shown on time schedule for taking-over the works any section or part of the works	Must not be done unreasonably
12.1	Issue taking-over certificate; or Notify contractor of items of work required to be done to render works fit and ready for taking-over; or Approve contractor's list of outstanding items of work; or Add items to the contractor's list	Contractor must have given notification that works are fit and ready for taking-over In last 3 cases, the taking-over certificate must be issued as soon as contractor has completed outstanding items. Taking-over certificate may be issued even if items are outstanding provided contractor gives written undertaking to complete outstanding items with due diligence
12.2	Instruct during maintenance period of 10 working days thereafter making good of defects etc	
15.3	Assign duties to QS where appointed	Not applicable to BPF edition
16.1	Require the contractor to submit documents, vouchers and receipts in support of interim application for payment	
17.3	Instruct contractor to comply with instruction where estimates not agreed; or Instruct him not to comply; or Refer him to adjudicator for decision	Clause 17.5 will apply and contractor is reimbursed Contractor has no claim Only if adjudication option applies (it is mandatory in BPF edition)
17.5	Dispense with need for contractor to submit estimates	By notice to contractor

Table 8.03: Architect's Powers under ACA2 and BPF/ACA – (continued)

Clause	Power	Comment
19.1	Require contractor to submit documents, vouchers and receipts in support of his final account	
19.5	Delete, correct or modify any sum which he has previously certified	May be done in *any* certificate

Table 8.04: Architect's Duties under ACA 2 and BPF/ACA

Clause	Duty	Comment
1.4	Correct any mistake in quantities or omission or misdescription of *items* in the bill and certify a fair adjustment to the contract sum	Where bills of quantities form part of the agreement
1.6	Issue instruction about infringement of statutory requirements	
2.1	Supply contractor with two copies of the contract documents immediately after the execution of the agreement	Applies to both alternatives
2.2	Supply the contractor with two copies or a negative of such drawings or details as are, in his opinion, reasonably necessary to explain or amplify the contract drawings or to enable the contractor to execute and complete the works	Not applicable to BPF edition. Alternative 1: contractor must make specific applications at the right time unless a date for supply is listed in the time schedule Alternative 2: duty limited to supplying drawings etc expressly stated to be the architect's responsibility
2.3	Return one copy of contractor's drawings etc with comments or "no comment" within 10 working days or other period specified in time schedule	After contractor's submission of drawings etc
2.6	Issue instructions as to how adverse ground conditions or articifial obstruction at the site are to be dealt with	Contractor must give written notification with details
6.4	Ascertain and certify a fair and reasonable adjustment to the contract sum in respect of restoration etc by the contractor of damaged works	Alternative 2: where employer has undertaken to insure
7.4	Give notice to contractor of acceptance of estimate or of wish to negotiate	

Table 8.04:   Architect's Duties under ACA2 and BPF/ACA – (continued)

Clause	Duty	Comment
8.3	Confirm any oral instructions in writing	
9.6	Consent to alternative sub-contractor where proposed named sub-contractor is unable to contract	The contractor must select another person and reason for failure must be beyond control of the contractor
9.7	Consent to substitute sub-contractor if named sub-contractor's employment is properly determined by main contractor	Determination or discharge must be in accordance with sub-contract terms
11.2	Issue certificate that works or sections of them not fit and ready for taking-over	Date specified in time schedule or any extended period must have elapsed
11.6	Grant in writing such extension of time as he estimates to be fair and reasonable	It must be reasonably apparent that the works will not be completed by the due date; *and* Contractor must have submitted written notice *unless* delay is caused by act, instruction, omission or default of employer or architect on his behalf; *and* Reasons for delay must be within the terms of whichever alternative applies (only one option in BPF edition)
11.7	Review extensions of time granted within a reasonable time after taking-over and notify contractor of final decision	Architect *must* do this and confirm dates even if no further extension is granted
11.8	Ascertain and certify a fair and reasonable adjustment of contract sum in respect of contractor's compliance	Architect may require contractor to give estimate of adjustment required before instructing acceleration
12.3	Ascertain and certify a fair and reasonable adjustment of contract sum where remedial works are not contractor's fault	Defective work is at contractor's cost unless due to employer's use or occupation or his or the architect's negligence, omission or default

Table 8.04: Architect's Duties under ACA2 and BPF/ACA – (continued)

Clause	Duty	Comment
13.3	Certify a fair and reasonable reduction of liquidated damages where employer takes-over part of the works	Contractor's consent to partial take-over is required. This duty does not apply if ACA 2, alternative 2 applies
14.2	Issue instructions if antiquities, etc, are discovered	Contractor must give written notice
16.2	Certify interim payments at monthly intervals until month when taking over occurs and thereafter as further amounts fall due	Contractor must make interim applications, supported by vouchers etc
17.2	Take reasonable steps to agree contractor's estimates of value of compliance with instructions; and Grant appropriate extension of time and appropriate adjustments to contract sum	Wherever in the opinion of either architect or contractor certain instructions will require adjustment to the contract sum and/or affect the time schedule, the contractor is to provide architect with estimates of the adjustment required Qualifying instructions: 1.5 Ambiguities or discrepancies 1.6 Statutory requirements 2.6 Ground conditions etc 3.5 Samples 8.1(c) Opening up etc; (d) Alteration of obligations as to working spaces, hours, etc; (e) Variations as such; (f) Other matters connected with the works 14 Finding antiquities
17.5	Ascertain and certify a fair and reasonable adjustment to contract sum and grant a fair and reasonable extension for the contractor's compliance	
18.3	Calculate substitute indices for fluctuations	Only when clause 18 applies and ACA index is not published or publication is delayed
19.2	Issue final certificate stating final contract sum	This must be done within 60 working days after completion by the contractor of all his obligations

Table 8.04:   Architect's Duties under ACA2 and BPF/ACA – (continued)

Clause	Duty	Comment
		The contractor must submit his vouched and documented final account within 60 working days after the maintenance period expires
22.1	Certify the amount of any loss, damage and/or expense suffered by the employer where employment has been terminated by the employer for contractor's fault	Exercisable only when the full and final cost of completion by others has been ascertained
22.2	Ascertain and certify the total amount due to contractor on termination by him for employer's fault	Also when termination due to no one's fault, but in that case no loss or expense is payable
25.1	Settle matters in dispute Give written notice to both parties of his decision about any dispute referred to him	Only where ACA 2 alternative 2 (settlement of disputes by arbitration) applies

Table 8.05:   Contractor's Powers under ACA 2 and BPF/ACA

Clause	Power	Comment
3.5	Request the architect to accept samples in lieu of drawings, etc	
4.3	Make reasonable objection to delegation of duties by architect	Only applies to the BPF edition Objection must be within 5 working days of notice
7.6	Refer estimate etc to adjudicator if appointed	If agreement cannot be reached within 20 working days of the architect's notice of his wish to negotiate an adjustment
9.1	Assign the contract	If the employer consents in writing
9.2	Sub-let any portion of the works	If the architect consents in writing
12.1	Submit to the architect a list of any outstanding works required to render the works fit and ready for taking-over Give a written undertaking to complete outstanding items with all due diligence	If appropriate
13.1	Consent to the employer's request to take-over part of the works	Consent must not be unreasonably withheld and damages will be proportionately reduced
20.1	Refer validity of default notice to adjudicator	If adjudication option applies
20.2	Serve a default notice on the employer	If the employer: Fails to pay any amount properly due and payable on any certificate; or Obstructs the issue of any certificate; or Is otherwise in breach of contract; and The breach has prevented the contractor from carrying out his obligations for a continuous period of 20 working days

Table 8.05: Contractor's Powers under ACA2 and BPF/ACA – (continued)

Clause	Power	Comment
20.2	Serve a termination notice on the employer terminating his employment under the contract forthwith	If the employer fails to remedy the default specified in the default notice within 10 working days. If the adjudication option applies and the employer has referred the dispute to the adjudicator, the termination notice cannot be served until adjudicator has given his decision
20.3	Serve a termination notice on the employer	Only applicable to insolvency, no previous default notice required
21	Serve a termination notice on the employer	If the contractor is prevented or delayed from executing the works for 60 consecutive working days by force majeure; or Occurrence of an insurance risk listed in clause 6.4; or War and allied causes
25.2	Refer any dispute etc to the named adjudicator	Only if adjudication provision applies
25.5	Give notice of arbitration	If dissatisfied with adjudicator's decision
25.1	Refer any dispute, etc, to the architect in writing for a decision	Not applicable to BPF edition Applicable where arbitration option applies Service of notice does not relieve either party from liability for due and punctual performance
25.3	Refer dispute, etc, to arbitration	Not applicable to BPF edition Applicable only where arbitration option applies, if dissatisfied with architect's decision

Table 8.06: Contractor's Duties under ACA 2 and BPF/ACA

Clause	Duty	Comment
1.1	Execute and complete the works in strict accordance with the contract documents Comply with and strictly adhere to the architect's instructions issued under the contract	
1.2	In performing his contractual obligations, to exercise all the skill, care and diligence to be expected of a properly qualified and competent contractor, who is experienced in carrying out work of a similar scope, nature and size to the works	
1.5	Notify the architect of any ambiguity or discrepancy contained in the contract documents	Compliance with the architect's subsequent instruction qualifies for payment unless the ambiguity etc, could reasonably have been foreseen at the date of the contract by a contractor showing the prescribed standard of skill, care and diligence
1.6, 1.7	Comply with statutory requirements in carrying out the works. Notify the architect of any infringement Make all statutory applications, give notices and pay fees unless otherwise instructed by the architect Idemnify employer against all damage, loss and/or expense which he incurs as a result of the contractor's breach	Compliance with architect's subsequent instruction qualifies for payment
2.1	Apply specifically to the architect for necessary drawings and details at a reasonable time	Not applicable to BPF edition Applies to ACA 2 alternative 1 unless a date is shown on the time schedule for supply of the information
2.2	Submit to the architect two copies or a negative of all	Not applicable to ACA 2 alternative 1 Where the contractor is to prepare further

Table 8.06: Contractor's Duties under ACA 2 and BPF/ACA – (continued)

Clause	Duty	Comment
	drawings etc which are reasonably necessary to explain and amplify the contract Drawings or specification; or To enable the contractor to execute and complete the works or comply with architect's instructions; or Are stated in the contract documents as being provided by the contractor	drawings, details or documents necessary to build the works. This must be done at a reasonable time
2.4	Take account of any comments by the architect on the drawings etc submitted, and resubmit to the architect under clause 2.2	As above
2.5	Ensure that all works shown on the drawings etc submitted by him, complies with statutory requirements	
2.6	Notify the architect if adverse ground conditions or artificial obstructions are encountered at the site Comply with any architect's instructions	Compliance with architect's instructions qualifies for payment unless competent contractors could reasonably have foreseen the situation
3.1	Responsible for the accuracy of all drawings etc prepared by him Must ensure that the works comply with any performance specification or requirement in the contract documents; and That the parts of the works designed by the contractor will be fit for their intended purpose	This express obligation is "without prejudice to any express or implied warranties or conditions" and is therefore an additional obligation
3.3	Must preserve confidentiality of information and not disclose to unauthorised third parties	

410

Table 8.06: Contractor's Duties under ACA 2 and BPF/ACA – (continued)

Clause	Duty	Comment
3.5	Provide samples Comply at his own cost with any procedures set out in the architect's consent to submission of samples	If the architect so requests The architect's consent must not be unreasonably withheld or delayed
4.1	Give the architect and his representatives full access to the works, to his own workshops and those of his sub-contractors etc	
4.2	Assist the architect and his representatives during site visits	
5.1	Provide all necessary inspection superintendence, supervision, planning and management to ensure proper performance of his contractual obligations	
5.2	Appoint a competent full-time site agent or manager	The architect must approve the appointment and any subsequent change
5.3	Ensure that the site agent or his other employees or sub-contractors etc, attend meetings convened by the architect in connection with the works	Only if the architect so requests
5.4	Employ only appropriate skilled personnel on the works	
6.1	Ensure that any goods or materials valued and included in an interim certificate are not removed except for delivery to site	Only applies if contract documents contain provision for payment for goods and materials before incorporation in the works
6.3	Indemnify the employer and insure against personal injury or death or damage to property as described in the agreement Ensure that his sub-contractors	Does not apply to property to be insured under clause 6.4

Table 8.06: Contractor's Duties under ACA 2 and BPF/ACA – (continued)

Clause	Duty	Comment
	insure as described in the agreement	
6.4	Insure in joint names of employer and contractor against all risks stated	There are alternative versions
	Restore and repair the works, replace goods, remove debris	Upon the occurrence of any event giving rise to an insurance claim
6.6	Take out professional indemnity insurance as required by contract documents	Only where contractor is responsible for preparing details, drawing etc and so assumes design liability: see clause 2, alternative 2
6.8	Pay insurance premiums promptly and produce insurance policies and premium receipts if requested by the employer	
7.2	Notify the architect	If it becomes apparent that there is likely to be disturbance to regular progess, and If an event giving rise to a money claim is likely to reoccur or has occurred
	Submit estimate of required adjustment to the contract sum with supporting documentation	On presentation of the next interim application for payment following the giving of notice
8.1	Immediately comply with all the architect's instructions	Instructions must be issued in writing, except in an emergency
9.3	Sub-let work or obtain goods or materials from named sub-contractors	Where the contract documents so provide
9.4	Comply with the architect's instructions as to named sub-contractor	Not applicable to BPF edition There must be a provisional sum and a person or list of persons in the contract documents
9.5	Comply with the architect's instructions requiring subletting	Not applicable to BPF edition There must be a provisional sum The contractor has a right to make reasonable objection within 5 working days of the date of the instruction

Table 8.06: Contractor's Duties under ACA 2 and BPF/ACA – (continued)

Clause	Duty	Comment
9.6	Negotiate and agree a price with any named sub-contractor or supplier	Not applicable to BPF edition
	Notify the architect of negotiations, meetings etc and permit him to attend them	
	Supply the architect with copy correspondence and documents	
	Select another person to carry out the specified work and obtain the architect's consent to the substitute	Only if negotiations do not result in a sub-contract; *and* If this is for reasons beyond the control of the contractor
	Keep proper and detailed accounts and records of all payments to named sub-contractors and suppliers and make available for inspection by the architect	
9.6	Select another person to carry out the specified work and obtain the architect's consent to the substitute	Only applies to the BPF edition Only if the contractor is unable to enter into a sub-contract with any of the persons named in the contract documents
9.7	Select another sub-contractor or supplier if the named sub-contractor fails and obtain the architect's consent to the substitution	
9.8	Responsible for any design carried out by all sub-contractors and suppliers	The contractor should obtain appropriate indemnities and/or insurance cover
9.9	Responsible for all sub-contractors etc	
10.1	Permit work to be done on site by the employer's licensees as provided in the contract documents	The work must not form part of the contract work
10.2	Permit work etc to be done by others engaged by the employer	The work must not form part of the contract. The contractor has the right of reasonable objection

Table 8.06: Contractor's Duties under ACA 2 and BPF/ACA – (continued)

Clause	Duty	Comment
10.3	Permit work to be executed by statutory undertakers	The work must not form part of the contract. It must be done pursuant to statutory obligations, eg mains installation
11.1	Immediately commence the execution of the works when possession of the site is given and proceed regularly and diligently with it in accordance with the time schedule so that the works (or sections) are fit and ready for taking-over on the due dates	Subject to any extensions of time granted by the architect or adjudicator (if appropriate)
11.3	Pay or allow to the employer liquidated damages at the rate specified in the time schedule	If the works are not fit and ready for taking-over *and* The architect has issued a clause 11.2 certificate to that effect (ACA 2, alternative 1 only)
11.5	Notify the architect immediately specifying the circumstance(s) in question Submit to the architect as soon as possible after the notice full and detailed particulars of the extension of time to which he considers himself entitled Submit any further particulars necessary to keep the architect up to date Prove to the satisfaction of the architect that taking-over is prevented by the specified circumstances	If it becomes reasonably apparent that taking-over by the prescribed date(s) will be prevented by one or more of the listed circumstances The architect may request additional details *Note*: ACA 2, alternative 1 is more limited *Alternative 2 only*
11.9	Submit a revised time schedule to the architect for his consent	Where the date for taking-over is adjusted Where the architect issues acceleration or postponement instructions under clause 11.8 or grants an extension under clause 11.6
12.1	Notify the architect when in his opinion the works (or a section) are fit and ready for taking-over	

414

Table 8.06: Contractor's Duties under ACA 2 and BPF/ACA – (continued)

Clause	Duty	Comment
12.2	With all due diligence complete any defective outstanding work during the maintenance period; *and* Immediately carry out any remedial work ordered by the architect	This may be instructed during the maintenance period or within 10 days of its expiry
12.3	Remedy all defective work at his own expense	Unless in the architect's opinion, it is due to the employer's use or occupation or the negligence etc of the employer or the architect
12.4	Bear the costs of remedying defective work by others	If contractor is in default; *and* Notice of default has been served on him
14.2	Immediately notify the architect if antiquities etc are found on site and not disturb or damage them	Compliance with any architect's instruction issued as a result will qualify for payment
16.1	Submit interim applications for payment to the architect with supporting documentation	On the last working day of each month (or other agreed intervals) up to and including the calendar month in which taking-over occurs Thereafter, as further amounts become due
17.1	Supply the architect with estimates of value, extension of time, and loss and expense or compliance with architect's instruction	If requested by the architect or in the contractor's opinion the contract sum etc will require adjustment
17.2	Take reasonable steps to agree those estimates with the architect	Contractor must comply with instructions if estimates agreed
19.1	Submit vouchered final account to the architect	Within 60 working days after the expiry of the maintenance period
19.4	Deliver to the employer all drawings etc prepared by or on behalf of the contractor	Must be done prior to the issue of the final certificate

Table 8.06: Contractor's Duties under ACA 2 and BPF/ACA – (continued)

Clause	Duty	Comment
20.1	Comply with employer's default notice	
22.4	Immediately deliver to the employer possession of the site and properly protect and secure the works	When a termination notice is served by either party, even if the contractor disputes its validity
22.6	Deliver to the employer all drawings, etc prepared by or on behalf of the contractor for the works	Upon any termination of the contractor's employment
22.7	To do all things necessary to effect assignment of sub-contracts etc	Upon any termination of the contractor's employment
24.3	Forthwith supply the employer with Inland Revenue form 715	If the contractor receives a payment from the employer without statutory tax deduction; *and* If the contractor is not the holder of Inland Revenue form 714c
24.4	State in any interim certificate application or in final account the amount included in respect of the true and accurate direct cost to the contractor etc of the materials and goods used in executing the works	Only where contractor does not provide form 714c or form 715
24.5	Indemnify employer against any damage, etc, suffered by non-compliance with clause 24 of obligations	
25.2	Provide any evidence required by adjudicator	If adjudication provision applies

Table 8.07: Employer's Powers under ACA 2 and BPF/ACA

Clause	Power	Comment
3.3	Use any drawings, detail, document or information prepared by or on behalf of the contractor for the purposes of the execution, completion, maintenance, repair, advertisement, letting or sale of the works	Prices contained in the schedule of rates must be kept confidential
6.4	Reduce value insured	If taking-over of part occurs prior to taking-over of the works
6.7	Approve insurers, terms and conditions for insurances placed by contractor under clauses 6.3, 6.4, 6.5 and 6.6	Approval must not be unreasonably withheld or delayed
6.9	Insure and deduct the cost, together with any damage, loss and/or expense suffered from the contractor's breach, from the contract sum	If the contractor or any sub-contractor is in breach of clauses 6.3, 6.4, 6.5, 6.6 or 6.8
6.10	Deduct from the contract sum any damage, loss and/or expense suffered from the contractor's failure and in making any claim on his own behalf	If the contract fails to make a due claim under clause 6.4
7.6	Refer the contractor's estimates to adjudicator for decision	Only if adjudication option applies If no agreement within 20 working days of architect's notice
9.1	Assign the contract	If the contractor consents in writing
11.3	Deduct liquidated damages or recover them from the contractor as a debt	If the works are not fit and ready for taking-over; and The architect has issued a clause 11.2 certificate to that effect (Not applicable to ACA 2, alternative 2)

Table 8.07:   Employer's Powers under ACA 2 and BPF/ACA – (continued)

Clause	Power	Comment
	Deduct damage, loss and/or expense from amount payable to contractor on any certificate	Only applicable to ACA 2, alternative 2
12.4	Employ and pay other persons to carry out work	If the contractor is in breach of any of his obligations under the agreement *and* If the contractor has failed to take steps to remedy his breach within 5 working days of the employer's notice. All damage, loss and/or expense suffered by the employer may be deducted from the contract sum
13.1	Request the contractor's consent to taking-over of any part of the works prior to the issue of a taking-over certificate in respect of that part	Consent must not be unreasonably withheld or delayed
15.2	Appoint a quantity surveyor in place of the quantity surveyor named in the contract	The contractor must be notified in writing
16.5	Deduct from monies held under clause 16.4 from time to time any amount	If the amount is due to the employer by adjustment to the contract sum; or Under express provision
20.1	Serve a termination notice on the contractor terminating his employment under the contract forthwith	If the employer fails to remedy the default specified in the default notice within 10 working days. If the adjudication option applies and the employer has referred the dispute to the adjudicator, the termination notice cannot be served until adjudicator has given his decision
20.3	Serve a termination notice on the contractor	Only applicable to insolvency, no previous default notice required
21	Serve a termination notice on the contractor	If the contractor is prevented or delayed from executing the works for 60 consecutive working days by *force majeure*; or Occurrence of an insurance risk listed in clause 6.4; or War and allied causes

Table 8.07: Employer's Powers under ACA 2 and BPF/ACA – (continued)

Clause	Power	Comment
22.7	Require novation to himself, without payment, the contractor's entire benefit, right and interest in and under any sub-contract	Upon termination of the contractor's employment under the contract
25.2	Refer any dispute etc to the named adjudicator	Only if the adjudication provision applies
25.5	Give notice of arbitration	If dissatisfied with the adjudicator's decision
25.1	Refer any dispute etc to the architect in writing for a decision	Not applicable to BPF edition Applicable where arbitration option applies Service of notice does not relieve either party from liability for due and punctual performance
25.3	Refer dispute etc to arbitration	Not applicable to BPF edition Applicable only where arbitration option applies, if dissatisfied with architect's decision

Table 8.08: Employer's Duties under ACA 2 and BPF/ACA

Clause	Duty	Comment
3.3	Must preserve confidentiality of information and not disclose to unauthorised third parties	
6.4	Insure in joint names of employer and contractor against all risks stated	Alternative 2 only
	Pay all monies received from insurers to contractor by instalments on certificates	Alternative 1 only If any event gives rise to a claim
11.4	Repay to the contractor amounts paid or recovered under clause 11.3 together with interest at the rate stated in the contract documents	If a certificate under clause 11.2 has been issued *and afterwards* a later date is fixed pursuant to clauses 11.6, 11.7 or 25.2 (where applicable)
16.3	Pay the contractor 95 % of the amount stated as due on any interim certificate	Within 10 working days of the date of the certificate
16.4	Hold 5% of the amount stated as due on any interim certificate as trustee for the contractor	The contract states that the employer has no obligation to account to the contractor for any interest accruing. The point is considered to be debatable
16.6	Pay the difference between the deduction of provisional sum and the addition of the price agreed in accordance with clause 9.6 or such other sum as is properly due	Not applicable to BPF edition The contract sum is to be adjusted
16.7	Pay to the contractor value added tax on goods and services	
20.2	Comply with contractor's default notice	

Table 8.08: Employer's Duties under ACA 2 and BPF/ACA – (continued)

Clause	Duty	Comment
22.2	Pay amounts properly due to the contractor up to the date of termination	If the contractor terminates his employment under clause 20.2 or 20.3. Payment must be made within 10 days of certification
24.1	Forthwith notify the contractor	If the employer becomes a "contractor" for the purposes of the relevant Acts
24.2	Make the statutory deduction from payments due to the contractor and provide him with a form SC 60	Unless the contractor provides with each interim application and with his final account a valid sub-contractor's tax certificate or other statutory document entitling the contractor to be paid without deduction
25.2	Provide any evidence required by the adjudicator	If adjudication provision applies

Table 8.09:   Clauses that May Give Rise to Claims under ACA 2 and BPF/ACA

Note: Due to the broad provisions of clause 7, all the following events may be the subject of contractual claims. But there is nothing to prevent the contractor pursuing any claim through the courts if he considers that such a course offers a better chance of success or more money or if the contractor has failed to comply with all the contractual provisions. In the normal course of events, all the following claims could be dealt with by the architect.

Clause	Event
1.3	Conflicting provisions in forms of agreement and contract documents
1.4	Mistake in contract bills (Not applicable to BPF edition, alternative 1)
1.5	Ambiguities or discrepancies in drawings and contract documents
1.6	Compliance with statutory requirements
2.1	Failure to supply drawings and documents immediately after the execution of the agreement
2.2	Incorrect drawings (applies to ACA 2, alternative 1 only)
2.3	Failure to deal with documents within the specified time period
2.6	Adverse ground conditions or artificial obstructions on site
3.2	Architect's failure to comply with clauses 2.2 to 2.4
3.3	Employer divulging confidential information, including prices, to a third party (except for the proviso in the clause)
3.5	Provision of samples requested by the architect
6.4	Accepted insurance claims
6.9	Unlawful deduction of monies by the employer
6.10	Unlawful deduction of monies by the employer
7.1	Damage, loss and/or expense
8.1	Instructions by employer
8.2	Architect's instructions
8.3	Failure to confirm oral instructions
9.1	Assignment by the employer without consent (except for matters in the proviso)
9.2	Unreasonably withholding or delaying consent to sub-letting
9.6	Interference by the architect in the contractor's negotiations with sub-contractors (Not applicable to BPF edition)
9.7	Unreasonably withholding or delaying consent to a selected person if the original named person's sub-contract is determined or discharged
10.4	Where the regular progress of the work, etc, is disrupted by the execution of work or installation of materials etc by the employer's licensees
11.1	Failure to give possession of the site on the due date
11.3	Failure to complete due to employer's or architect's action or inaction and damages deducted
11.6	The architect's failure to award extension of time
11.7	The architect's failure to carry out a review of extensions of time granted
11.8	Acceleration or postponement
12.1	Failure to issue certificate(s) in due time
12.3	Remedial work due to the fault of employer or architect
12.4	Wrongful employment of other persons and deduction of money
13.1	Taking-over without consent
13.3	Failure to issue certificate in due time
15.1	Wrongful adjustment of the contract sum
15.3	Quantity surveyor's actions outside his authority
16.2	Failure to issue certificate or failure to issue it in proper form

Table 8.09:   Clauses that May Give Rise to Claims under ACA 2 and BPF/ACA – (continued)

16.3	Failure to pay on time
16.4	Failure to hold retention monies in separate bank account
16.6	Wrongful adjustment of the contract sum (Not applicable to BPF edition)
16.7	Recovery of VAT
17.1	Variations, damage, loss and/or expense
17.3	Failure to act after time limit
18	Fluctuations
19.2	Failure to issue final certificate in proper form or in proper time
19.3	Failure to pay on time
20.1, 20.3, and 21	Invalid termination
22.2	Payment after contractor's termination
23.1	Failure to properly serve notices

Table 8.10: Certificates to be Issued under ACA 2 and BPF/ACA

Clause	Event
1.4	Adjustments to the contract sum to take account of mistake, omission or mis-description of items in the contract bills (Not applicable to BPF edition, alternative 1)
1.7	In respect of statutory fees paid by contractor
6.4	Adjustment to contract sum in respect of restoration, repair, replacement and/or renewal (Applicable only to alternative 2)
11.2	Works not fit and ready for taking-over
11.8	Adjustment to the contract sum in respect of the contractor's compliance with acceleration or postponement instructions and any damage, loss and/or expense arising out of or in connection with it
12.1	Works fit and ready for taking-over
12.3	Adjustment to the contract sum in respect of remedial work which is the fault of the employer
13.3	Fair and reasonable reduction to the liquidated damages sum within 10 working days of the employer taking-over part of the works under clause 13 (Not applicable if clause 11.3, alternative 2 is in operation)
16.2	Interim certificates stating the amount due to the contractor
17.5	Adjustment to the contract sum in respect of instructions, damage, loss and/or expense
19.2	Final certificate stating the balance due to the contractor or the employer
22.1	Amount of damage, loss and/or expense suffered by the employer after termination under clause 20.1 or 20.3
22.2	Total amount due to the contractor up to the date of termination

Table 8.11: Architect's Instructions Empowered by ACA 2

Clause	Instruction
8.1(a)	For the removal from site of work or goods not in accordance with the contract
8.1(b)	For the dismissal of incompetent or negligent persons employed upon the works
8.1(c)	For the opening up and inspection or testing of goods or the work
8.1(d)	For the amendment of obligations in respect of working space, hours, access or use of the site
8.1(e)	For the alteration of design or quality or quantity of the works including removal from site of any materials brought on to the site
8.1(f)	For any matter connected with the works
8.1(g)	Discrepancies (clause 1.5)
	Infringement of statutory notices (clause 1.7)
	Ground conditions and artificial obstructions (clause 2.6)
	To provide samples (clause 3.5)
	With regard to named sub-contractors (clause 9.4)
	With regard to sub-letting (clause 9.5)
	Requiring the contractor to permit work by others (clause 10.2)
	Regarding acceleration or postponement (clause 11.8)
	Regarding defective work during or immediately after the maintenance period (clause 12.2)
	Regarding antiquities (clause 14)

Table 8.12: Adjustment of Contract Sum under ACA 2 and BPF/ACA

Clause	Adjustment
1.4	For an error in the bills of quantities (Not applicable to BPF edition, alternative 1)
1.7	Fees in relation to statutory authorities etc
6.4	Repair and removal of debris (alternative 2 only)
6.9	If the contractor fails to insure
6.10	If the contractor fails to make an insurance claim – employer's loss and/or expense and expenses in making his own claim
7.4	Damage, loss and/or expense
11.8	Acceleration or postponement
12.3	Work required due to employer's or architect's default
12.4	Contractor in breach of his obligations
16.6	Provisional sums (Not applicable to BPF edition)
17	Variations
18	Fluctuations
25.2	Decisions of adjudicator (Not applicable to ACA 2, alternatives 2 and 3)

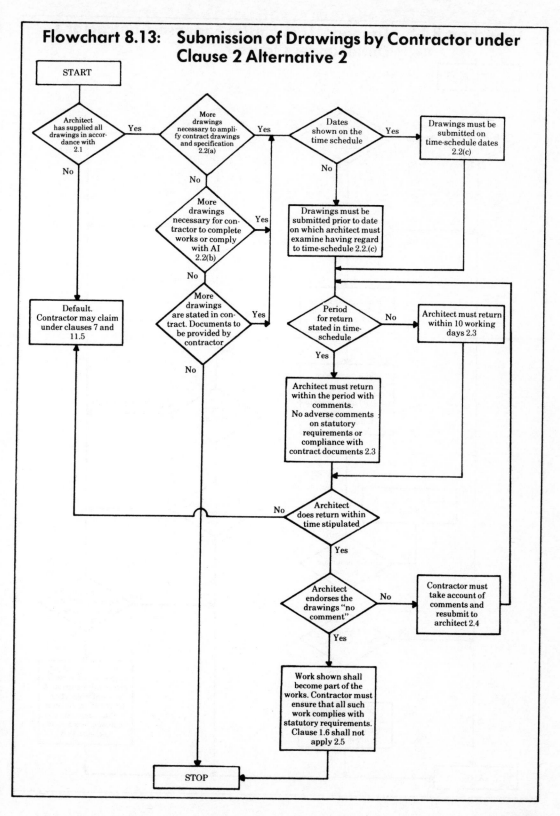

Flowchart 8.13: Submission of Drawings by Contractor under Clause 2 Alternative 2

START

Architect has supplied all drawings in accordance with 2.1

More drawings necessary to amplify contract drawings and specification 2.2(a)

Dates shown on the time schedule

Drawings must be submitted on time-schedule dates 2.2(c)

More drawings necessary for contractor to complete works or comply with AI 2.2(b)

Drawings must be submitted prior to date on which architect must examine having regard to time-schedule 2.2.(c)

Default. Contractor may claim under clauses 7 and 11.5

More drawings are stated in contract. Documents to be provided by contractor

Period for return stated in time-schedule

Architect must return within 10 working days 2.3

Architect must return within the period with comments.
No adverse comments on statutory requirements or compliance with contract documents 2.3

Architect does return within time stipulated

Architect endorses the drawings "no comment"

Contractor must take account of comments and resubmit to architect 2.4

Work shown shall become part of the works. Contractor must ensure that all such work complies with statutory requirements. Clause 1.6 shall not apply 2.5

STOP

Flowchart 8.14: Damage, Loss and/or Expense: Contractor's Duties under Clause 7

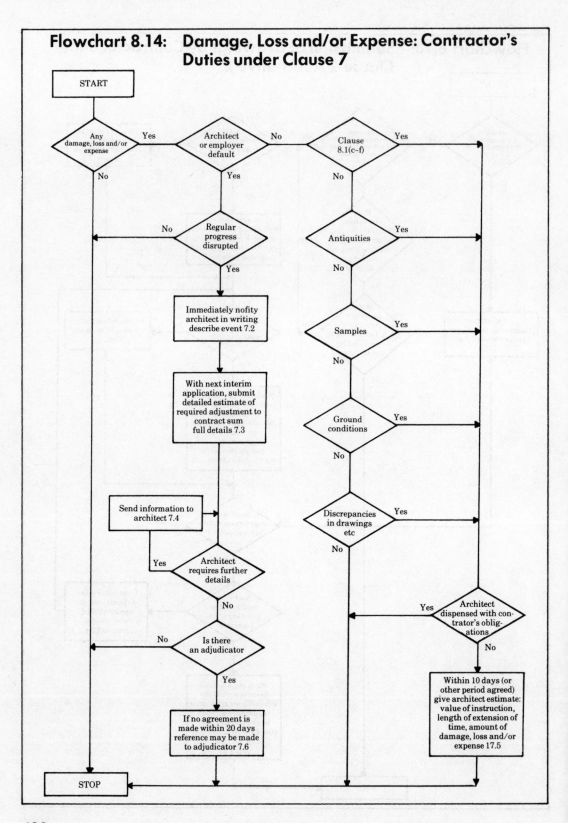

Flowchart 8.15: Damage, Loss and/or Expense: Architect's Duties under Clause 7

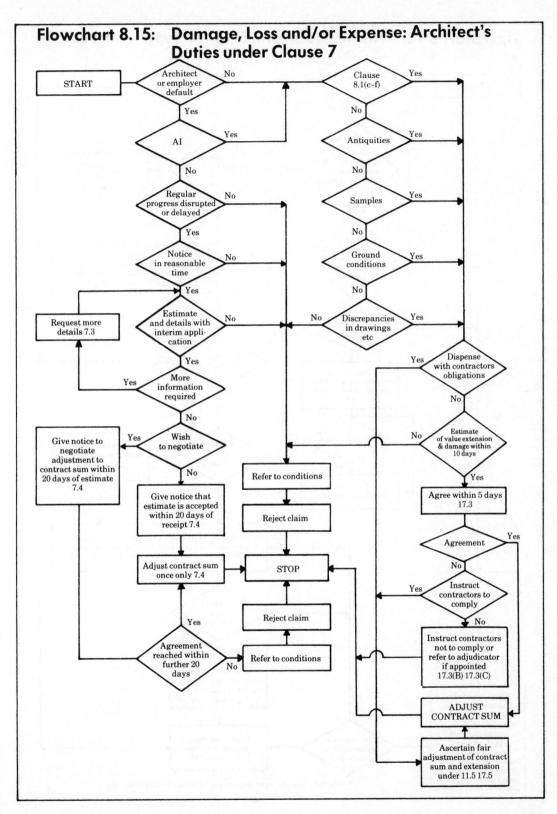

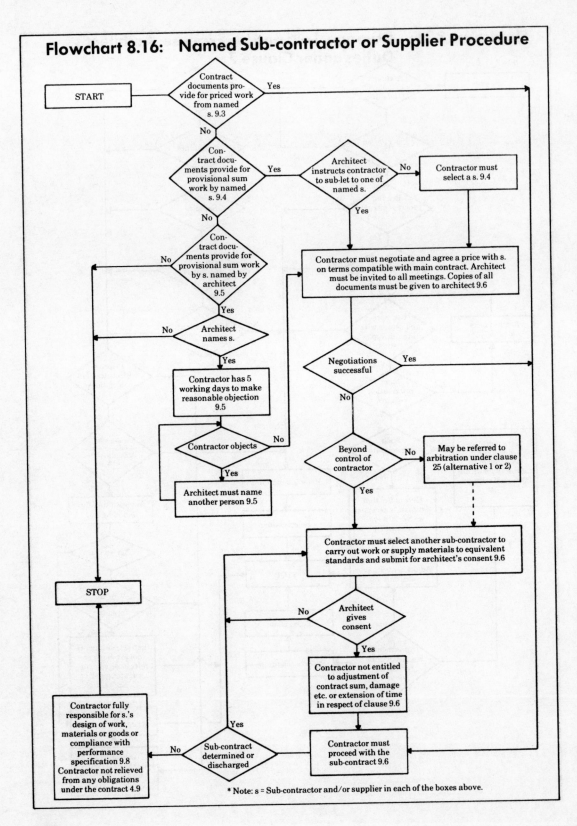

Flowchart 8.16: Named Sub-contractor or Supplier Procedure

START

Contract documents provide for priced work from named s. 9.3 — Yes

No

Contract documents provide for provisional sum work by named s. 9.4 — Yes → Architect instructs contractor to sub-let to one of named s. — No → Contractor must select a s. 9.4

No

Yes

Contract documents provide for provisional sum work by s. named by architect 9.5 — No

Yes

Architect names s. — No

Yes

Contractor has 5 working days to make reasonable objection 9.5

Contractor objects — No

Yes

Architect must name another person 9.5

Contractor must negotiate and agree a price with s. on terms compatible with main contract. Architect must be invited to all meetings. Copies of all documents must be given to architect 9.6

Negotiations successful — Yes

No

Beyond control of contractor — No → May be referred to arbitration under clause 25 (alternative 1 or 2)

Yes

Contractor must select another sub-contractor to carry out work or supply materials to equivalent standards and submit for architect's consent 9.6

Architect gives consent — No

Yes

Contractor not entitled to adjustment of contract sum, damage etc. or extension of time in respect of clause 9.6

STOP

Contractor fully responsible for s.'s design of work, materials or goods or compliance with performance specification 9.8 Contractor not relieved from any obligations under the contract 4.9 — No

Sub-contract determined or discharged — Yes

Contractor must proceed with the sub-contract 9.6

* Note: s = Sub-contractor and/or supplier in each of the boxes above.

430

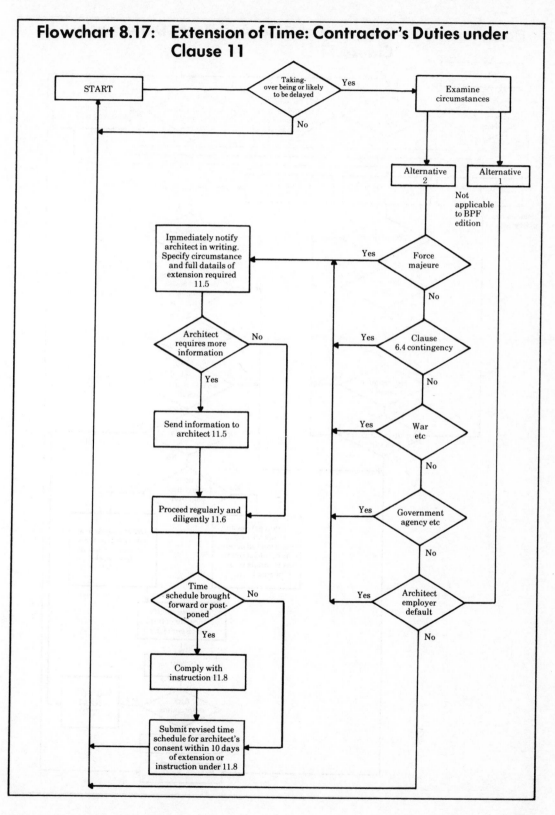

Flowchart 8.17: Extension of Time: Contractor's Duties under Clause 11

START

Taking-over being or likely to be delayed — Yes → Examine circumstances

No

Alternative 2

Alternative 1

Not applicable to BPF edition

Immediately notify architect in writing. Specify circumstance and full datails of extension required 11.5 ← Yes — Force majeure

No

Architect requires more information — No

Yes

Clause 6.4 contingency ← Yes

No

Send information to architect 11.5

War etc ← Yes

No

Proceed regularly and diligently 11.6 ← Yes — Government agency etc

No

Time schedule brought forward or post-poned — No

Yes

Architect employer default ← Yes

No

Comply with instruction 11.8

Submit revised time schedule for architect's consent within 10 days of extension or instruction under 11.8

Flowchart 8.18: Extension of Time: Architect's Duties under Clause 11

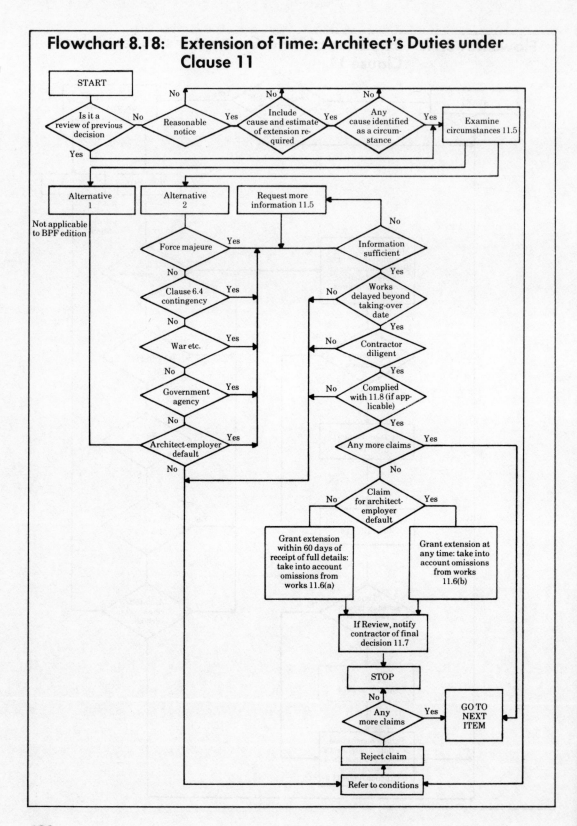

Flowchart 8.19: Taking-over under Clause 12.1

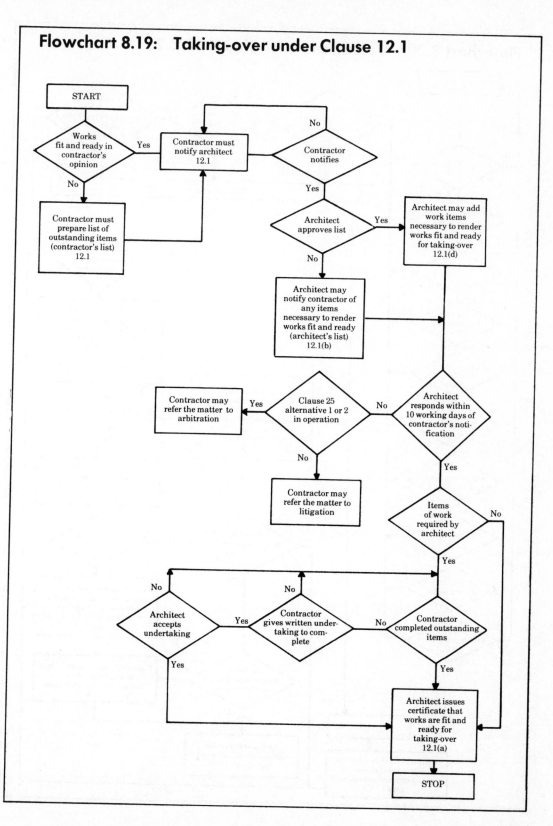

Flowchart 8.20: Valuation under Clause 17/8.2

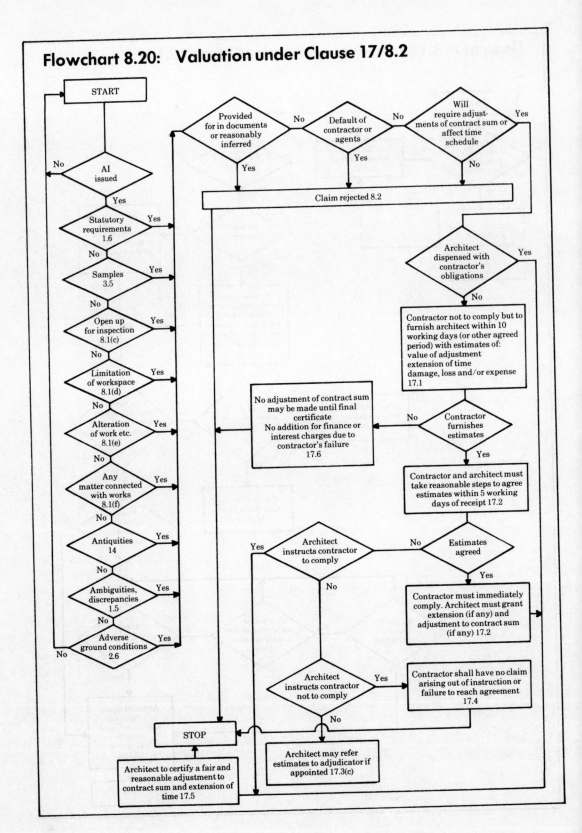

START

AI issued — No / Yes

Statutory requirements 1.6 — Yes / No

Samples 3.5 — Yes / No

Open up for inspection 8.1(c) — Yes / No

Limitation of workspace 8.1(d) — Yes / No

Alteration of work etc. 8.1(e) — Yes / No

Any matter connected with works 8.1(f) — Yes / No

Antiquities 14 — Yes / No

Ambiguities, discrepancies 1.5 — Yes / No

Adverse ground conditions 2.6 — Yes / No

Provided for in documents or reasonably inferred — No / Yes

Default of contractor or agents — No / Yes

Will require adjustments of contract sum or affect time schedule — Yes / No

Claim rejected 8.2

Architect dispensed with contractor's obligations — Yes / No

Contractor not to comply but to furnish architect within 10 working days (or other agreed period) with estimates of: value of adjustment extension of time damage, loss and/or expense 17.1

Contractor furnishes estimates — No / Yes

No adjustment of contract sum may be made until final certificate No addition for finance or interest charges due to contractor's failure 17.6

Contractor and architect must take reasonable steps to agree estimates within 5 working days of receipt 17.2

Architect instructs contractor to comply — Yes / No

Estimates agreed — No / Yes

Contractor must immediately comply. Architect must grant extension (if any) and adjustment to contract sum (if any) 17.2

Architect instructs contractor not to comply — Yes / No

Contractor shall have no claim arising out of instruction or failure to reach agreement 17.4

Architect may refer estimates to adjudicator if appointed 17.3(c)

STOP

Architect to certify a fair and reasonable adjustment to contract sum and extension of time 17.5

Flowchart 8.21: Termination by Employer under Clause 20.1

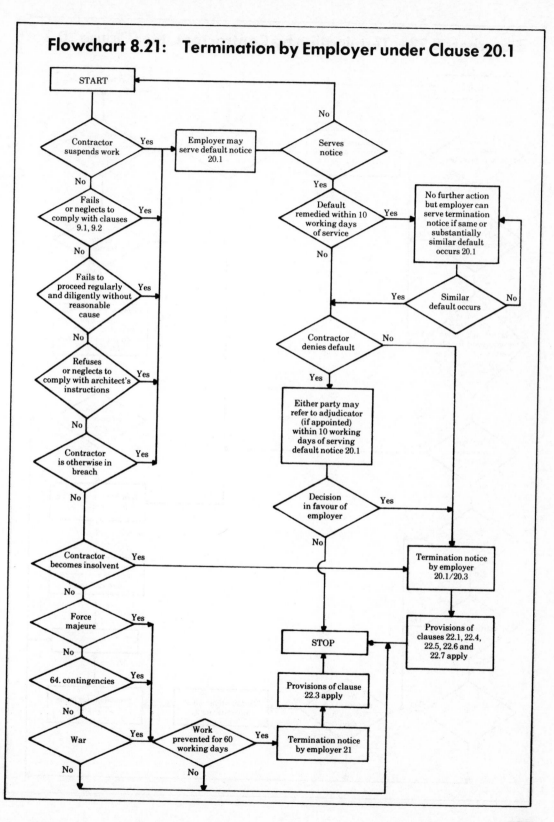

Flowchart 8.22:   Termination by Contractor under Clause 20.2

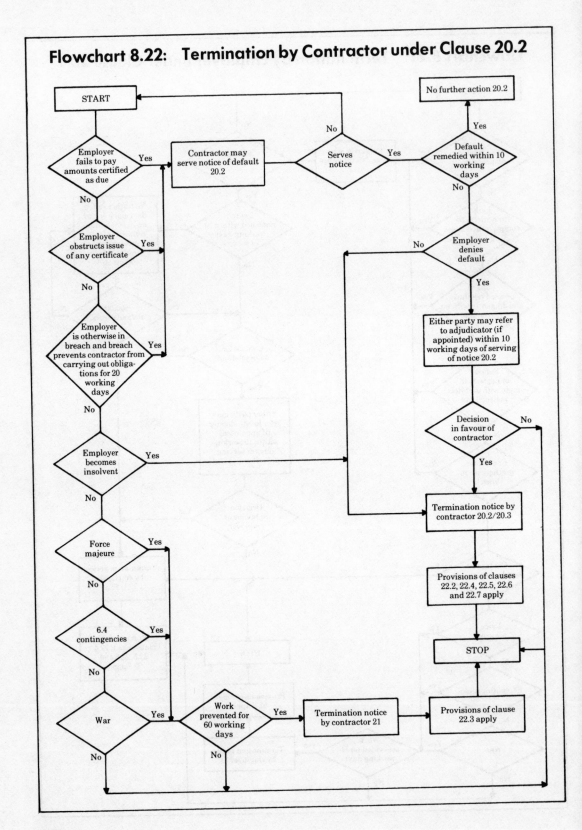

Flowchart 8.23:   Adjudication under Clause 25 Alternative 1

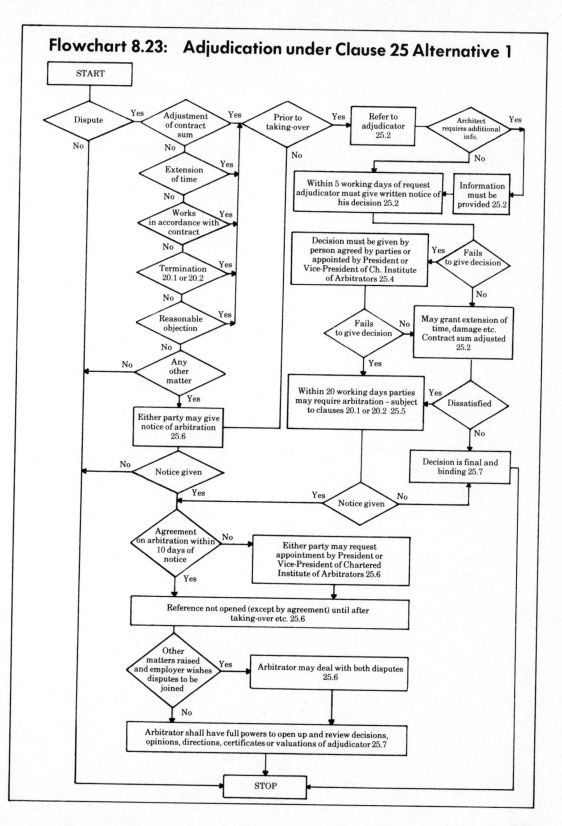

9: The Government Conditions of Contract (GC/Works/1)

9.01 Introduction

The second edition of this standard form was published in September 1977, and has been amended on four occasions, the last amendment being issued in 1987. GC/Works/1 is the Government counterpart of JCT 80, although there is little similarity between the two sets of conditions. Its full title is General Conditions of Government Contracts for Building and Civil Engineering Works (form GC/Works/1). Although drafted unilaterally on the part of the Government – and thus tending to be more clear cut than negotiated forms – it is partly the result of consultations with interested bodies.

Some contractors allege that it is unfair. In fact, it protects the employer's legitimate interests, and its special features (eg the unilateral power of determination conferred on the employer by clause 44) result from the special circumstances surrounding Government projects. If this – and certain other special provisions – are deleted there is no reason in principle why the form should not be used for private projects, provided appropriate insurance provisions are inserted.

In principle it is intended for use on contracts over £50,000 in value and is usually – but not necessarily – on a with quantities basis (there is a special set of conditions – Form GC/Works/2 (1974) – for use on smaller projects). Its distinguishing features are:

- The employer (called "the Authority") has extensive powers. A number of decisions are stated to be "final and conclusive" and not referable to arbitration
- The architect (called "the superintending officer") has very wide powers to give instructions, including a catch-all provision entitling him to give instructions on "any other matters ... necessary or expedient"
- The treatment of nominated sub-contractors differs from the JCT pattern, and the contractor is fully responsible for nominated sub-contractors and must make good any loss or expense suffered by the employer as a result of a sub-contractor's default or failure
- There is no contractual provision entitling the contractor to terminate the contract. He must rely on his common law rights. In contrast, the employer is given express contractual power to determine, not only for contractor's default, but also without reason
- Separate articles of agreement must be prepared incorporating the conditions by reference.

Table 9.01 summarises the contents of the form.

Edition 3 of GC/Works/1 comes into use on 1 April 1990, but Edition 2 will continue to be used for some time. Edition 3 is substantially different from Edition 2. Major provisions are:

- *Clause 1* refers to the Project Manager, who seems to be equivalent to the old Superintending Officer, and to a Stage Payment Chart which sets out the amounts to be paid to the contractor and the periods between payments. The payments can be adjusted in accordance with the provisions of clause 53
- *Clause 8* provides that the contractor must maintain his own insurance to cover the usual risks or, alternatively, that he must take out insurance in joint names in accordance with the synopsis attached to the Abstract of Particulars
- *Clause 10* provides for the situation if the contractor or sub-contractor is required to undertake design. In both instances the contractor is to be liable although his liability is confined to that of a professional person carrying out the work with proper care and skill. He is not required to warrant fitness for purpose but in certain instances the contractor could be under a higher liability, eg where a performance specification is included
- *Clause 20* provides that the contractor must indemnify the Crown against all claims in connection with loss or disclosure of personal data (which is to have the same meaning as in section 1(3) of the Data Protection Act 1984)
- *Clause 26* makes the contractor responsible for keeping all records necessary for contract purposes and obliges him to give the project manager and quantity surveyor access to them

440

- *Clause 33* requires the contractor to submit a fully resourced programme within 21 days of acceptance of his tender
- *Clause 35* places an obligation on the contractor's agent to attend progress meetings which are to be held at not less than monthly intervals. Details of time and place and pre-meeting reports are noted together with a procedure the project manager must adopt to notify the contractor of delays and extensions of time
- *Clause 38* provides for acceleration by agreement
- *Clause 40* makes provision for an option to require the contractor to submit a quotation for a variation instruction
- *Clause 46* provides a definition of "expense" as money expended by the contractor, but not including interest or finance charges
- *Clause 47* lays down the circumstances in which the authority will finance charges at a prescribed rate
- *Clause 52* allows the contractor to submit cost saving proposals at any time. If accepted, the contractor is entitled to 50% of the saving in cost
- *Clause 60* provides for the appointment of an officer of the Property Services Agency who is not associated with the letting or management of the project to act as adjudicator. His decision on any matter referred to him by the contractor is final until after completion of the works.

9.02   Contractor's Obligations

Clause 6 states that, on being given possession of the site or the order to commence, "the contractor shall thereupon commence the execution of the Works and shall proceed with diligence and expedition in regular progression or as may be directed by the [architect] so that the whole of the Works shall be completed by the date for completion". The wording should be noted, and the reference to architect's instructions is to the very wide powers conferred by clause 7(1), which imposes a further obligation on the contractor.

He is to "carry out and complete the execution of the Works to the satisfaction of the" architect. There is a definition of "the Works" in clause 1(2) and it is so phrased as to include all contractual obligations. In fact – save in a few cases where the architect's opinion is stated to be final and conclusive – whether or not the works are to the architect's satisfaction is a matter which can be reviewed in arbitration.

The contractor's obligation is re-emphasised in clause 28(1) (date for completion: extension of time) which goes on to impose a further obligation on the contractor: "All unused things for incorporation and all things not for incorporation, the removal of which is ordered by the [architect] shall be removed and the site and the Works cleared of rubbish and delivered up to his satisfaction *on or before* the date for completion".

Clause 2(1) states that the contractor is "deemed to have satisfied himself as to the conditions affecting execution of the Works" and to have obtained his own information on all matters affecting the works and his tendered prices. Its effect is to put him in the same position as if he had satisfied himself by inspecting the site and so on. The exception to this provision is that it has no application to information given or referred to in the bills of quantities as required by the SMM being used. Subject to that – and to the provisions of clause 2A – the contractor is not entitled to any additional payment on the ground of any misunderstanding or misrepresentation in respect of the matters referred to in the clause, nor is he to be released from any resultant contractual risks or obligations or because he could not or did not foresee any matter affecting the works.

Clause 2A – inserted by amendment No 4 in November 1987 – provides an exception in the case of *unforeseeable ground conditions* encountered during the execution of the works of which he did not know or which he could not reasonably have foreseen having regard to any information which he had or ought reasonably to have had. Unforeseeable ground conditions include artificial obstructions but exclude ground conditions caused by weather. If he encounters such conditions the contractor must notify the architect immediately, specifying the conditions and the measures he proposes to take to deal with them. If the architect agrees that the ground conditions could not have been reasonably foreseen, he is to certify accordingly. He must inform the contractor in writing of his decision. The contractor is entitled to payment in respect of any work carried out or omitted as a result of certified unforeseeable ground conditions as well as to any necessary extension of time.

9.03   Contract Documentation and Information

The contract documentation differs from that of the other standard forms. Clause 1 (1) defines "the Contract" in the following terms:

"The Contract means the documents forming the tender and acceptance thereof, together with the documents referred to therein including these Conditions (except as set out in the Abstract of Particulars), the Specification, the Bills of Quantities and the Drawings, and all these documents taken together shall be deemed to form one contract. When there are no Bills of Quantities all references to Bills of Quantities ... shall be treated as cancelled, except that where the context so admits the Schedule of Rates shall be substituted therefor".

The contract documents therefore comprise:
- The contractor's tender and employer's acceptance *and*
- The contract drawings *and*
- The printed conditions *and*
- A specification
  together with
- Bills of Quantities *or*
- A schedule of rates.

This choice of documentation makes for flexibility, but also requires the greatest care at tender stage. The employer's acceptance of the contractor's tender will create a binding contract.

The *abstract of particulars* is a vital document and is referred to in several of the contract conditions. It fulfils some of the functions of the appendix in JCT 80 and related forms, identifies the employer, the architect and the quantity surveyor, as well as giving dates for completion, amount of liquidated damages, length of the maintenance period and other vital information. It can be used to modify the printed conditions themselves. Clause 4 is important in that it provides that, in case of discrepancy between the conditions and the specification and/or bills and/or drawings only, the printed conditions prevail.

Clause 5(1) deals with errors in description or in quantity and omissions in the bills (if applicable); where the contract sum is based on the quantities in the bills, errors or omissions are to be treated as a variation and valued accordingly. The appropriate method of measurement must be specified. The contractor is bound by errors, omissions or wrong estimates in his bill prices, etc.

The abstract of particulars must also list the dates after acceptance for the supply of certain information (see clause 53(2)) and the period(s) which the contractor requires for sub-contract nominations. Value added tax and price fluctuations must also be covered.

If the employer decides to provide either bills or a schedule of rates, then the contractor can be required to provide a priced schedule of rates as the control document: see clause 5B. Where provisional or approximate bills or a schedule of rates are used, the value of the whole work properly executed will be subjected to measurement and valuation.

Further information by way of drawings, schedules, levels and other design information is to be provided by the architect from time to time, and breach of this duty is one of the grounds giving rise to a money claim under clause 53(1)(d) as well as to extension of time under clause 28(1). Clause 7(1) refers to the architect's obligation to issue such further information "from time to time" – an obligation which would be otherwise implied under the general law. Under clause 12 the architect must supply dimensioned drawings, levels and other information necessary to enable the contractor to set out the works. The information/supply schedule in the abstract of particulars – akin, in some respects, to the ACA time schedule, is vitally important.

9.04   Commencement and Completion

Clause 6 states that possession of the site or a written order to commence is to be given to the contractor. The conditions themselves say nothing about when possession is to be given nor is any period of notice to commence specified. These matters must be dealt with in the abstract of particulars. Possession of the site, or the issue of a written order to commence, is a pre-condition to the contractor's duty to commence the works and proceed with their execution with all due dispatch and expedition and complete them by the specified completion date, as altered under the provisions relating to extensions of time. If the contractor fails so to complete – and clear the site – on or before the completion date, liquidated damages are recoverable by the employer under clause 29(1).

Clause 29 is straightforward in its wording and application. If the contractor fails to complete the works and clear the site on or before the date for completion, the agreed damages are payable "for the period during which the Works or any section, shall remain uncompleted and the site, or any relevant part, is duly delivered up to the satisfaction of the architect not cleared after the date for completion". Although the clause uses the phrase "the contractor shall pay", in the normal course the employer will deduct the liquidated damages from monies due or to become due to the contractor – on interim valuations for example – in virtue of the power conferred by clause 43.

The liquidated damages provision is very tightly-drafted and the terms of clause 29(3) are particularly important. The effect of this provision is that the employer may give written notice to the contractor stating that, in his opinion, the contractor is not entitled to any further extension of time. The effect of such a notice is that the employer can deduct the sums claimed as liquidated damages, leaving the reasonableness or otherwise of the employer's decision to be settled by arbitration after the contract comes to an end. This overcomes some of the problems thrown up under other contract forms.

Clause 28(1) deals with completion, and the wording indicates that it is practical or substantial completion that is required. Sectional completion is provided for. Only if the contractor has not so completed by the date for completion stated in the abstract of particulars is he in breach. By clause 42(1) the architect is required to issue a certificate stating the date on which the works are completed to his satisfaction. The consequences of that certificate are:

- The contractor's liability for liquidated damages (clause 29) ends
- The contractor is entitled to be paid the amount which the employer estimates will represent the final sum *less* half the amount of the reserve (clause 41(1))
- The maintenance period begins to run (clause 32)
- The contractor's liability for frost damage ends (clause 32(2))
- Reference to arbitration can be opened (clause 61(2))

Defects liability is governed by clause 32 which deals with defects which appear after completion and during the maintenance period which is set out in the abstract of particulars. The contractor is under an obligation to remedy defects so appearing provided:

- They arise from his neglect or failure or that of any of his sub-contractors or suppliers in the proper performance of the contract; *or*
- They are due to frost occurring before completion.

Such defects are to be made good by the contractor at his own cost and to the satisfaction of the architect. In most respects the obligations imposed by and the operation of this provision closely resemble the JCT position.

9.05 Extensions of Time

Extensions of time are dealt with by clause 28(2) which requires the employer to allow the contractor "a reasonable extension of time for completion" for delays to the works or any section specified in the abstract of particulars caused by specified events. These are:

- The execution of any modified or additional work
- Weather conditions which make continuance of work *impracticable*
- Any act or default of the employer. This would, it is suggested, cover acts or defaults of those – such as the architect – for whom the employer is responsible in law: see *Croudace Ltd* v *London Borough of Lambeth* (1986) 6 ConLR 70
- Strikes or lock-outs of workpeople employed in the building and related trades in the area where the work is being executed or those employed in the manufacture or preparation of goods and materials
- Any of the accepted risks as defined in clause 1(2)
- Any unforeseeable ground conditions
- Any other circumstance which is wholly beyond the control of the contractor.

The grant of the extension of time is subject to three important provisos:

- Written notice by the contractor is a pre-condition to the operation of the clause, unless the employer otherwise decides. The contractor must give notice immediately he becomes aware that delay has been or will be caused and his notice – served on the architect – must be specific in its terms
- The effect of any authorised omission from the works may be taken into account in determining the length of any extension of time
- The contractor is not entitled to an extension of time if any delay is attributable to his negligence, default or improper conduct.

9.06 Architect's Instructions

The architect is empowered to issue instructions in writing or orally, but in the case of oral instructions there must be written confirmation (clause 7(2)). "If any ... instructions issued orally have not been confirmed in writing ... such confirmation shall be given upon a reasonable request by the contractor".

All instructions must be given or confirmed in writing in the manner prescribed by the employer. No time limit for the confirmation of oral instructions is imposed.

Failure of the contractor to comply with architect's instructions is covered by clause 8.

The sanction for failure to comply is that the architect is to issue a written notice requiring compliance within a period specified in the notice. Should the contractor still fail to comply, the employer may have the work involved done by others, recovering from the contractor the additional costs and expenses incurred in so doing, which in practice will be done by way of set-off under clause 43. The employer's power to employ others to carry out the work involved is said to be without prejudice to his right to determine the contract under clause 45.

The instructions which the architect may give are listed in clause 7(1), which could scarcely be more widely phrased. The clause empowers the architect to issue instructions from time to time with regard to thirteen specified matters, including variation instructions, and the last ground is a sweeping-up provision. The architect is empowered to issue instructions about "any other matter as to which it is necessary or expedient for [him] to issue" and, significantly, his decision that any such instruction is necessary or expedient is declared to be "final and conclusive" (clause 7(3)).

Naturally, the contract sum is to be adjusted accordingly (clause 9). Moreover, compliance with an architect's instruction may result in the contractor making a claim for both extension of time and for money, and – despite the seemingly draconian nature of the clause – problems do not seem to arise in practice. There are adequate safeguards for the contractor as regards any loss or expense which he suffers or incurs as a result of compliance.

9.07 Contractor's Claims

There is a comprehensive provision (clause 53) dealing with contractor's claims for prolongation and disruption expenses, the object of which is to reimburse the contractor for any *expense* which he incurs in performing the contract as a result of regular progress of the whole or part of the works being *materially disrupted or prolonged* as a result of one or more specified matters. The claims clause is hedged about with restrictions and a number of points should be noted:

- Although the reference is to *expense* this does not limit the sums claimable to sums paid out, although a more restrictive interpretation is supportable. The PSA – the principal users of GC/Works/1 allow finance charges as an element of claim
- That expense must be one which is "beyond that otherwise provided for in or reasonably contemplated by the contract"
- It must also be an expense which the contractor would not otherwise have incurred
- The expense must have been "properly and directly incurred" by the contractor as a result of the matters specified.

These limitations make the claims clause more limited than its counterpart in other contracts.

The matters which may give rise to a claim for prolongation or disruption expenses are:

- Compliance with any architect's instruction
- The making good of loss and or damage which is caused by the default or neglect of the employer's own employees and agents (clause 26(2)) and the insurance risks
- Direct works carried out by the employer contemporeaneously with the contract works (clause 50, which deals effectively with employer's licensees)
- Late information, which is the architect's responsibility to provide
- Work or the supply of goods, which is to be undertaken or ordered direct by the employer, except where this arises through the contractor's own default
- The employer's or architect's instructions "regarding the nomination or appointment of any person" and closely related matters
- Any unforeseeable ground condition.

Apart from these inherent limitations, merely because one of the listed events occurs does not, of itself, give rise to a claim by the contractor, because there are further limitations imposed by the terms of clause 53(3)).

It is precondition ("condition precedent") to any claim that:

- The contractor must give written notice to the architect "immediately upon becoming aware that... regular progress... has been or is likely to be disrupted or prolonged"
- The contractor's notice must
  - Specify the circumstances causing or expected to cause disruption or prolongation
  - State that he is or expects to be entitled to an increase inthe contract sum
- As soon as reasonably practicable after incurring the expense the contractor must provide the quantity surveyor with all necessary information and documents "certified in such a manner as the quantity surveyor may require"
- If the claim results from compliance with an architect's instruction, that instruction must have been given or confirmed in writing and must not have been rendered necessary because of default by the contractor
- If the claim relates to late information, etc the contractor must have given written notice to the architect specifying the item and the date by which it was reasonably required and he must have done this "neither unreasonably early nor unreasonably late". The exception is where a date for the provision of the information was agreed with the architect.

Amounts ascertained are to be included in the next interim certificate.

Claims may also arise under clause 9(2)(a)(i). This provides for the contract sum to be increased by the amount of "any expense beyond that otherwise provided for in or reasonably contemplated by the Contract in complying with any" instructions of the architect, other than variation instructions.

Two preconditions must be met before a claim is allowed under clause 9(2)(a)(i):

- The contractor must have provided the quantity surveyor with all necessary documents and information in respect of the expense claimed. He must do this as soon as reasonably practicable after incurring the expense
- The instruction must not have been rendered necessary as a result of any default on the contractor's part.

9.08 Certificates and Payment

The scheme of payment is set out in clauses 40 to 42. As the works progress, the contractor is paid 97% of the value of work properly executed on site and materials reasonably brought on site for incorporation, and adequately stored and protected, the balance of 3% being accumulated by the employer as a reserve. There is an interesting provision (clause 42(3)) which says that the employer's decision as to the sums certified from time to time is "final and conclusive", although this does not apply to the final certificate.

Payment is conditioned on the contractor submitting claims for payment at not less than monthly intervals, although where the contract sum exceeds £100,000 the contractor may make application at fortnightly intervals. Entitlements under clauses 9(2) and 53(1) are included in these advances on account, the amount not being subject to retention.

Where the contractor is unable to satisfy the architect, on request, that amounts due to sub-contactors or suppliers and covered by previous advances have been paid, such payments may be withheld until the employer is satisfied. Nominated sub-contractors and suppliers may be paid direct if the architect certifies that they have not been paid, with recovery from the contractor.

Interim certificates are not conclusive and may be subsequently modified or corrected.

Final payment and the release of the 3% reserve is covered by clause 41. When the architect certifies the date on which the works are completed to his satisfaction, the contractor is entitled to be paid the amount which the employer estimates will be the final sum, less half the reserve, with a discretionary power in the employer to pay further sums in reduction of the reserve thereafter.

As soon as possible after completion of the works, the quantity surveyor must send a copy of the final account to the contractor, who is bound to provide all necessary documents and information for the calculation of the final sum. If required, the contractor must also arrange for a representative to attend the site with the quantity surveyor for final measurement.

The contractor is entitled to final payment at the end of the maintenance period, on the architect certifying that the works are in a satisfactory state. This releases the balance of the reserve (1.5%) along with any balance in respect of the final sum. There is a provision (clause 41(4)) under which the final sum may be calculated and agreed before the end of the maintenance period, but this would be an unusual situation.

Clause 42 is a comprehensive provision dealing with certificates and makes clear (clause 42(2)) that "no interim certificate... shall of itself be conclusive evidence that any work or things to which it relates are in accordance with the contract". The form is silent as to the nature of the final certificate and it seems, therefore, that it does not have even the limited conclusive evidential effect ascribed to it under the JCT forms. Disputes about the contractor's right to a certificate or as to sums to be certified are to be referred to the employer, whose decision is made final and conclusive (ie is not subject to review on arbitration or otherwise) except in three cases – the most important, in practical terms, being disputes about the amount of the balance of the final sum due and those about the contractor's right to a certificate that the works are in a satisfactory state.

Clause 43 is important: it confers on the employer an express right of set-off, enabling him to recover sums due from the contractor under "this or any other contract".

9.09 Sub-contractors and Employer's Licensees

Clause 27 is a clearly-worded prohibition against the contractor assigning or transferring his contractual rights to third parties, without the employer's consent. Sub-letting – as opposed to assignment – is covered by clause 30. This says (clause 30(1)) that the contractor is not to sub-let any part of the contract without the previous written consent of the architect. This is not subject to any qualification that the consent should not be unreasonably withheld.

Where sub-letting is permitted, the resulting sub-contract must contain certain minimum terms, namely:

- Provision to determine the sub-contract should the employer determine the main contract under clause 46
- A vesting clause in respect of the sub-contractor's materials
- Terms enabling the main contractor to fulfil his obligations to the employer
- Terms against assignment or sub-letting without consent, for replacement of employees, against corrupt practices and in respect of secrecy
- A fluctuations clause if appropriate in terms of clause 11G(1)(2).

A specially designed form of sub-contract for use with GC/Works/1 is available, having been prepared on behalf of the Building Employer's Confederation.

Clause 31 deals not only with sub-contractors and suppliers generally, but also with nominated specialists and in this connection must be read in conjunction with clause 38. Clause 31 makes three points crystal clear:

- Neither the employer nor the architect may nominate anyone to whom the contractor shall make a reasonable objection
- The contractor is fully responsible for all sub-contractors or suppliers whom he employs, whether domestic, nominated or otherwise
- The contractor is responsible to the employer for making good any loss or expense suffered or incurred by the employer because of any sub-contractor's or supplier's default or failure. This restates in express terms what whould otherwise be the position under the general law. Thus, for example, the contractor cannot claim any extension of time for delays by sub-contractors or suppliers.

Clause 38 (prime cost items) deals with nomination. It also empowers the employer to contract direct in respect of all prime cost items. After defining PC items and dealing with discounts and payments, the provision confers a power of nomination on the employer or the architect:

"All prime cost items shall be reserved for the execution of work or the supply of things by persons to be nominated or otherwise appointed in such ways as may be directed" by the employer or the architect.

The contractor must not order PC work or items without a written instruction from the architect or the employer's written consent. Where the employer exercises his power to contract direct in respect of PC items, the contract sum is adjusted accordingly. Delay caused through the exercise of the power in this clause may give rise to a disruption claim under clause 53(2)(6).

Clause 38(5) should be read with care. Should a nominated sub-contract be terminated, it is for the contractor to either:

- Select another person to undertake or complete the work (the employer's written consent is required) *or*
- Undertake that work himself.

In either event, the contractor is then entitled to payment of the amount which would have been payable to the nominated person, together with any allowances for profit and attendances contained in the priced documents.

Under clause 50, the employer is empowered to have other work done on the site while the contact is in progress and the contractor is to give reasonable facilities for this purpose. Claims for extensions of time and for prolongation and disruption caused as a result of the exercise of this power may be made as appropriate.

9.10 Statutory Obligations

Curiously, there is no express term requiring the contractor to comply with the substantive provisions of legislation, but such a term is clearly to be implied under the general law. Clause 14 requires the contractor to give all statutory and allied notices and indemnify the employer against statutory fees and charges. Clause 48 deals with damage to public roads, and under its terms the employer undertakes to indemnify the contractor against any claims against him by the local highway authority in respect of such damage. Provided the contractor takes reasonable steps to prevent damage by "extraordinary traffic" and complies with any relevant instructions of the architect in this regard, this indemnity is operative.

In addition, clause 25(2) imposes on the contractor a duty to comply with any statutory regulations governing the storage and use of things which are brought on site, whether or not they are things for incorporation.

9.11 Injury, Damage and Insurance

Under the printed terms, the contractor is not bound to provide insurance cover for employer's and public liability risks and, if used for private work, appropriate insurance clauses must be drafted.

There is a very wide indemnity clause (clause 47) dealing with claims for damage to persons and property brought by third parties, while clauses 25 and 26 deal respectively with precautions against fire and other risks and damage to the works themselves.

Clause 25(1) requires the contractor to:

- Take all reasonable precautions to prevent loss or damage from any of the "accepted risks" such as war. A full definition is contained in clause 1(2) and, since amendment 4 issued in 1987, the accepted risks no longer include fire
- Take all reasonable precautions to minimise the amount of any loss or damage caused by the accepted risks or by a Crown servant. If used in private practice, this provision would need amendment.

The contractor's liability for damage to the works is set out in clause 26. Plant is at the contractor's sole risk and he must immediately make good any loss or damage.

Clause 26(2) deals with damage to the works themselves or to materials for incorporation and reinforces clause 7(1). Any damage must be made good at the contractor's expense with all speed – unless the employer determines the contract – unless caused by the accepted risks or unforeseeable ground conditions or by the neglect or default of a Crown servant, when the employer will meet the cost, in whole or in part as the case may be.

Commercially, it is essential for adequate insurance cover to be maintained if the contractor is to meet the extensive obligations imposed on him by these related clauses.

9.12 Determination

There are two determination clauses in form GC/Works/1 (clauses 44 and 45), but in both cases the power of determination is exercisable only by the employer. The contractor is given no express right to terminate his own employment under the contract and must, therefore, rely on his common law rights. If, for example, the employer were guilty of a serious breach of contract going to the very root of the bargain, the contractor would be entitled to accept that breach and treat the contract as at an end under the general law. For discussion of this very difficult topic reference may usefully be made to *Determination and Suspension of Construction Contracts* by V Powell-Smith and J Sims (Blackwell Scientific Publications 1985), especially Chapter 1.

Determination for default by contractor

Clause 45 gives the employer a right to terminate the contract for specific defaults by the contractor. These are:

- The contractor's failure to comply within 7 days with a notice from the architect requiring rectification of work which is defective or which is being carried out in an inefficient or improper manner
- The contractor delaying or suspending the execution of the work so that the architect is of the opinion that the work will not be completed on time
- Insolvency and financial difficulties
- Contractor's failure to comply with the contract provisions about admission to the site (clause 56), and the employer decides that this breach is prejudicial to the interests of the state
- Corrupt practices under clause 55.

Termination is brought about by written notice served on the contractor by the employer, and no length of notice is specified. The notice may be served whether or not the completion date has elapsed and the wording of the clause makes plain that the right of termination is additional to the employer's common law rights.

Clause 46 deals with the consequences of termination under clauses 45 or 55. These may be summarised briefly:

- All sums of money then due cease to be due
- The employer may enter on site and take possession of all equipment, materials, etc on site
- The employer may hire anyone employed by the contractor.

The employer may do all things necessary for completion of the works

- Except in an insolvency situation, the contractor must assign (without payment) the benefit of any sub-contract or supply contract
- The employer may pay nominated sub-contractors and suppliers direct.

The contractor has no claim at all in respect of any action so taken by the employer.

The cost of completion is to be certified by the architect and if there is (unusually) a credit due to the contractor, this is paid to him, though in view of the wide terms of the clause and the powers of the employer, the more usual situation is that the deficit is recoverable from him.

Special power of determination

Clause 44, which would of course be deleted if the form were being used in the private sector, entitles the employer to terminate the contract at any time in his absolute discretion, termination being by notice, and the contractor having no legally enforceable claim for any loss or damage suffered or incurred by him in consequence. There is, however, express (but unnecessary) provision for the authority to consider a hardship (*ex gratia*) claim (clause 44(5)).

9.13 Disputes

Arbitration is the chosen method of disputes settlement, and clause 61 is very much in common form. Arbitration is to take place on all disputes and differences between the contracting parties, except that the following are excluded from the scope of the arbitration agreement:

- Decisions said by the contract to be final and conclusive (**see Table 9.13**).

Unless both parties agree, arbitration cannot take place during the currency of the contract, but must await its completion, alleged completion or abandonment or determination (clause 61(2)).

Table 9.01: Contents of GC/Works/1 Summarised

Clause	Content
1	Definitions
2	Contractor deemed to have satisfied himself as to conditions affecting execution of the works
2A	Unforeseeable ground conditions
3	Vesting of works etc in authority: things not to be removed
4	Specifications, bills of quantities and drawings
5	Bills of quantities
5A	Authority's schedule of rates
5B	Contractor's schedule of rates
6	Progress of the works
7	SO's (architect's) instructions
8	Failure of contractor to comply with instructions
9	Valuation of instructions
10	Valuation by measurement
11A to F	Variation of price (as applicable)
11G	Variation of price (labour-tax matters)
12	Setting out of works
13	Things for incorporation and workmanship to conform to description
14	Local and other authorities' notices and fees
15	Patent rights
16	Resident engineer or clerk of works
17	Watching, lighting and protection of works
18	Precautions to prevent nuisance
19	Removal of rubbish
20	Excavations and materials arising therefrom
21	Foundations
22	Notice prior to covering-up work
23	Suspension for frost etc
24	Daywork
25	Precautions against fire and other risks
26	Damage to the works or other things
27	Assignment or transfer
28	Date for completion: extensions of time
28A	Partial possession before completion
29	Liquidated damages
30	Sub-letting
31	Sub-contractors and suppliers
32	Defects liability
33	Contractor's agent
34	Daily returns
35	Contractor to conform to regulations
36	Replacement of contractor's employees
37	Attending for measurement and provision of information
38	Prime cost items
39	Provisional sums and provisional quantities
40	Advances on account
41	Payment on and after completion
42	Certificates
43	Recovery of sums due from the contractor
44	Special powers of determination
45	Determination due to contractor's default or failure
46	Provisions in case of determination

Table 9.01: Contents of GC/Works/1 Summarised – (continued)

Clause	Content
47	Injury to persons: loss of property
48	Damage to public roads
49	Emergency powers
50	Facilities for other works
52	Racial discrimination
53	Prolongation and disruption expenses
54	Not used
55	Corrupt gifts and payments
56	Admission to the site
57	Passes
58	Photographs
59	Secrecy
60	Not used
61	Arbitration

Table 9.02: GC/Works/1 – Time Chart

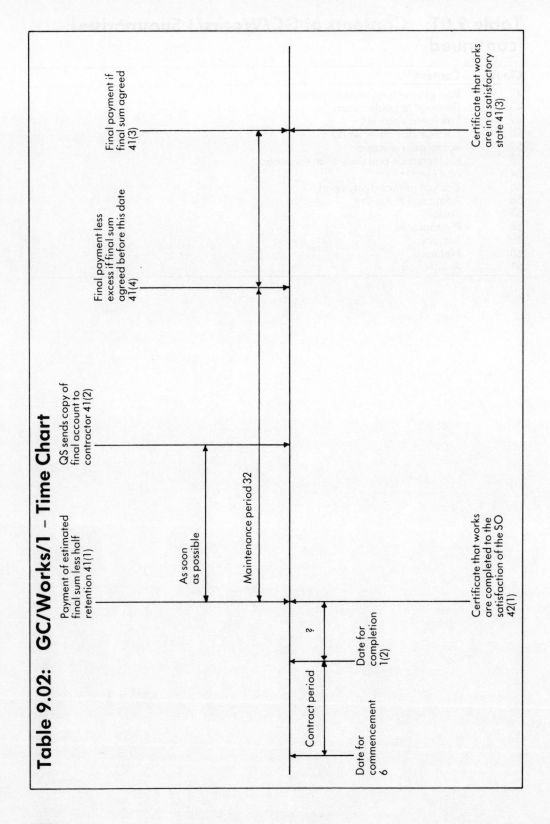

Payment of estimated final sum less half retention 41(1)

QS sends copy of final account to contractor 41(2)

Final payment less excess if final sum agreed before this date 41(4)

Final payment if final sum agreed 41(3)

As soon as possible

Maintenance period 32

Certificate that works are in a satisfactory state 41(3)

Date for commencement 6

Contract period

Date for completion 1(2)

?

Certificate that works are completed to the satisfaction of the SO 42(1)

Table 9.03: Architect's [SO's] Powers under GC/Works/1

Clause	Power	Comment
3(2)	Order or permit the contractor to remove things from site	The superintending officer's decision in case of dispute is final and conclusive
4(4)	Require the contractor to return the specification, bills, drawings, including copies or extracts	On completion of the works or earlier determination of the contract
7(1)	Issue further drawings, details and/or instructions, directions and explanations from time to time	The list in clause 7(1) is exhaustive and the superintending officer's decision as to whether any instruction is necessary or expedient is, by clause 7(3) made final and conclusive
8	Require the contractor to comply with an instruction within a specified period	This notice is a precondition to the exercise of default powers by the employer
13(1)	Request the contractor to prove that things for incorporation and workmanship comply with description	
13(2)	Inspect and examine the works etc	
13(3)	Require testing of things for incorporation supplied	At the superintending officer's discretion, an independent expert may be employed
16	Notify contractor of any delegation of powers to resident engineer or clerk of works	
21	Examine and approve excavations for foundations	
23	Direct suspensions of works because of frost etc	
28A(1)(b)	Instruct partial possession before completion	

Table 9.03:   Architect's [SO's] Powers under GC/Works/1 – (continued)

Clause	Power	Comment
30(1)	Consent in writing to sub-letting	
32(2)	Require the making-good of defects	
33	Require site agent's attendance at his office	
36(1)	Require contractor to cease to employ and to replace foremen and below if he forms the opinion that continued employment is undesirable	
39	Require expenditure of provisional sums	
49	Decide on urgent measures in an emergency	

Table 9.04: Architect's [SO's] Duties under GC/Works/1

Clause	Duty	Comment
2A(2)	Certify unforeseeable ground conditions Inform contractor of his decision	If he agrees that ground conditions notified by the contractor are unforeseeable
7(2)	Confirm in writing in prescribed manner any oral instructions	If so requested by the contractor
12	Supply dimensioned drawings, levels and other information necessary to enable the contractor to set out the works	
20(3)	Issue instructions about objects found on site	If the contractor has reported the find
24	Certify daywork vouchers	
28A(6)	Decide disputes about partial possession before completion	Decision final and conclusive
40(3)	Certify the sum to be paid by way of advance	When the valuation has been agreed
42(1)	Certify from time to time the sums to which the contractor is entitled under clauses 40 and 41 Certify the date on which the works are completed to his satisfaction Certify when the works are in a satisfactory state after the end of the maintenance period	
46(1)(e)	Certify the cost of completion after determination of the contract	

Table 9.05:   Contractor's Powers under GC/Works/1

Clause	Power	Comment
3(2)	Remove things from site	With the written consent of superintending officer
7(2)	Request to confirm oral instructions in writing	The request must be made within 14 days of the issue of the oral instruction
30(1)	Sub-let part of the contract	If the superintending officer previously consents in writing
31(1)	Object to proposed nominated sub-contractors/ suppliers	The objection must be reasonable
40(3)	Submit claims for payment of advances on account	At intervals of not less than one month Claims must be supported by a valuation
42(3)	Refer disputes as to his right to a certificate to the employer	The decision is generally final and conclusive
44(5)	Claim a hardship allowance by referring the circumstances to the employer	Payment is absolutely discretionary
61(1)	Request appointment of an arbitrator	
61(2)	Agree to arbitration during the progress of the works	

Table 9.06: Contractor's Duties under GC/Works/1

Clause	Duty	Comment
2(1)	Satisfy himself as to conditions affecting execution of the works	He is deemed to have so satisfied himself
2A(1)	Notify the SO immediately he encounters unforeseeable ground conditions, specifying the conditions and the measures he proposes to take to deal with them	The duty arises if the contractor becomes aware of ground conditions (excluding those caused by weather) including artificial obstructions which he did not know of and which he could not reasonably have foreseen having regard to any information which he had or ought reasonably to have had
3(1)	Be responsible for the protection and preservation of the works etc until termination of the contract	
3(2)	Not to remove things brought on site in connection with the contract	Unless the superintending officer consents in writing
	Remove things from site forthwith	If the superintending officer so directs or orders
4(3)	Keep a copy of all drawings and the specification on site	The superintending officer or his representative have a right of access to them at all reasonable times
4(4)	Return specification, bills, etc to the superintending officer on completion of the works or earlier determination of the contract	If the superintending officer so requires
5B	Supply the authority with a full and detailed schedule of rates	If bills or a schedule of rates is not supplied by the authority
6	Commence execution of the works and proceed with diligence and expedition in regular progression or as directed by the superintending officer so that the whole of the works are completed by the due date	On being given possession of the site or the order to commence

Table 9.06: Contractor's Duties under GC/Works/1 – (continued)

Clause	Duty	Comment
7(1)	Carry out and complete the works to the satisfaction of the superintending officer	
7(3)	Obey the superintending officer's authorised instructions	
7(4)	Only vary the works pursuant to a superintending officer's instructions	
11G(4)	Give notice to the superintending officer of relevant increases or decreases and furnish such further information as required by the employer Keep proper books of account and other records	Labour-tax matters only
12	Set out the works in accordance with dimensioned drawings etc supplied by the superintending officer and provide all necessary templates etc	The contractor is solely responsible for the accuracy of the setting-out
13(1)	Prove that things for incorporation and workmanship conform to description	If the superintending officer so requests
13(2)	Give the superintending officer or his representative access to site, etc and provide such facilities as may be required for inspection	
13(3)	Provide all facilities which the superintending officer requires for testing Comply with any prescribed testing procedures	

Table 9.06: Contractor's Duties under GC/Works/1 – (continued)

Clause	Duty	Comment
	Pay independent expert's charges if employed	Only if tests not in the contractor's favour
13(4)	Execute the works in a workmanlike manner and to the superintending officer's satisfaction Replace defective workmanship and materials	
14	Give all statutory and allied notices paying any fees involved and supplying all drawings etc required	
15	Indemnify the employer against patent proceedings and claims	Contractor entitled to payment if patented articles used on superintending officer's instructions
16	Allow resident engineer or clerk of works access to site	If appointed
17	Provide all necessary watching, lighting and protection	
18	Take all reasonable precautions to prevent nuisance to third parties	
19	Keep the site free from rubbish and debris at all times	If they arise from the execution of the works
20(2)	Notify superintending officer of discovery of fossils etc and take all necessary steps to preserve them etc	
21	Lay foundations only when the excavations have been examined and approved by superintending officer	

Table 9.06:   Contractor's Duties under GC/Works/1 – (continued)

Clause	Duty	Comment
22	Give superintending officer due notice before covering work	In default, superintending officer can require uncovering at the expense of the contractor
23	Suspend execution of the work	If so instructed by superintending officer for frost, etc. Work must not be resumed until superintending officer permits. There is no entitlement to payment unless the contractor proves that he has complied with all relevant specification requirements
24	Give reasonable notice to superintending officer before commencing daywork	Supporting vouchers etc must be provided
25(1)	Take all reasonable steps and precautions to prevent and minimise the extent of loss or damage to the works, etc arising from any cause whatsoever	
25(2)	Comply with statutory regulations about storage and use of things brought on site	Even if the regulations are not binding on the Crown
26(1)	Be responsible for all damage to the works etc Make good any damage etc with all possible speed	
26(2)	Bear the cost of making good	The cost of making good is to be borne by the contractor unless caused by Crown servants, the accepted risks, or unforeseeable ground conditions There are provisions for apportionment where Crown servants are at fault
29(1)	Pay liquidated damages	If: Works not completed and site cleared on or before date for completion; or any specified section is not completed Subject to provisions for extension of time

Table 9.06: Contractor's Duties under GC/Works/1 – (continued)

Clause	Duty	Comment
30(4)	Ensure that sub-contractors comply with and perform obligations specified in clause 30(2)	This is conditioned on the superintending officer's request The specified provisions should be set out in the sub-contract
31(2)	Be responsible for all sub-contractors and suppliers	Includes nominated or approved sub-contractors
31(3)	Make good any loss suffered or expense incurred by the employer as a result of any total or partial default or failure on the part of any sub-contractor or supplier	
32(2)	Make good at his own cost to the satisfaction of the superintending officer defects during the maintenance period or appropriate sub-contract maintenance period	
32(3)	Bear all costs and expenses if the employer exercises default powers and employs others	
33	Employ a competent agent to superintend the works	
35	Conform to any relevant rules and regulations	Where works are executed in a Government establishment
36	Replace employees as instructed by superintending officer	
37(1)	Attend for measurement and provide necessary information	If quantity surveyor so requires

Table 9.06: Contractor's Duties under GC/Works/1 – (continued)

Clause	Duty	Comment
38(3)	Produce to the quantity surveyor invoices etc in respect of prime cost items to show details of sums paid by the contractor	
38(4)	Order prime cost items only if instructed to do so by superintending officer or employer	
38(5)	Select a substitute sub-contractor or supplier or undertake to complete the work or supply items himself	If sub-contract is terminated. The employer's consent is needed
40(6)	Satisfy the superintending officer that amounts due to sub-contractors etc covered by a previous advance have been paid	If superintending officer so requests
44(2)	Comply with all reasonable despatch with employer's directions as to: Performance of further work Protection of work so executed Removal of things from site Removal of rubbish from site Termination or transfer of sub-contracts etc Other matters as necessary	If the employer exercises the special powers of determination by written notice
44(6)	Take similar special powers of determination in any substantial contract or sub-contract	
46(1)	Assign the benefit of sub-contracts etc to the employer	If the employer has determined the contract for default under clauses 45 or 55
47(2)	Be responsible for and reinstate and make good or make compensation for any	

Table 9.06: Contractor's Duties under GC/Works/1 – (continued)

Clause	Duty	Comment
	loss of property suffered by the employer Indemnify employer against relevant claims and proceedings	Personal injury and property damage
48(2)	Take resonable steps to prevent damage to public roads through extraordinary traffic and select routes etc accordingly	
48(3)	Comply with relevant superintending officer's instructions	
48(4)	Notify employer of any claim etc for damage to public roads	
50	Give reasonable facilities for other works to be executed on site	
52(1)	Refrain from unlawful racial discrimination	
52(2)	Take reasonable steps to ensure that employees etc do not racially discriminate	
53(3)	Give written notice to the superintending officer specifying circumstances causing or expected to cause disruption or prolongation and provide such documents and information as required by the quantity surveyor	Notice must be given immediately the contractor becomes aware that regular progress of the works or part has been or is likely to be disrupted or prolonged by specified events
55(1)	Refrain from corrupt practices	

Table 9.06: Contractor's Duties under GC/Works/1 – (continued)

Clause	Duty	Comment
56(1)	Take reasonable steps to prevent the admission to site of specified persons	If employer gives notice
56(2)	Take such steps as superintending officer may reasonably require to prevent aliens being admitted to site	The employer's consent to their admission is needed EC citizens are not aliens
57	Provide the superintending officer with a list of workpeople etc	So that site passes may be issued. These are returnable on demand and in any case on completion of the works
58	Take reasonable steps to prevent unauthorised photography	
59(1)	Ensure that employees are aware of the application of the security legislation in force	
59(3)	Observe confidentiality of information	

Table 9.07: Employer's Powers under GC/Works/1

Clause	Power	Comment
5B	Require the contractor to provide a schedule of rates	If neither bills nor an employer's schedule of rates are provided
8	Provide labour and/or things or enter into contracts for the execution of work etc if the contractor fails to comply with a superintending officer's instruction Recover additional costs and expenses from contractor	This is without prejudice to the employer's right to determine the contract under clause 45 NB Notice of compliance must have been served by superintending officer
11G(4)	Require information from the contractor in respect of fluctuations	
16	Appoint a resident engineer or clerk of works	
27	Consent in writing to assignment or transfer of the contract	
28(2)(i)	Waive the requirement for notice	
28(2)(iii)	Take the effect of authorised omissions into account when granting extensions of time	
28A	Take partial possession before completion	
29(3)	Notify the contractor that he has no entitlement to any or a further extension of time	Sum representing the amount of liquidated damages then becomes recoverable under clause 43
30(4)	Request the contractor to take necessary action to ensure that his sub-contractors comply with and perform all relevant obligations	

Table 9.07: Employer's Powers under GC/Works/1 – (continued)

Clause	Power	Comment
32(3)	Provide labour etc and contract with others if the contractor fails to make good defects and recover costs involved from the contractor	
36(2)	Require replacement of contractor's employees	
38(4)	Direct contractor as regards PC items	
40(6)(a)	Withhold payment of any amount due to a sub-contractor or supplier	Until superintending officer is satisfied that earlier payments made
40(6)(b)	Pay nominated sub-contractors and suppliers direct	If superintending officer certifies that they have not been paid Direct payments are recoverable from the contractor
41(1)	Estimate the amount of the final sum Pay further sums in reduction of the reserve	
44(1)	Determine the contract without reason	Determination is by notice
44(2)(b)	Vary any directions given to the contractor consequent on determination	
44(3)(a)(iii)	Consent to the contractor electing not to retain things for incorporation	
44(3)(d)	Require the contractor to provide documentation necessary for the operation of the clause	

Table 9.07:   Employer's Powers under GC/Works/1 – (continued)

Clause	Power	Comment
44(5)	Pay the contractor a hardship allowance	Payment is discretionary
45	Determine the contract for default or failure by the contractor	The grounds are traditional and determination is by notice
46(1)(c)	Require assignment of the benefit of contracts and sub-contracts Recover from the contractor any payments to sub-contractors covered by previous advances	If superintending officer so certifies
46(1)(d)	Pay any nominated sub-contractor or supplier direct and recover such payments from contractor	
46(1)(e)	Decide percentage of establishment and superintendence charges	Decision is final and conclusive
46(3)	Sell things on site and apply proceeds of sale to reduce contractor's indebtedness	Would not be effective against third-parties
48(4)	Decide whether any claim or proceedings is due wholly or partly to contractor's default or failure and recover costs and expenses from contractor	
49	Carry out emergency work by others and recover from contractor as appropriate	Note wording of clause
50	Execute other works on site contemporaneously with the contract works	

Table 9.07: Employer's Powers under GC/Works/1 – (continued)

Clause	Power	Comment
56(1)	Limit admission of persons to site	By notice to contractor
56(4)	Decide disputes under the clause	Decision final and conclusive
58	Consent in writing to photographs etc	
59(3)	Consent to disclosure of information	
61(1)	Request appointment of an arbitrator	
61(2)	Agree to arbitration during the contract	

Table 9.08:   Employer's Duties under GC/Works/1

Clause	Duty	Comment
5A	Provide a schedule of rates	If so stated in tender
6	Give possession of the site to the contractor	
26(2)(b)	Pay the contractor for making good loss or damage to the works if the loss etc is wholly or partly caused by a Crown employee's neglect or default	Payment is proportionate The employee must have been acting in the course of employment
	Similarly pay where loss or damage is caused by the accepted risks	These are the insured risks Payment may be proportionate
28(2)	Allow the contractor a reasonable extension of time for completion of the works in specified circumstances	The specified circumstances are: Execution of modified or additional work Weather conditions which make continuance of work impracticable Any act or default of the employer Strikes etc in the building allied trades Accepted risks Unforeseeable ground conditions Other circumstances wholly beyond the contractor's control The contractor must observe the procedural provisions
28A(5)	Apportion accumulated reserve Pay one half of the reserve to the contractor on the date of certification and pay the second half at the end of the maintenance period as certified by superintending officer	If partial possession is taken before completion
38(5)	Pay the contractor sums which would have been payable to him had sub-contract not been terminated	If a nominated sub-contract is terminated NB Contractor must either select someone else or do the work himself
40(1)	Pay advances on account and accumulate 3% as a reserve	97% is payable Clause 40(2) covers unfixed materials

Table 9.08:   Employer's Duties under GC/Works/1 – (continued)

Clause	Duty	Comment
41(1)	Pay the contractor the amount of the estimated final sum less half the amount of the reserve	On completion as certified by the superintending officer
41(3)	Pay balance to the contractor	After the end of the maintenance period if superintending officer has certified satisfactory completion; *and* If final sum has been calculated and agreed
42(3)	Decide disputes about the contractor's right to a certificate	In most cases the decision is final and conclusive
44(2)(a)	Give directions to the contractor about specified matters	If the employer has exercised its right of special determination Directions must be given within 3 months from the determination notice; *or* Of the period up to the date of completion
44(3)(a)	Pay amounts as specified to the contractor	
47(4)(a)	Notify the contractor of any claim or proceedings made or brought in respect of personal injury or loss of property covered by the clause	
48(1)	Indemnify the contractor against claims etc in respect of damage to public roads etc	Subject to the conditions set out in the clause
53(1)	Reimburse the contractor any prolongation or disruption expenses properly incurred	Subject to the provisions of the clause
55(3)	Decide any dispute over corrupt gifts etc	The decision is final and conclusive

Table 9.09: Clauses that may Give Rise to Claims under GC/Works/1

Clause	Event	Type
5(2)	Errors in bills of quantities	C
5(3)	Unforeseeable ground conditions	C
6	Failure to give possession of the site	CL
7(1)(a)	Variations in design, quality or quantity of work	C
7(1)(b)	Discrepancies in or between: Specification; or Bills of quantities; or Drawings	C
7(1)(c)	Removal of goods for incorporation from site and substitution of other goods	C
7(1)(e)	Order of carrying out any part of the work	C
7(1)(f)	Hours of working, extent of overtime or night work	C
7(1)(i)	Opening up of work found in accordance with the contract	C
7(1)(k)	Emergency work	C
7(1)(m)	Any instruction other than those in 7(1)(a)–7(1)(l) inclusive	C
9	Variations	C
9(1)	Failure to value in accordance with the rules	CL

Table 9.09: Clauses that may Give Rise to Claims under GC/Works/1 – (continued)

Clause	Event	Type
12	Failure to supply levels, dimensioned drawings or other information required for setting out	CL
13(3)	Goods found to be in accordance with the contract after testing	C
15	Royalties and patent rights	C
21	Failure to examine and approve excavations for foundations	CL
23	Making good defects due to frost or inclement weather not the contractor's fault	C
26(2)(b)(i)	Damage to works or other things caused by the authority	C
26(2)(b)(ii)	Damage to works or other things caused by any of the accepted risks	C
28	Financial claims for faulty procedure	CL
28A(1)	Possession without contractor's consent	CL
28A(3)	Failure to certify	CL
28A(5)	Failure to release reserve	CL

Table 9.09: Clauses that may Give Rise to Claims under GC/Works/1 – (continued)

Clause	Event	Type
38	Prime cost sums	C
38(2)	Fixing goods	C
38(3)	Failure to adjust contract sum	CL
39	Provisional sums	C
40(1)(2)	Failure to pay 97% of value of work executed or goods brought on to site for incorporation	CL
40(3)	Failure to value or certify in accordance with the rules	CL
41(1)	Failure to pay the final sum less one half the reserve on completion	CL
41(3)	Failure to pay the sum remaining due after certification of satisfaction and sum has been agreed	CL
41(4)	Failure to pay in accordance with this clause	CL
42(1)	Failure to certify or failure to certify properly	CL
44(3)	Failure to operate provisions after determination	CL
44(3) & 46(2)	Payment after determination	C
50	Works by the authority	CL

Table 9.09: Clauses that may Give Rise to Claims under GC/Works/1 – (continued)

Clause	Event	Type
53	Prolongation and disruption	C

KEY
C = Contractual claims
CL = Common law claims
Contractual claims are usually dealt with by the superintending officer
Common law claims are usually dealt with by the authority

Table 9.10: Certificates to be Issued by the Superintending Officer under GC/Works/1

Clause	Certificates
2A(2)	Unforeseeable ground conditions
24	Vouchers for daywork
28A(1)	Satisfactory completion of part of the works
40(3)	Certification of advances on account
40(6)(b)	Amount not paid to nominated sub-contractor or supplier
42(1)	Certificate of payment under clauses 40 and 41
	Satisfactory completion of the works
	Works in a satisfactory state at the end of the maintenance period
46(1)(e)	Cost of completion after determination

Table 9.11: Superintending Officer's Instructions Empowered by GC/Works/1

Clause	Instruction
7(1)(a)	Regarding the variation of the design, quality or quantity of work
7(1)(b)	Regarding discrepancies between specification and/or bills of quantities and/or drawings
7(1)(c)	For the removal from site of things for incorporation brought by the contractor and the substitution of other things
7(1)(d)	For the removal and re-execution of contractor's work
7(1)(e)	For the order of carrying out of work
7(1)(f)	For working hours, overtime and nightwork
7(1)(g)	For the suspension of the work
7(1)(h)	Regarding the replacement of men graded foreman or below
7(1)(i)	For opening up the work for inspection
7(1)(j)	To make good defects under clause 32
7(1)(k)	To carry out emergency work
7(1)(l)	To use excavated materials
7(1)(m)	Regarding any other necessary or expedient matter
20(3)	Finding antiquities
23	Suspension due to frost
25	To prevent loss or damage from accepted risks
28A(1)(b)	Possession of part before completion of the whole of the works
38(4)	Instruct contractor to order work under prime cost items

Table 9.12: Adjustment of Contract Sum under GC/Works/1

Clause	Adjustment
2A(3)	Unforeseen ground conditions
5(2)	Errors in the bills
9	Variations
11G(2)	Labour-tax matters
11G(3)	Sub-contract reductions or increases
15	Patent rights
20(1)	Use of the authority's property
23	Suspension for frost etc
26(2)(c)	Damage to the works
38(3)	Prime cost sums
38(4)	Prime cost sums
39	Provisional sums
44(3)(a)	After determination by use of special powers
50	Damage caused by the authority's works
53	Expense incurred by the contractor

Table 9.13: Decisions which are Final and Conclusive

Clause	Decision
3(2)	Architect's decision about removal of things from site
7(3)	Architect's decision as to whether instruction necessary or expedient
9(3)	Quantity surveyor's decision as to value of alterations and additions
13(4)	Expert's reports on tests
28A	Architect's decision about partial possession
36	Replacement of contractor's employees: employer or architect
40(3) and 40(6)	Architect's decisions about advances on account and employer's decision about NSC payments
42(3)	Employer's decision about certificates, etc
44	Employer's decisions consequent on special determination
45	Whether contractor's breach of clause 56 against national interest
55(3)	Employer's decisions about corruption
56(4)	Employer's decision about admission to site

Flowchart 9.14: Superintending Officer's Instructions

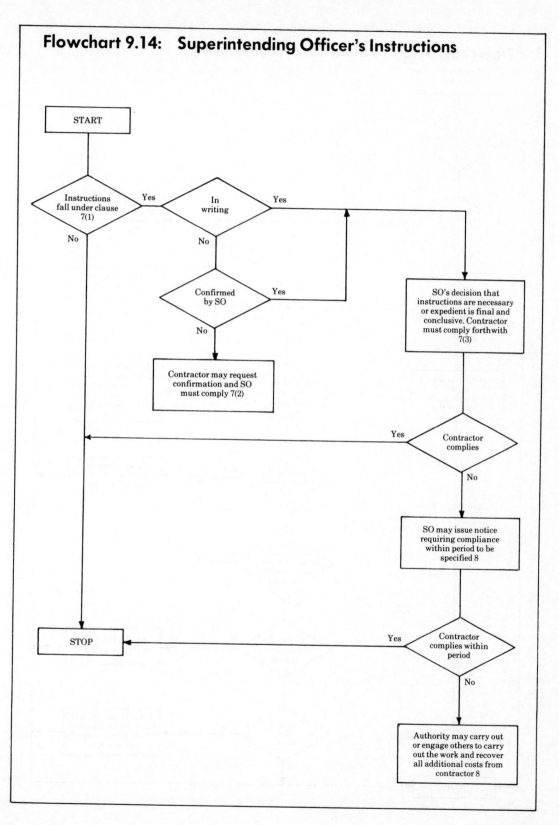

START

Instructions fall under clause 7(1)

Yes

No

In writing

Yes

No

Confirmed by SO

Yes

No

SO's decision that instructions are necessary or expedient is final and conclusive. Contractor must comply forthwith 7(3)

Contractor may request confirmation and SO must comply 7(2)

Contractor complies

Yes

No

SO may issue notice requiring compliance within period to be specified 8

Contractor complies within period

Yes

No

STOP

Authority may carry out or engage others to carry out the work and recover all additional costs from contractor 8

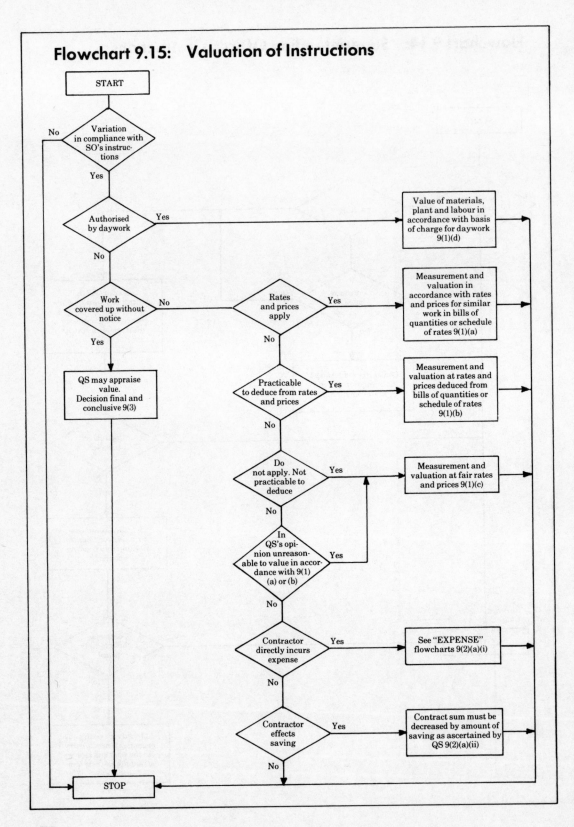

Flowchart 9.15:   Valuation of Instructions

START

Variation in compliance with SO's instructions — No

Yes

Authorised by daywork — Yes → Value of materials, plant and labour in accordance with basis of charge for daywork 9(1)(d)

No

Work covered up without notice — No → Rates and prices apply — Yes → Measurement and valuation in accordance with rates and prices for similar work in bills of quantities or schedule of rates 9(1)(a)

Yes

QS may appraise value. Decision final and conclusive 9(3)

No

Practicable to deduce from rates and prices — Yes → Measurement and valuation at rates and prices deduced from bills of quantities or schedule of rates 9(1)(b)

No

Do not apply. Not practicable to deduce — Yes → Measurement and valuation at fair rates and prices 9(1)(c)

No

In QS's opinion unreasonable to value in accordance with 9(1) (a) or (b) — Yes

No

Contractor directly incurs expense — Yes → See "EXPENSE" flowcharts 9(2)(a)(i)

No

Contractor effects saving — Yes → Contract sum must be decreased by amount of saving as ascertained by QS 9(2)(a)(ii)

No

STOP

Flowchart 9.16: Extension of Time: Superintending Officer's Duties

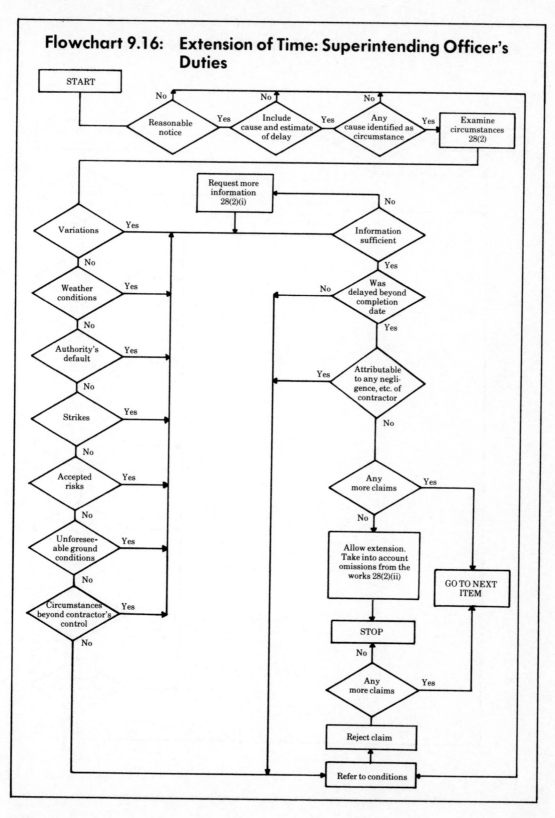

Flowchart 9.17: Extension of Time: Contractor's Duties

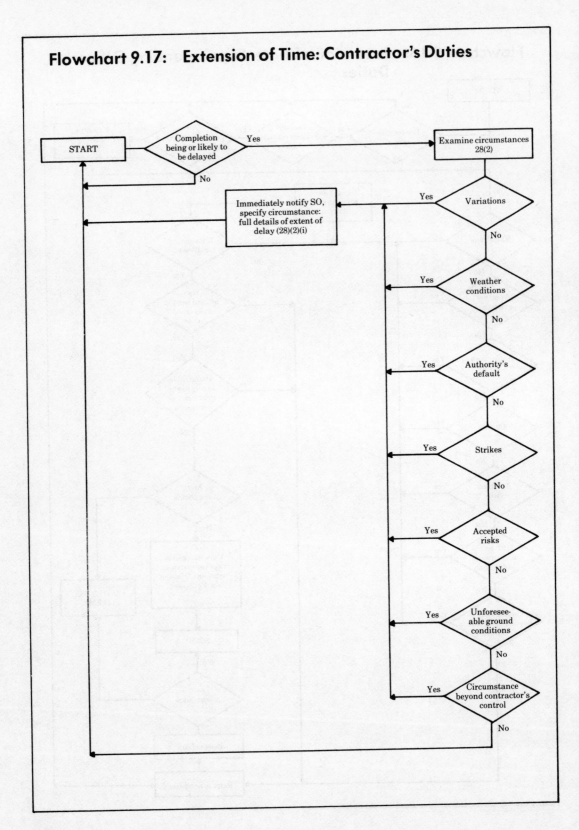

START

Completion being or likely to be delayed — Yes → Examine circumstances 28(2)

No

Immediately notify SO, specify circumstance: full details of extent of delay (28)(2)(i)

Yes ← Variations

No

Yes ← Weather conditions

No

Yes ← Authority's default

No

Yes ← Strikes

No

Yes ← Accepted risks

No

Yes ← Unforeseeable ground conditions

No

Yes ← Circumstance beyond contractor's control

No

Flowchart 9.18: Expense: Superintending Officer's Duties

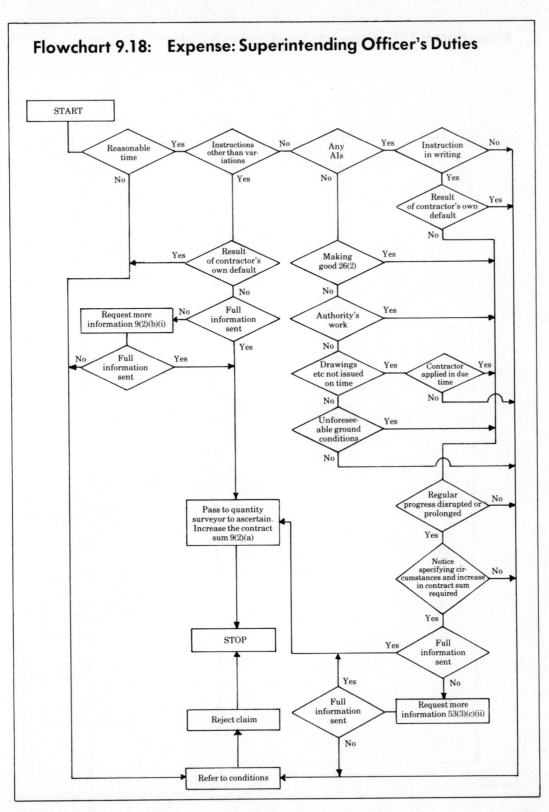

Flowchart 9.19: Expense: Contractor's Duties

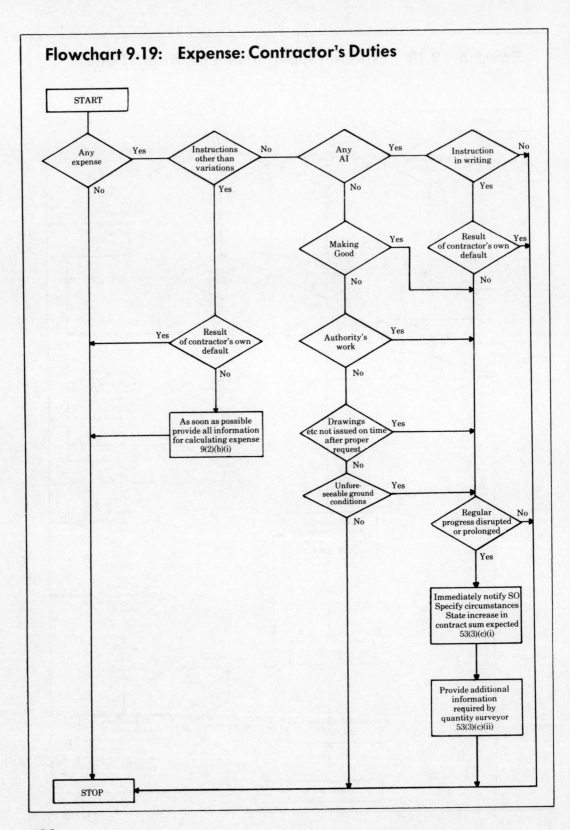

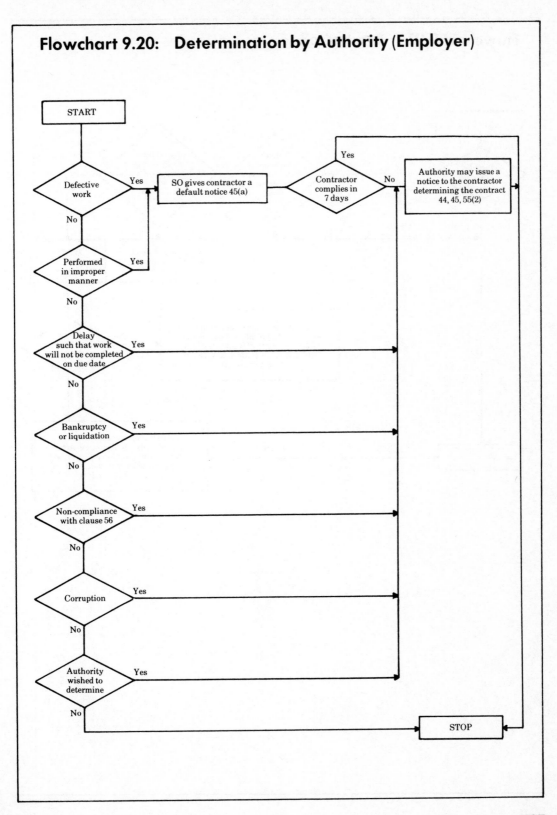

Flowchart 9.20:   Determination by Authority (Employer)

START

Defective work — Yes → SO gives contractor a default notice 45(a) → Contractor complies in 7 days — Yes

Defective work — No

Performed in improper manner — Yes

Performed in improper manner — No

Delay such that work will not be completed on due date — Yes

Delay such that work will not be completed on due date — No

Bankruptcy or liquidation — Yes

Bankruptcy or liquidation — No

Non-compliance with clause 56 — Yes

Non-compliance with clause 56 — No

Corruption — Yes

Corruption — No

Authority wished to determine — Yes

Authority wished to determine — No

Contractor complies in 7 days — No → Authority may issue a notice to the contractor determining the contract 44, 45, 55(2)

STOP

Flowchart 9.21:   Arbitration

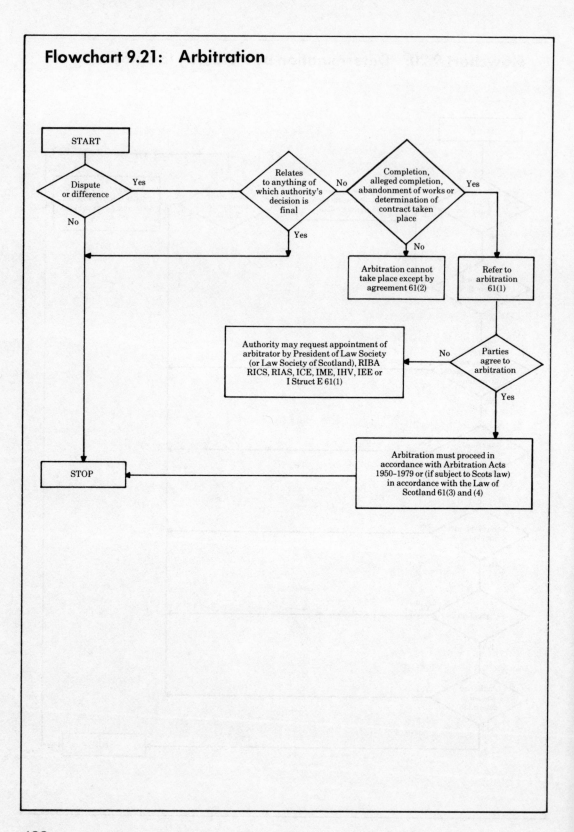

START

Dispute or difference — Yes →

No ↓

Relates to anything of which authority's decision is final — No →

Yes ↓

Completion, alleged completion, abandonment of works or determination of contract taken place — Yes →

No ↓

Arbitration cannot take place except by agreement 61(2)

Refer to arbitration 61(1)

Parties agree to arbitration

No → Authority may request appointment of arbitrator by President of Law Society (or Law Society of Scotland), RIBA RICS, RIAS, ICE, IME, IHV, IEE or I Struct E 61(1)

Yes ↓

Arbitration must proceed in accordance with Arbitration Acts 1950–1979 or (if subject to Scots law) in accordance with the Law of Scotland 61(3) and (4)

STOP

Bibliography

1   Contract Choice and Comparison

Bickford-Smith, S, Anderson, A J, Freeth, E, Powell-Smith, V (1980), *Emden's Building Contracts and Practice*, 8th edn, 2 vols, with supplement.
London: Butterworth.

Keating, D (1978), *Building Contracts*, 4th edn, with supplement.
London: Sweet & Maxwell.

Powell-Smith, V, Chappell, D (1990), *A Building Contract Dictionary*, 2nd edn.
London: Legal Studies & Services Ltd.

Powell-Smith, V, Furmston, M (1990), *A Building Contract Casebook*, 2nd edn.
London: Blackwell Scientific Publications.

Speaight, A, Stone, G (1990), *AJ Legal Handbook*, 5th edn.
London: Butterworth.

Wallace, I N D (1970), *Hudson's Building & Engineering Contracts*, 10th edn, with supplement.
London: Sweet & Maxwell.

2   The JCT Standard Form of Building Contract (JCT 80)

Parris, J (1985), *The Standard Form of Building Contract: JCT 80*, 2nd edn.
London: Blackwell Scientific Publications.

Powell-Smith, V (1989), *A Contractor's Guide to the JCT Standard Form of Building Contract (JCT 80)*, 2nd edn.
London: Legal Studies & Services Ltd.

3   The JCT Intermediate Form of Contract (IFC 84)

Chappell, D, Powell-Smith V (1990), *The JCT Intermediate Form of Contract: An Architect's Guide*, 2nd edn.
London: Legal Studies & Services Ltd.

Jones, N F, Bergman, D (1985), *A Commentary on the JCT Intermediate Form of Building Contract.*
London: Blackwell Scientific Publications.

Powell-Smith, V (1985), *The Intermediate Form of Building Contract (IFC 84).*
Sutton: Business Press International.

4   The JCT Agreement for Minor Building Works

Chappell, D, Powell-Smith, V (1990), *The JCT Minor Works Form of Contract: An Architect's Guide*, 2nd edn.
London: Legal Studies & Services Ltd.

Clamp, H (1988), *The Shorter Form of Building Contract*, 2nd edn.
London: Blackwell Scientific Publications.

5   The JCT Standard Form of Management Contract (JCT 87)

Powell-Smith, V, Sims, J (1988), *The JCT Management Contract – A Practical Guide.*
London: Eclipse Publications.

8   The ACA Form of Building Agreement (ACA 2)

Powell-Smith, V (1985), *Guide to the ACA Form of Building Agreement 1982,* (2nd edn, 1984).
London: The Association of Consultant Architects.

9   The Government Conditions of Contract (GC/Works/1)

Powell-Smith, V (1984), *The General Conditions of Government Contracts for Building and Civil Engineering Works.*
Sutton: Business Press International.

Powell-Smith, V (1990), *GC/Works/1 – Edition 3 – The Government General Conditions of Contract for Building and Civil Engineering.*
London: Blackwell Scientific Publications.